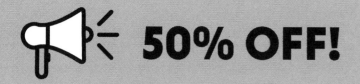 **50% OFF!**

FREE VIDEO

Essential Test Tips Video from Trivium Test Prep!

Thank you for purchasing from Trivium Test Prep!
We're honored to help you prepare for your exam.
To show our appreciation, we're offering a

FREE *Essential Test Tips* Video

Our video includes 35 test preparation strategies that will make you successful
on your big exam. All we ask is that you email us your feedback and describe
your experience with our product. Amazing, awful, or just so-so:
we want to hear what you have to say!

To receive your **FREE** *Essential Test Tips* **Video**, please email us at
5star@triviumtestprep.com.

Include "Free 5 Star" in the subject line and the following information in your email:

1. The title of the product you purchased.

2. Your rating from 1 – 5 (with 5 being the best).

3. Your feedback about the product, including how our materials helped you meet
   your goals and ways in which we can improve our products.

4. Your full name and shipping address so we can send your
   FREE *Essential Test Tips* **Video**.

If you have any questions or concerns please feel free to contact us directly at:
5star@triviumtestprep.com.

Thank you!

– Trivium Test Prep Team

Certified Medical Assistant Exam Prep 2023-2024:

800+ Practice Questions, Study Guide for CMA and RMA Tests

E.M. Falgout

TABLE OF CONTENTS

ONLINE RESOURCES

Ascencia Test Prep includes online resources with the purchase of this study guide to help you fully prepare for your Medical Assistant exam.

REVIEW QUESTIONS

Need more practice? Our review questions use a variety of formats to help you memorize key terms and concepts.

FLASH CARDS

Ascencia's flash cards allow you to review important terms easily on your computer or smartphone.

CHEAT SHEETS

Review the core skills you need to master the exam with easy-to-read Cheat Sheets.

FROM STRESS TO SUCCESS

Watch "From Stress to Success," a brief but insightful YouTube video that offers the tips, tricks, and secrets experts use to score higher on the exam.

REVIEWS

Leave a review, send us helpful feedback, or sign up for Ascencia Test Prep promotions—including free books!

Access these materials at:
https://www.ascenciatestprep.com/medical-assistant-online-resources

INTRODUCTION

Congratulations on choosing to become a certified medical assistant! Passing the medical assistant exam is an important step forward in your health care career. This guide will help prepare you for test day so you can take the medical assistant exam with confidence.

What is a Certified/Registered Medical Assistant?

Medical assistants support physicians in various medical settings, offices, and clinics. They perform in both administrative and clinical areas, with a focus on helping patients feel comfortable and informed. Medical assistants can choose between two programs to become either a certified medical assistant (CMA) or registered medical assistant (RMA). These certifications are important for medical assistants to demonstrate they possess the knowledge and skills necessary to provide quality health care service.

The Certified Medical Assistant (CMA) Exam

WHAT IS A CERTIFIED MEDICAL ASSISTANT (CMA)?

The **Certified Medical Assistant (CMA)** title recognizes medical assistants who pass the CMA exam, which is given by the **American Association of Medical Assistants (AAMA)**. To be eligible for certification, you must have graduated or be within 30 days of graduating from a certified medical assistant program. You can see if you are eligible at www.aama-ntl.org/cma-aama-exam/eligibility. CMA candidates are required to recertify their credentials every five years.

What's on the CMA Exam?

The CMA exam is a computerized test consisting of **200 multiple-choice questions**. Only 180 questions are scored; the remaining questions are used to plan future tests. You will have 160 minutes (two hours and 40 minutes) to answer all the exam questions, which are administered in four 40-minute sections. The exam covers three general areas: clinical competency, general, and administrative.

CMA Test Content		
Category	**Sections**	**Number of Questions**
Clinical Competency	A. Clinical Workflow: Patient Intake and Discharge B. Safety and Infection Control C. Procedures/Examinations D. Pharmacology	106
General	E. Legal and Ethical Issues F. Communication	38
Administrative	G. Billing, Coding, and Insurance H. Schedule Appointments and Health Information Management	36
Total (scored questions)		180

For the full exam content outline, visit www.aama-ntl.org/cma-aama-exam/study/content outline.

How is the CMA Exam Administered?

The CMA exam is a computerized test administered by Prometric. Before you take the test, make sure you meet the requirements listed on the AAMA website. To schedule an exam appointment, you can find a testing center near you at www.prometric.com. The testing fees and required forms of documentation vary depending on your eligibility. Special provisions must be requested through a special accommodations form.

On the day of the test you will have the option to complete a 15-minute tutorial (it will not count as part of the exam time). The exam will then be administered in four sections. You will have 40 minutes to complete each section, for a total of 160 minutes of test time. Twenty minutes total is allowed for breaks. The maximum allotted time to complete the exam, including breaks and the tutorial, is three hours and 15 minutes.

You will receive a pass/fail notification upon completion of the test, and exam scores will be sent by mail within three weeks of taking the CMA exam. If you do not pass, you may reapply immediately. Candidates are allowed a total of three exam attempts.

How is the CMA Exam Scored?

The CMA exam consists of 200 questions, 20 of which are unscored. These are pretest questions being considered for future exams. However, you will not know which questions are unscored and there is no penalty for wrong answers, so you should answer every question to the best of your ability.

Your CMA exam scores are calculated based on the total number of correct responses and converted to a scaled score. The AAMA requires a minimum scaled score of 430 to pass the exam. Candidates who pass the exam will earn their official CMA credential, valid for five years after certification.

The Registered Medical Assistant (RMA) Exam

WHAT IS A REGISTERED MEDICAL ASSISTANT (RMA)?

The Registered Medical Assistant (RMA) title recognizes medical assistants who pass the RMA exam, which is given by the American Medical Technologists (AMT). To qualify for the exam, you must have graduated from an accredited MA program or have five years of relevant work experience (within the last seven years). You can see if you are eligible at www.americanmedtech.org/Certification/Get-Certified/RMA-Eligibility. RMA candidates must recertify their credentials every three years.

What's on the RMA Exam?

The RMA examination is available to take in either paper-and-pencil or computerized format. It consists of 200 – 210 multiple-choice questions with four answer choices each. Candidates will have 180 minutes (three hours) to complete the exam.

Section	Work Area	Number of Questions
Anatomy and Physiology	Body Systems Medical Terminology	46
Administrative Medical Assisting	Insurance Financial Bookkeeping Medical Receptionist/Secretarial/Clerical Medical Laws and Ethics Human Relations	75
Clinical Medical Assisting	Asepsis Sterilization Instruments Laboratory Procedures Minor Surgery	31
Clinical Patient Interactions	Patient Education Vitals Signs and Measurement Physical Examinations Clinical Pharmacology Therapeutic Modalities Laboratory Procedures First Aid, CPR, and Emergency Response	58
Total		210

How is the RMA Exam Administered?

The RMA exam is available to take in both paper-and-pencil and computerized formats. Before you take the test, you must be officially approved by the AMT and have received an "authorization to test" letter. Ensure you are eligible and apply on their website at https://www.americanmedtech.org/.

The computerized test is administered by Pearson VUE; testing locations may be found at www.pearsonvue.com, where you may also schedule an exam appointment. The paper-and-pencil tests are only administered at certain times as scheduled by the AMT.

Results are available immediately for computerized exams. Paper-and-pencil exam results are sent out within eight weeks of taking the test. RMA candidates who do not pass can retake the exam three times.

How is the RMA Exam Scored?

The minimum passing score for the RMA exam is a 70, on a scale from 1 – 100. Each question is weighted based on difficulty and converted to a scaled score. Your raw score is the total number of correct answers, which is then converted to a standard score. Candidates who pass the exam will earn their official RMA credential, valid for three years after certification.

About This Guide

This guide will help you master the most important test topics and develop critical test-taking skills. We have built features into our books to prepare you for your test and increase your score. We offer an overview of the content knowledge required to pass the test. In the review, you'll find sidebars that provide interesting information, highlight key concepts, and review content so that you can solidify your understanding of important concepts. You can also test your knowledge with sample questions throughout the text and a full practice test at the end of the guide.

Ascencia Test Prep

With health care fields such as nursing, pharmacy, emergency care, and physical therapy becoming the fastest-growing industries in the United States, individuals looking to enter the health care industry or rise in their field need high-quality, reliable resources. Ascencia Test Prep's study guides and test preparation materials are developed by credentialed industry professionals with years of experience in their respective fields. Ascencia recognizes that health care professionals nurture bodies and spirits, and save lives. Ascencia Test Prep's mission is to help health care workers grow.

1 PATIENT INTAKE AND DISCHARGE

The purpose of the patient intake and physical examination is to assess the patient's state of health and wellness and to determine the cause of the chief complaint. The medical assistant must greet the patient, obtain necessary vital signs and measurements, document the chief complaint, interview the patient, and provide the patient with a sense of support and security. The CMA assists the physician by:

- preparing the exam room and necessary equipment
- making sure the exam room is clean and free of clutter
- preparing the patient for the exam by giving instructions
- helping with draping/gowning
- assisting with the exam

Vital Signs

Vital signs monitored in the health care environment include temperature, heart and pulse rate, respiratory rate, and blood pressure. These vital signs can change with age, illness, injury, and health status. Pain is also sometimes considered a vital sign and should be addressed by the CMA during intake.

Body Temperature

Body temperature can be measured with a **thermometer** by various routes, such as oral, axillary, forehead, or rectal. Average normal body temperature is 98.6°F (37°C) but can vary depending on the location used for measurement and among patients.

TABLE 1.1. Measuring Body Temperature

Method	Location	Baseline
Axillary	armpit	97.6°F (36.5°C)
Oral	under tongue	98.6°F (37.0°C)
Rectal	rectum	99.6°F (37.5°C)
Temporal artery	forehead	99.6°F (37.5°C)
Tympanic membrane	inside ear	98.6°F (37.0°C)

Elevated temperature, or **fever**, is defined as a temperature higher than 100.4°F (38°C) (although this is not a universal standard—some physicians may use a different cutoff temperature). Fever is often a symptom of infection or inflammation, but it can be caused by other conditions, including stress, dehydration, exercise, the environment, and thyroid disorders. **Hypothermia** (body temperature below 95°F [35°C]) can occur when the body is exposed to cold weather or due to medical conditions such as a thyroid disorder.

PULSE

The heart beats a certain number of times each minute, a value called the **pulse**, or **heart rate**. The pulse can be taken at a number of locations on the body.

- **carotid pulse**: to the side of the trachea
- **radial pulse**: on the thumb side of the inner wrist
- **brachial pulse**: on the side of the crease of the elbow
- **pedal pulse**: on the top of the foot
- **apical pulse**: at the apex of the heart (with stethoscope)

The pulse is measured as the number of times the heart beats in 1 minute. The radial pulse is the most common place to take a pulse, by pressing with two or three fingers and counting for a full minute (or for 30 seconds and multiplying by 2).

Heart rate is also usually found on the readouts of equipment used to test cardiovascular performance, including pulse oximeters and electrocardiograms (ECGs).

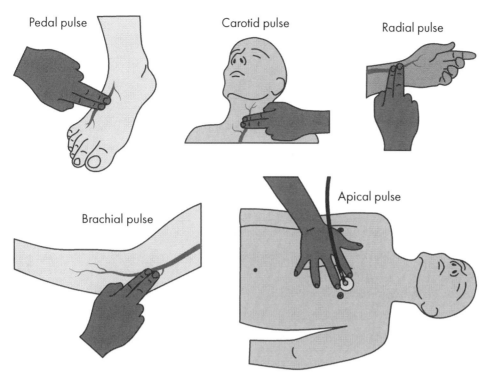

Figure 1.1. Locations for Measuring Heart Rate

The average adult's heart rate at rest is between 60 and 100 beats per minute. The normal heart rate is higher in children and infants.

TABLE 1.2. Normal Heart Rate	
Age	**Beats per Minute (bpm)**
Adults and adolescents	60 – 100
Children (2 – 10 years)	60 – 140
Infants and toddlers	100 – 190
Newborns (< 3 months)	85 – 205

A rapid heart rate (**tachycardia**) can be caused by a wide range of conditions, including infection, dehydration, shock, anemia, stress, anxiety, thyroid conditions, and heart conditions. Similarly, a slow pulse rate (**bradycardia**) can be caused by many factors, including certain medications (e.g., beta blockers and digoxin), fainting, and various heart conditions.

RESPIRATORY RATE

A person's **respiratory rate (RR)** is the number of breaths taken per minute. Respiratory rate is usually found by having the patient lie on their back (although this is not required) and counting the rise and fall of their chest.

For an accurate measurement, the patient should be allowed to rest before the respiratory rate is measured.

A normal adult's RR is 12 to 20 breaths per minute, although this rate can vary in adults over 65. Conditions that can elevate the respiratory rate include acute respiratory distress, asthma, COPD, pneumonia, heart failure, bronchitis, and tuberculosis. Use of opioids, drug overdose, or a diabetic coma can lower the respiratory rate.

BLOOD PRESSURE

Blood pressure (BP) is the measurement of the force of blood as it flows against the walls of the arteries, measured in mm Hg. Blood pressure is written as two numbers: systolic pressure and diastolic pressure. **Systolic pressure** is the pressure that occurs while the heart is contracting; **diastolic pressure** occurs while the heart is relaxed. A healthy blood pressure has a systolic value of 100 to 139 mm Hg and a diastolic value of 60 to 79 mm Hg.

Blood pressure can be taken manually using a blood pressure cuff and stethoscope or by using an automatic or semiautomatic blood pressure monitor. (Both the cuff and electronic monitors are referred to as **sphygmomanometers**.) For both methods, the patient should be upright, with their feet on the floor and uncrossed, and the arm being used for the measurement should be at heart height.

To take a blood pressure manually, the CMA should wrap a properly sized cuff around the patient's upper arm and lightly press the stethoscope over the brachial pulse. The cuff should be inflated to 180 mm Hg; this prevents blood from flowing through the brachial artery. Releasing the valve allows air to slowly leave the cuff. When the pressure in the cuff is equal to the patient's blood pressure, the blood will rush through the artery, creating a distinctive sound called the **Korotkoff sound**. The pressure at which the first sound is heard is the systolic pressure, and the pressure at which the last sound is heard is the diastolic pressure.

To use an **automatic blood pressure monitor**, the medical assistant wraps the cuff around the patient's upper arm and turns on the monitor. It will automatically inflate, deflate, and provide a pressure reading. A **semiautomatic monitor** requires manual inflation but will automatically deflate and provide a pressure reading.

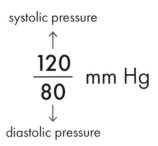

Figure 1.2. Systolic and Diastolic Blood Pressure

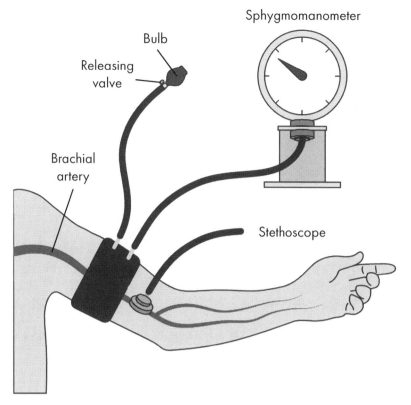

Figure 1.3. How to Take a Manual Blood Pressure Reading

High blood pressure is called **hypertension.** Smoking, stress, exercise, eating, caffeine, certain medications, salt intake, and a full bladder can all elevate blood pressure. Prolonged hypertension can result in atherosclerosis, stroke, and heart failure. **Hypotension** (low BP) can be caused by hypothermia, shock, diuretics, and fainting. Some people, particularly those over 65, may experience orthostatic hypotension, which occurs when standing up too quickly.

HEIGHT AND WEIGHT

The patient's **height** is assessed by using a fixed bar on the weight scale or wall. Height measurements are recorded in feet (ft) and inches (in) or in centimeters

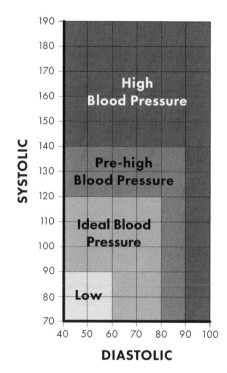

Figure 1.4. Classifying Blood Pressure

(cm). The patient's **weight** is measured using a balanced scale and recorded in pounds (lb) or kilograms (kg).

Body mass index (BMI) is a measurement of body fat that is based on a person's height and weight. To calculate the BMI, divide the weight in kilograms by the height in meters squared.

TABLE 1.3. BMI Scale	
<15	Very severely underweight
15 – 15.99	Severely underweight
16 – 18.49	Underweight
18.5 – 24.9	Normal weight
25 – 29.9	Overweight
30 – 39.9	Obese
>40	Morbidly obese

OXYGEN SATURATION AND PULSE OXIMETRY

Oxygen saturation is a measurement of the amount of oxygen in the blood. Specifically, it measures the amount of oxygen-saturated hemoglobin (the substance in red blood cells that carries oxygen) relative to unsaturated hemoglobin. Normal blood oxygen level is 94 to 100 percent. Oxygen saturation is measured using a pulse oximeter, which is usually placed on the patient's finger.

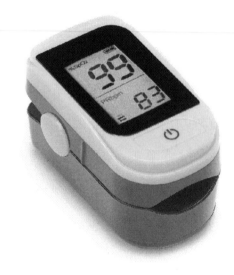

Figure 1.5. Pulse Oximeter

PAIN

If a patient presents with pain, the medical assistant will need to assess pain during intake. The letters **PQRST** can be used as a mnemonic device.

- **Provoking:** What was happening when the pain started? What makes the pain better or worse?

- **Quality:** What does the pain feel like? Is it sharp, stabbing, dull, aching, burning, etc.?
- **Region:** Where is the pain located? Does the pain radiate or move to another area of the body?
- **Severity:** On a scale of 0 – 10 (10 being the worst pain imaginable), how bad is the pain?
- **Timing:** How long has this pain gone on? When did it start? How long does it typically last?

For pediatric patients or patients with communication barriers, the CMA may use a "faces" pain scale.

0   2   4   6   8   10

Figure 1.6. The Wong-Baker FACES Pain Rating Scale

REVIEW QUESTIONS

1. Where is the carotid pulse taken?

   _____

2. What is systolic blood pressure?

   _____

3. How is oxygen saturation measured?

   _____

4. What is the normal resting heart rate for adults?

   _____

5. What is the normal body temperature found using a tympanic membrane thermometer?

   _____

6. What pain scale should be used for pediatric patients?

   _____

7. A patient's BMI is 17. Is the patient underweight, normal weight, or overweight?

   _____

8. What sound is heard when noting the blood pressure?

   _____

Interview Techniques

Patient interviewing is a skill medical assistants must develop in order to obtain important health information from patients. Some general interview techniques are discussed below.

- **Active listening** is the process of actively concentrating on the patient and responding appropriately to what they say. (See chapter 9, "Communication" for more discussion of active listening.)

- **Open-ended questions** cannot be answered with a simple yes or no. Asking open-ended questions encourages patients to provide more detailed information during the interview.

- **Adaptive questioning** is the use of guided questions that get progressively more specific, while allowing the patient to provide information in an uninterrupted narrative.

- **Echoing** is repeating words used by the patient in the form of a question in order to elicit more information.

- **Showing empathy and concern** when the patient is speaking can make the patient feel comfortable.

- **Providing validation and reassurance** to patients will make them feel like their experiences are important and will encourage them to speak more freely.

REVIEW QUESTIONS

9. What interview techniques can be used to get the most detailed information from patients?

_____

10. How can the CMA help a patient feel more comfortable during an interview?

_____

Documentation of Care

During **intake**, the CMA gathers both objective data (i.e., that measured by the CMA) and **subjective data** (i.e., that reported by the patient). Objective data includes the results of the physical exam (e.g., pulse, temperature) and any laboratory screenings. The CMA should collect the following subjective data:

- **chief complaint**: the problem or symptom that the patient describes (e.g., cough, fever, runny nose)

- **present illness**: the symptoms and how long the illness has been present (e.g., fever of 101.0°F [38.3°C] for 3 days, dry cough for 2 days)

- **medical history**: medical history over a lifetime (e.g., previous medical diagnoses, allergies, mental illness, surgeries, hospitalizations)
- **family history**: medical history of biologically related family members, such as parents, grandparents, siblings, aunts, uncles, and cousins (e.g., hypertension, diabetes, cancers)
- **social and occupational history**: the patient's personal habits (e.g., drinking, smoking, drug use), social history, and work history
- **review of symptoms**: a list of questions used by the physician to diagnose different medical conditions (e.g., respiratory symptoms, cardiovascular symptoms, etc.)

All data gathered by the CMA should be included in the patient's medical record, along with a full record of the care the patient receives during the visit. This record should include intake information, diagnosis, and treatment recommendations. During intake of returning patients, the CMA may also verify that the patient is in compliance with previous treatment recommendations. If necessary, changes and corrections can be made to the medical record with an addendum.

REVIEW QUESTIONS

11. What should be reviewed when gathering the patient's past medical history?

_____

12. The patient reports a sore throat, runny nose, and itchy eyes. Is this subjective or objective data?

_____

13. What should be documented in the patient record?

_____

Patient Screenings and Wellness Assessments

Medical assistants must be knowledgeable about wellness and preventive care for patients. A CMA should be able to provide education and answer patient questions about the following topics:

- **cancer screenings**: Pap smear and colonoscopy screenings to check for abnormalities of the cervix and colon
- **sexually transmitted infections (STIs)**: symptoms, risk factors, diagnosis, and treatment
- **hygiene**: importance of and step-by-step instructions for handwashing and cough etiquette

- **smoking risks and cessation**: harm caused by smoking and techniques for quitting
- **osteoporosis screening/bone density scan**: done in patients over 50, smokers, people with vitamin D deficiency

Medical assistants should also be able to recognize the signs of substance abuse and domestic violence. When these signs are seen, the medical office's substance abuse and domestic violence policies should be followed.

- recognition of **substance abuse**: abusing illegal drugs or prescription drugs, isolation from family and friends, engaging in criminal activity, excessive drinking, and changes in behavior
- **domestic violence** screening and detection: bruises, lacerations, burns, or other injuries; making excuses for injuries; excessive canceling of appointments; withdrawal, depression, or anxiety

As part of intake, CMAs may also screen patients for depression and suicidal thinking or behaviors. **Depression** is a mood disorder that has both emotional and physical symptoms. Patients who are depressed report feelings of sadness and hopelessness that last longer than 2 weeks and may report physical symptoms such as sleep disruption and changes in appetite.

Self-harm is the process of hurting oneself (such as cutting or burning the skin) as a response to emotional distress. Patients who self-harm may have patterns of injuries in varying stages of healing.

Suicide is intentionally causing one's own death. Risk factors for suicide include behavioral health disorders like depression and bipolar disorder; a history of trauma or abuse; and environmental stressors like bullying, divorce, or job loss. People who have previously attempted suicide are at a much higher risk for suicide attempts.

The medical assistant should notify their supervisor as soon as possible if they see signs of self-harm or if a patient reports suicidal thinking or behaviors.

REVIEW QUESTIONS

14. The CMA sees cuts along a patient's wrist when putting on the blood pressure cuff. What should they do?

_____

15. What patient population should be screened for osteoporosis?

_____

16. What are the signs of domestic violence the CMA should look for during patient screenings?

_____

Patient Education

Some educational plans require little preparation and planning, such as simple medication instructions. Other plans require a multidisciplinary approach that will include physician office workers, physical therapists, and home health workers. Depending on the patient's needs, the steps of education planning are:

1. Identify the topic and purpose.
2. Assess the patient's abilities and needs.
3. Develop the plan and decide who will do what and how it will be done.
4. Implement the plan.
5. Evaluate the patient's understanding.
6. Document the education in the medical record.
7. Reevaluate the plan on follow-up.

DIABETIC TEACHING AND HOME CARE

CMAs may be asked to educate patients on the importance of diabetic care. This process may include:

- printing out a diabetic diet for the patient to take home.
- teaching the patient how to examine their feet and look for abnormalities such as calluses, sores, and discoloration and to note any numbness.
- encouraging patients to keep follow-up appointments with their physician for medication management and laboratory work (hemoglobin A1C, CMP, CBC, TSH, lipids, and vitamin B-12).

PATIENT MOBILITY EQUIPMENT AND ASSISTIVE DEVICES

Some patients require **mobility equipment** to assist them in getting around, such as electric wheelchairs, walkers, scooters, lift chairs, or crutches. The CMA should educate the patient on safely using these devices, and provide educational material on mobility equipment and safety measures.

PRE-OP AND POST-OP CARE INSTRUCTIONS

Surgery procedures are invasive and require the patient to follow precise instructions to prevent infection. When giving **pre-op instructions**, the CMA should instruct the patient to wash with antiseptic soap the night before and the day of surgery. They should not apply any lotions, deodorants, or perfumes the day of surgery and should not wear jewelry or watches. The

CMA should explain what medications the patient can and cannot take the day of the procedure.

For **post-op care**, the patient should be educated on signs and symptoms of possible complications, medications they can take, prescriptions sent to their pharmacy, and when to follow up with the surgeon. These steps will help ensure patient compliance and reduce infection.

PATIENT-ADMINISTERED MEDICATIONS

Patients must understand the importance of taking their medications according to instructions. The CMA should print out for the patient a list of their medications and the prescribed dosages and frequencies. They should also describe to the patient the signs and symptoms to look for if starting new medications. The patient should repeat the instructions they were given to verify that they understand them.

Medical assistants may be asked to help educate patients who self-administer medications using nebulizers, inhalers, or IM injections.

- A **nebulizer** is a machine that allows patients to inhale medication in the form of a fine mist. They are commonly prescribed for patients with COPD or asthma. Medical assistants must receive training before assisting patients with nebulizers.

- Patients with asthma may have a prescribed **metered-dose inhaler (MDI)** that contains a bronchodilator (usually albuterol). To administer the medication, the patient exhales completely and then breathes in slowly and deeply while pressing down on the medication canister.

- Some **IM injections** may be self-administered by the patient. These include epinephrine (EpiPens), interferon, hormones, and anti-arthritis drugs. Patients should understand how to clean the injection site, prepare the syringe, administer the injection, and properly dispose of the syringe.

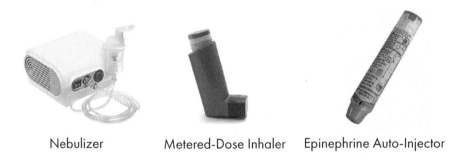

Nebulizer   Metered-Dose Inhaler   Epinephrine Auto-Injector

Figure 1.7. Self-Administered Medication Devices

HOME MONITORING

Some patients need to monitor their blood pressure at home. They should check their blood pressure once or twice a day and document the readings in a notebook. They should be given educational materials on monitoring blood pressure to take home.

The use of anticoagulants, or blood thinners, prevents blood clots in patients at high risk for thrombotic events. Conditions that may require anticoagulants include previous thrombotic events (e.g., myocardial infarction, pulmonary embolism) and dysrhythmias (e.g., atrial fibrillation). Some post-op patients may also be prescribed anticoagulants. Patients on anticoagulants must adhere strictly to physicians' instructions; small changes in dosages can result in life-threatening bleeding.

INR (international normalized ratio) is a laboratory test that measures the time it takes for the blood to clot. Patients who take anticoagulants need to have their INR measured regularly either at home or in a medical office to ensure they are taking the correct dose. The CMA should educate patients to ensure they are aware of their INR testing procedures. They should also educate patients to look for signs and symptoms of over-anticoagulation such as bruising, nosebleeds, bleeding gums, blood in stools, and blood in vomit.

Patients with diabetes will need to monitor their blood sugar (glucose) levels. Glucose levels in the blood can be tested at home with small, portable **glucose meters**. A small amount of blood from a skin puncture is placed on the test strip, and the meter provides a readout of the glucose level. Patients should know how to puncture the skin with the lancet, apply blood to the test strip, and read the meter.

> **HELPFUL HINT:**
>
> Anticoagulant drugs include heparin, warfarin, apixaban (Eliquis), enoxaparin sodium (Lovenox), and rivaroxaban (Xarelto).

> **HELPFUL HINT:**
>
> Normal blood glucose levels are 70 – 100 mg/dL.

REVIEW QUESTIONS

17. What should be taught to patients with diabetes about foot health?

_____

18. What range of blood glucose is considered normal?

_____

19. What instructions should be provided for post-op patients?

_____

20. Describe how to educate a patient on the proper use of an MDI.

_____

21. What lab is commonly used to evaluate effectiveness of anticoagulants?

_____

→

CONTINUE

Nutrition

Basics of Nutrition

Nutrition is the process of acquiring the energy and other resources needed for growth and development. A healthy diet includes sufficient amounts of necessary nutrients, including:

- carbohydrates: sugars that provide an immediate source of energy
- fats: stored energy that can be broken down and used for fuel by the body
- proteins: molecules composed of amino acids that play an integral role in most bodily functions
- vitamins: essential compounds that are required in small amounts
- minerals: elements (such as calcium and phosphorus) that are essential for life
- electrolytes: ions (such as sodium and potassium) that play an important role in maintaining the balance of water in the human body

Special Dietary Needs

Medical assistants should have the knowledge to educate and care for patients with various nutritional disorders and needs. **Malnutrition** occurs when a person's diet has a deficiency of necessary nutrients. Some patients take dietary supplements to replenish missing nutrients. Patients with osteoporosis, for example, may take calcium supplements, and pregnant women are advised to take vitamins containing folic acid.

Patients may have special dietary requirements that need to be accommodated in health care settings. Patients with allergies should be provided with meals that do not contain potentially dangerous allergens. Some other special dietary needs are listed in the table below.

TABLE 1.4. Special Dietary Needs	
Condition	**Dietary Needs**
Diabetes	diet low in sugar
Cardiovascular disease or hypertension	diet low in salt and fat
Lactose sensitivity/intolerance	no dairy or dairy products
Celiac disease	no gluten (a protein found in wheat)

A high-protein diet low in fats and sugars can also help with **weight control** in some patients, if needed. Some patients may also be on diets that restrict specific types of foods for reasons other than medical. **Vegans** do not eat any animal products at all. These patients are at risk for deficiencies in vitamins B-12 and D, zinc, iron, calcium, protein, and omega-3 fatty acids. **Pesco-vegetarians** eat seafood and fish but no other animal or dairy products. **Lacto-vegetarians** eat dairy products but no meat or eggs. Finally, **lacto-ovo-vegetarians** eat dairy products and eggs but no meat or seafood.

THERAPEUTIC DIETS

Patients may be put on therapeutic diets that are designed to help alleviate the symptoms of specific medical conditions. A **clear liquid diet** consists of fluids and some electrolytes to prevent dehydration. A clear liquid diet is often given to a malnourished patient who has not eaten for some time. Before many intestinal tests and surgeries, patients are often placed on a clear liquid diet. Allowed food items might include water, broth, clear beverages, gelatin, popsicles, hard candy, and diluted fruit juices.

A **full liquid diet** is used as a transition when going from clear liquids to altered or soft foods. Patients are often placed on a full liquid diet following surgery, or when they have difficulty swallowing, chewing, or tolerating solid foods. Foods on this diet can include ice cream, milk, pudding, custard, sherbet, strained soups, refined cooked cereals, juices, and breakfast drinks.

Mechanically altered diets are used when a patient has difficulty chewing and swallowing. Foods on this diet should be soft and moist and can include moistened bread products, cooked cereals, canned fruit, pureed soups, meat in very small pieces served with sauce or gravy, and well-cooked vegetables.

Similarly, a **soft diet** is used for patients with swallowing or chewing problems, as well as those with ulcerations of the mouth, gums, or throat. Foods that contain nuts and seeds are not allowed, and patients should be careful with raw fruits and vegetables and whole grains.

Patients with inflammation or scarring of the gastrointestinal tract or with decreased motility may be put on a **low-residue, low-fiber diet**. Foods include refined cooked cereals, white bread, cooked potatoes, refined pasta, white rice, eggs, fresh fruit without skin or seeds, and dairy products.

In contrast, a **high-fiber diet** is used for patients with constipation, obesity, diabetes, diverticulosis, and high cholesterol. Foods include whole-grain products, seeds, nuts, beans, leafy vegetables, and fruits.

EATING DISORDERS

People with **eating disorders** have abnormal or extreme behaviors and thoughts and feelings related to food and body image. Eating disorders are more common in women but occur in men as well.

DID YOU KNOW?

Eating disorders are a mental and physical illness. Patients should be treated with sensitivity.

An extreme desire for thinness and fear of gaining weight characterize **anorexia nervosa.** Individuals with anorexia sometimes abstain from food to such a degree that they do not maintain healthy levels of body fat and do not consume enough essential nutrients to meet requirements.

Bulimia nervosa is also associated with an individual's obsession over weight and body image, but it is characterized by an uncontrollable urge to binge followed by compensatory actions, such as purging, fasting, excessive exercise, or the use of laxatives, enemas, or diuretics to try to lose the calories consumed during the binge.

REVIEW QUESTIONS

22. A patient states that they are a lacto-vegetarian. Which foods does this patient NOT eat?

_____

23. What types of foods should a patient requiring a high-fiber diet be encouraged to eat?

_____

24. What type of food does a patient with celiac disease need to avoid?

_____

25. What types of foods can be offered to a patient on a full liquid diet?

_____

26. Why would a patient be placed on a clear liquid diet?

_____

ANSWER KEY

1. The carotid pulse is taken to the side of the trachea.

2. Systolic blood pressure is the pressure that occurs while the heart is contracting.

3. Oxygen saturation is measured with a pulse oximeter, which is usually placed on the patient's finger.

4. The normal resting heart rate for adults is between 60 and 100 beats per minute.

5. The normal body temperature found using a tympanic membrane thermometer is 98.6°F (37.0°C).

6. The Wong-Baker FACES Pain Rating Scale should be used for pediatric patients.

7. Body mass index (BMI) is a measurement of body fat based on a person's height and weight. A patient with a BMI of 17 is underweight.

8. When the pressure in the blood pressure cuff is equal to the patient's blood pressure, the blood will rush through the artery, creating the Korotkoff sound.

9. Open-ended questions that require more than a simple yes or no answer and echoing are techniques that elicit more information.

10. Showing empathy and concern as well as providing validation and reassurance during the interview can enhance patient comfort levels.

11. The CMA should review the patient's subjective data, including previous medical diagnoses, allergies, mental illness, surgeries, and hospitalizations.

12. Any report of a symptom by the patient is considered subjective data.

13. The CMA should document the data gathered through assessment and the care given during the visit, including intake information, compliance with ordered therapies, diagnosis, and treatment recommendations.

14. The CMA should immediately report possible self-harm or suicidal behavior to their supervisor.

15. Osteoporosis screening should be performed in patients over 50, who smoke, or who have vitamin D deficiency.

16. The CMA should look for bruises, lacerations, burns, or other injuries; making excuses for injuries; excessive canceling of appointments; withdrawal, depression, or anxiety.

17. The patient should be taught how to examine their feet and look for abnormalities such as calluses, sores, and discoloration and to note any numbness.

18. A normal blood glucose range is between 70 and 100 mg/dL.

19. Patients should be instructed on signs and symptoms of possible complications, medications they can take, prescriptions sent to their pharmacy, and when to follow up with the surgeon.

20. To administer the medication, the patient exhales completely and then breathes in slowly and deeply while pressing down on the medication canister.

21. The INR is a laboratory test that measures the time it takes for the blood to clot.

22. A lacto-vegetarian patient would not eat meat or eggs.

23. A patient on a high-fiber diet should eat whole-grain products, seeds, nuts, beans, leafy vegetables, and fruits.

$\longrightarrow$
CONTINUE

24. A patient with celiac disease should avoid foods containing gluten (a protein found in wheat).

25. A patient on a full liquid diet is allowed to eat ice cream, milk, pudding, custard, sherbet, strained soups, refined cooked cereals, juices, and breakfast drinks.

26. A clear liquid diet is often given to a malnourished patient who has not eaten for some time. Before many intestinal tests and surgeries, patients are often placed on a clear liquid diet.

2 SAFETY AND INFECTION CONTROL

The goal of **infection control** is to intervene in the chain of infection at the point where infection is most likely to occur in order to prevent its spread. To do this, medical assistants must understand how infections occur and are transmitted as well as the principles of proper anti-infective treatment, infection control measures, and preventive disease precautions. Using aseptic techniques and adhering to universal precautions can help control the spread of infection.

Infection Cycle and the Chain of Infection

When an organism establishes an opportunistic relationship with a host, the process is called **infection**. The process of infection starts with the transmission of organisms and ends with the development of infectious disease. There are four stages of the infection process.

1. During the **incubation period** the organism establishes a presence in the susceptible host, but the host does not show any symptoms.

2. In the **prodromal stage** the symptoms of infection begin to appear.

3. Throughout **acute illness** the organisms grow and spread quickly inside the host.

4. In the **convalescent stage** the damaged tissue begins healing, and symptoms resolve.

Infections can be mild or severe, and the acuteness of an infection depends on the disease-causing potential of the infectious agent and the ability of the body to defend itself. Infections can be caused by many different **infectious agents**.

- **Bacteria** are single-celled prokaryotic organisms that are responsible for many common infections such as strep throat, urinary tract infections, and many food-borne illnesses.

- **Viruses** are composed of a nucleic acid (DNA or RNA) wrapped in a protein capsid. They invade host cells and hijack cell machinery to reproduce. Viral infections include the common cold, influenza, and human immunodeficiency virus (HIV).

- **Protozoa** are single-celled eukaryotic organisms. Protozoan infections include giardia (an intestinal infection) and African sleeping sickness.

- **Fungi** are a group of eukaryotic organisms that include yeasts, molds, and mushrooms. Common fungal infections are athlete's foot, ringworm, and oral and vaginal yeast infections.

- Parasitic diseases are caused by **parasites** that live in or on the human body and use its resources. Common human parasites include worms (e.g., tapeworms), flukes, and ectoparasites like lice and ticks, which live on the outside of the body.

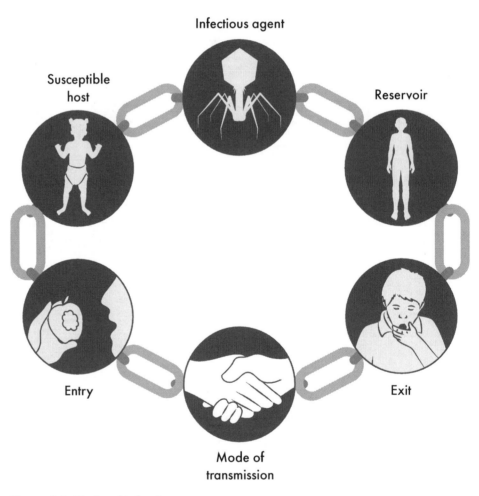

Figure 2.1. Chain of Infection

Infections travel from person to person via the **chain of infection.** The chain starts with a **causative organism** (e.g., a bacteria or virus). The organism needs a **reservoir**, or place to live. This may be biological, such as people or animals, or it may be environmental. For example, in a medical office, equipment and office surfaces may act as reservoirs. In order to spread, the infectious agent needs a way to **exit** the reservoir, such as being expelled as droplets during a sneeze.

For the infection chain to continue, the infectious agent needs to encounter a susceptible host—a person who can become infected. Finally, the infectious agent needs a way to **enter** the host, such as through inhalation or drinking contaminated water. There are a variety of modes of transmission for infectious agents.

- **Direct contact** is transmission from one infected person to another during physical contact with blood or other body fluids (e.g., transmission of herpes during sexual intercourse).

- **Indirect contact** is transmission of the disease through a nonbiological reservoir (e.g., drinking water contaminated with giardia).

- **Droplets** are infectious agents trapped in moisture that are expelled when an infected person sneezes or coughs. They can enter the respiratory system of other people and cause infection (e.g., transmission of influenza when an infected person sneezes).

- Some droplets are light enough to remain **airborne**, meaning people may inhale infectious agents from the air long after the initial cough or sneeze (e.g., measles, which can live in airborne droplets for up to 2 hours).

- Some diseases are carried by organisms called **vectors** that spread the disease; the infection does not require direct physical contact between people (e.g., mosquitoes carrying malaria).

HELPFUL HINT:

See chapter 3, "Anatomy and Physiology," for more information on the human body's natural barriers to infection.

DID YOU KNOW?

Infectious disease precautions are categorized based on how the disease is transmitted. For example, droplet precautions require only a surgical mask, but airborne precautions require an N-95 respirator to prevent transmission.

REVIEW QUESTIONS

1. During which stage of infection has the infectious organism invaded the host, but the host does not yet have symptoms?

   _____

2. What type of infectious organism causes influenza?

   _____

3. What role does a reservoir play in the chain of infection?

   _____

4. How does droplet transmission of disease occur?

   _____

Asepsis

MEDICAL ASEPSIS

Asepsis is the absence of infectious organisms, and **medical asepsis** is the practice of destroying infectious agents outside the body to prevent the spread of disease. An object that has had all infectious agents removed or destroyed is **sterile**.

Medical asepsis is different from **clean technique**, which also aims to minimize the spread of infectious agents, but it does not require sterilization. Wearing gloves is an example of clean technique; the gloves are not sterile, but they provide a barrier that prevents the spread of infection from patient to provider.

The most important tool used for medical asepsis is handwashing. **Aseptic handwashing** is a specific technique intended to remove all infectious agents

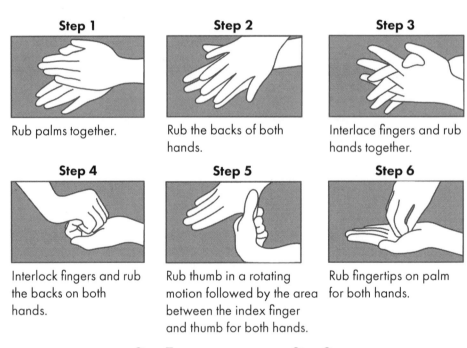

Step 1
Rub palms together.

Step 2
Rub the backs of both hands.

Step 3
Interlace fingers and rub hands together.

Step 4
Interlock fingers and rub the backs on both hands.

Step 5
Rub thumb in a rotating motion followed by the area between the index finger and thumb for both hands.

Step 6
Rub fingertips on palm for both hands.

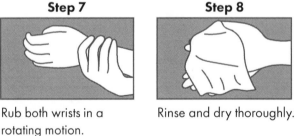

Step 7
Rub both wrists in a rotating motion.

Step 8
Rinse and dry thoroughly.

Figure 2.2. Aseptic Handwashing Technique

from the hands and wrists. Aseptic handwashing should be performed whenever the CMA is going to interact with a sterile field (e.g., when applying a sterile dressing).

Medical asepsis also includes the removal of infectious agents from equipment and other surfaces. This process has three general levels.

1. **Cleaning** removes dirt and some infectious agents.

2. **Disinfection** kills all pathogens except bacterial spores. Most surfaces in health care settings are disinfected using liquid chemical agents such as alcohol or chlorine bleach.

3. **Sterilization** kills all infectious agents, including bacterial spores. Medical equipment is sterilized using heat (e.g., autoclave) or chemicals (e.g., ethylene oxide).

Disinfectants are regulated by the EPA, and medical offices must use EPA-approved disinfectants. The EPA maintains a list of disinfectants that are approved for specific infectious agents. These products have registration numbers that should be checked by the staff members who purchase cleaning supplies.

SURGICAL ASEPSIS

Surgical asepsis is the practice of removing all infectious pathogens from all equipment involved in invasive procedures. Medical assistants may be asked to help sterilize equipment and may also be required to do a surgical scrub if participating in an invasive procedure.

Sterilization is the process of destroying living organisms. **Chemical sterilization** is also known as cold sterilization, and is used for heat-sensitive equipment, such as endoscopes. The equipment is soaked in closed containers with strong chemical agents.

Two types of heat are also used in sterilization: dry and steam. Dry heat is used for sterilizing instruments that corrode easily, and it requires 1 hour of heat at 320°F (160°C). The use of steam heat in an **autoclave** is the most common method used in medical offices. The steam achieves high temperatures, usually 250°F – 254°F (121°C – 123°C), under pressure. Instruments must be wrapped in special packaging for autoclaving. The time required in the autoclave varies from 20 to 40 minutes, depending on how tightly the items are wrapped.

Items must be wrapped following specific procedures before being autoclaved.

1. Position open wrap on a flat surface in a diamond shape with one of the points toward the body.

2. Place cleaned and dried instruments in the center of the wrap.

3. Fold the corner closest to the body over the instrument and fold the point back down to create a tab.

4. Fold the first side corner toward the center, covering the instrument. Fold the extra material back to form a tab.

5. Repeat step 4 with the second side corner.

6. Fold the last corner toward the center, completely covering the instrument.

7. Fasten the packet with sterilization tape.

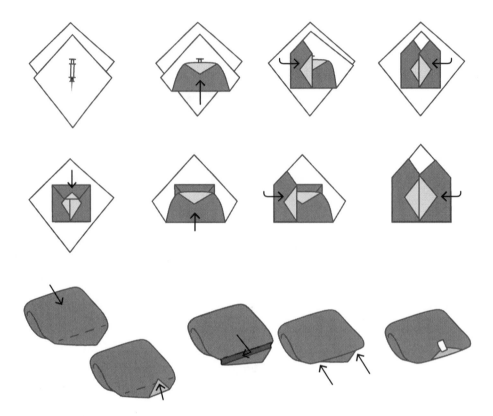

Figure 2.3. How to Wrap an Instrument for the Autoclave

Before surgical procedures, all health care team members must do a **surgical scrub**.

1. Remove all jewelry.

2. Wash hands, wrists, and forearms at foot- or knee-controlled faucet.

3. Cleanse for 10 minutes.

4. Hold hands upward while rinsing.

5. Dry with a sterile towel.

6. Apply sterile gloves.

The **sterile field** is a pathogen-free area that contains the sterile instruments, solutions, and other items that will be used in the procedure. This also includes the hands and anterior neck-to-waist region of the physician and assistants.

In the sterile field, specific guidelines must be followed.

- Check for sterile indicators and dates on all items before opening them and putting them in the sterile field.
- Examine each item for breaks in packaging or for moisture.
- Open the packages per instructions.
- Maintain a border of 1 inch between non-sterile and sterile areas.
- Do not reach over the sterile field.
- Do not cough, talk, or sneeze over the sterile field.

REVIEW QUESTIONS

6. Which level of medical asepsis—cleaning, disinfection, or sterilization—kills all infectious agents, including bacterial spores?

_____

7. How long should a surgical hand scrub last?

_____

8. What areas of the surgeon and assistants are considered sterile?

_____

9. What must be done with sterile packaged instruments before they are opened?

_____

10. How is heat-sensitive equipment like an endoscope sterilized?

_____

Standard Precautions and Exposure Control

Personal protective equipment (PPE) is any item necessary for the prevention of microorganism transmission. PPE includes gloves, gowns, goggles, eye shields, and masks. Gloves and gowns help prevent the spread of pathogens from patients or equipment to other patients or equipment. The CDC recommends that health care workers remove fluid-resistant gowns before leaving a patient's room and before performing hand hygiene. Masks, goggles, and face shields should be used by health care workers when there is a likelihood of blood or body fluid splashes. All of these PPE devices protect the mucous membranes of the mouth, nose, and eyes from infected particles.

Standard precautions (also called universal precautions) are based on the assumption that all patients are infected with microorganisms, whether or

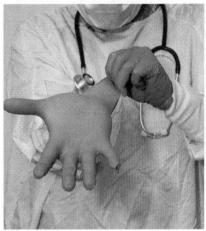

Figure 2.4. PPE

not there are symptoms or a diagnosis. Standard precautions decrease the risk of transmission of microorganisms from blood and other body fluids. The standards apply to contact with blood; all body fluids, secretions, and excretions (except sweat); non-intact skin; and mucous membranes.

This set of principles is used by all health care workers who have direct or indirect contact with patients. When working with patients and specimens, the CMA should always follow these standard precautions.

- Assume that all patients are carrying a microorganism.
- Practice hand hygiene:
  - Use soap and water when hands are visibly soiled.
  - Antimicrobial foam or gel may be used if hands are not visibly soiled.
- Wear gloves:
  - Gloves must be discarded between each patient.
  - Gloves may need to be discarded when soiled and a new pair applied.
  - Practice hand hygiene after removing gloves.
- Prevent needlesticks:
  - Immediately place used needles in puncture-resistant containers.
  - Recap needles using a mechanical device or a one-handed technique.
- Wear appropriate PPE if there is a possibility of body fluids splashing or spraying.
- Clean and disinfect surfaces after each patient.
- Use disposable barriers to protect surfaces that are hard to disinfect.

Additional precautions may be needed for patients with known infections. These precautions are based on the transmission route for the infection.

- Airborne precautions:
  - Wear N-95 respirator mask; place on before entering the room and keep on until after leaving the room.
  - Place N-95 or surgical mask on patient during transport.
  - Patient may be placed in a private room with a negative-pressure air system with the door kept closed.
- Droplet precautions:
  - Place patient in a private room; the door may remain open.
  - Wear appropriate PPE within 3 feet of patient.
  - Wash hands with antimicrobial soap after removing gloves and mask, before leaving the patient's room.
  - Place surgical mask on patient during transport.
- Contact precautions:
  - Place the patient in a private room; the door may remain open.
  - Wear gloves.
  - Change gloves after touching infected materials.
  - Remove gloves before leaving patient's room.
  - Wear gown; remove before leaving patient's room.
  - Use patient-dedicated equipment if possible; community equipment is to be cleaned and disinfected between patients.
  - During transport keep precautions in place and notify different areas or departments as needed.

OSHA maintains standards for universal precautions and blood-borne pathogens, and employers may face penalties if these protocols are not followed. According to the standards, employers must provide:

- all necessary PPE
- environmental control methods, including access to clean air and water and appropriate processes for waste disposal
- training on blood-borne pathogens for employees
- an **exposure control plan** that explains steps to be taken by employees exposed to blood-borne pathogens

Exposure to blood-borne pathogens requires immediate action. For a needlestick, remove object from wound and clean the site with soap and water. For membrane exposure (splashes), flush site with water or saline for 10 minutes.

11. When should health care workers remove fluid-resistant gowns?

12. When hands are visibly soiled, which type of hand hygiene should be used?

13. A patient on airborne precautions should be kept in which type of room?

14. What steps can be taken to prevent needlesticks?

15. What is an exposure control plan?

Biohazard Disposal and Regulated Waste

Regulated medical waste (RMW) (also called biohazardous waste) is any waste that is or may be contaminated with infectious materials, including blood, secretions, and excretions. Regulated medical waste must be handled carefully to prevent the possibility of an exposure incident. The disposal of RMW is governed by federal, state, and local regulations that vary by location. Some general waste disposal guidelines are given below.

DID YOU KNOW?

Infectious material that is not blood is referred to as "other potentially infectious material" (OPIM).

- Sharps should be disposed of in a biohazard sharps container. The term "sharps" refers to needles, lancets, blood tubes, capillary tubes, razor blades, suturing needles, hypodermic needles, and microscope slides and coverslips.

Figure 2.5. Sharps Container

- Blood and body fluids, such as urine, sputum, semen, amniotic fluid, and cerebrospinal fluid, can be disposed of in a drain, toilet, or utility sink. State and local regulations may limit the amount of fluid that can be disposed of into the sewage system.

- Feces should be flushed in a toilet.

- Bandages, dressing gauzes, and gloves with small amounts of RMW can be put in regular garbage disposal cans.

- Dirty linen should be put in a separate receptacle; if very soiled by blood, it should be put in a biohazard bag.

- Chemicals should be stored and disposed of according to the information in the **safety data sheets (SDSs)**, which are provided by the manufacturer. The SDSs will also include a color code for potential hazards:
  - red: flammable
  - blue: health hazard/toxic
  - yellow: reactive/oxidizing
  - white: contact hazard
  - green: not hazardous/suitable for general storage

Spill kits are a collection of substances and PPE that assist in cleaning and containing infectious agents or chemical agents after a spill. Spill kits may be general purpose, or they may be tailored to a specific substance, such as mercury or body fluids.

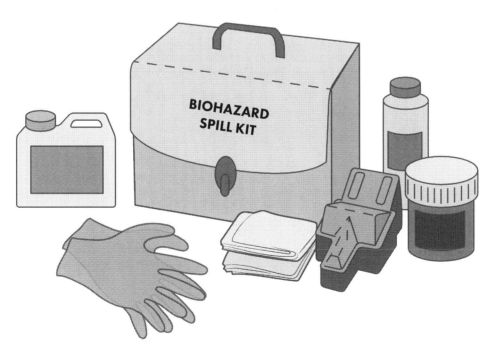

Figure 2.6. Biohazard Spill Kit

Workplace Safety

Although rare, fires in physician offices do occur. The medical assistant should be aware of certain fire safety measures:

- Keeping open spaces free of clutter.
- Marking fire exits.
- Knowing the locations of fire exits, alarms, and extinguishers.
- Knowing the fire drill and evacuation plan of the health care facility.
- Not using the elevator when a fire occurs.
- Turning off oxygen in the vicinity of a fire.

Before use, **electrical equipment** should be inspected for defects and safety by checking three-pronged outlets and reading warning labels. Any electrical cords that are exposed, damaged, or frayed should be discarded, and circuits should not be overloaded. Safety measures include:

- Never running electrical wiring under carpets.
- Not pulling a plug by yanking the cord.
- Never using electrical appliances near bathtubs, sinks, or other water sources.
- Disconnecting plugs from the outlet before cleaning appliances or equipment.
- Never operating unfamiliar equipment.

Radiation safety involves the use of various protocols and guidelines of the health care facility. Radiation exposure is monitored with a film badge. Safety measures include:

- Labeling potentially radioactive material.
- Limiting time spent near the source.
- Using a shielding device to protect vital organs.
- Placing the patient with radiation implants in a private room.

A **poison** is any substance that destroys or impairs health or life when inhaled, ingested, or otherwise absorbed by the body. The reversibility of the poison effect is determined by the capacity of the body tissue to recover from the poison. Poisonous substances can alter various body systems, including the respiratory, central nervous, circulatory, hepatic, renal, and gastrointestinal systems. Safety measures include:

- Keeping the poison control center phone number visible.
- Removing obvious substances/materials from the patient's mouth, eyes, or body area.
- If the patient vomits, saving the vomitus for examination.
- Never inducing vomiting unless specified in poison control policies.
- Never inducing vomiting in an unconscious patient.

Warning signs and labels are used to warn staff and patients about potential dangers in the workplace.

- **Danger** signs indicate an immediate hazard that could result in death or serious injury.
- **Warning** signs indicate a hazardous situation that could result in death or serious injury.
- **Caution** signs identify potentially hazardous situations that could result in minor or moderate injury or equipment damage, or to caution against unsafe practices.
- **Biological hazard** signs identify the potential presence of a biohazard.
- **Notice** signs provide general information.
- **General safety** signs provide notices of general office practices and safety measures.
- **Fire safety** signs indicate the location of emergency firefighting equipment.

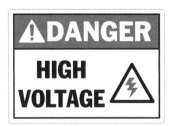

Figure 2.7. Examples of Safety Signs

REVIEW QUESTIONS

19. If there is a fire in a medical office, what should be done with an oxygen tank?

20. How is radiation exposure monitored in a health care facility?

_____

21. What does a _Danger_ sign indicate?

_____

Emergency Procedures

It is important that a medical office have a crash cart or area where emergency equipment is easily accessible. Medical assistants should be familiar with the location of emergency equipment and how it is used. The CMA may be asked to retrieve or use supplies from the crash cart. The table below provides a list of common medical equipment that may be needed in an emergency.

TABLE 2.1. Common Emergency Medical Equipment	
Equipment	**Use**
Automated external defibrillator (AED)	restarts normal cardiac rhythm in patients with specific dysrhythmias
Portable oxygen tank	provides oxygen to patients with hypoxia (low oxygen saturation)
Suction equipment	clears airways
Endotracheal tubes	opens airways and provides mechanical ventilation
Cardiopulmonary resuscitation mask	covers patient's mouth during CPR
Bag valve mask (this may have an oxygen hookup)	provides ventilation during cardiac or respiratory arrest
Emergency medications	epinephrine: anaphylactic shock and cardiac arrest atropine: slow heart rate (bradycardia) sodium bicarb: high acid levels in blood and some types of overdoses activated charcoal: some poisonings ipecac: to induce vomiting aspirin: for patients experiencing symptoms of acute coronary distress
IV supplies	for administration of fluids and medications
Dressings	for controlling bleeding and dressing wounds
PPE, including gowns, gloves, surgical masks, and N-95 respirators	to prevent spread of infections

The office should have an established emergency response plan that details the CMA's role and responsibilities. Staff should review how to respond to a medical emergency at least quarterly. Common emergency procedures and appropriate responses should be detailed. Emergency plans will vary by office, but in general the medical assistant should expect to:

- alert providers to emergencies
- provide immediate assistance as directed by the provider
- help direct other office personnel

During an emergency it is important to communicate clearly and work as a team. Important telephone numbers (e.g., poison control and the nearest hospital) should be clearly posted. All staff should be trained in CPR, and a list of everyone with CPR and first aid training should be available.

In the event that the office needs to be evacuated, CMAs should be familiar with the approved exit routes. Many offices have an evacuation map posted. Medical assistants should understand their role in evacuating patients and be prepared to provide calm, clear directions. The most important thing to remember when responding to an emergency is to remain calm.

REVIEW QUESTIONS

22. What is the purpose of an automated external defibrillator (AED)?

_____

23. What is the CMA's role during an emergency?

_____

24. What common medical equipment is used to clear a patient's airway?

_____

Risk Management and Quality Assurance

A medical assistant's primary responsibility is protecting the dignity, confidentiality, and safety of the patient. Unfortunately, there may be a time when the CMA observes the unsafe or unethical behaviors of a coworker or even a physician. In most cases, the most appropriate course of action is to report these behaviors to a supervisor. It is important to document the conversation in writing and to establish a timeline for resolution of the problem. If the situation is not resolved, the next step is to report the problem to the appropriate government agency (e.g., nursing board, medical board).

Most health care providers will make a mistake at some point in their careers. In some cases, these **incidents** will cause no adverse effects for the patient, while in others there could be extensive damage or even fatality.

- A **variance** is a deviation from standard protocols or from a patient's care plan. It may directly impact a patient's care, or it may not lead to patient harm. A patient fall or a medication administered at the wrong time are examples of variances.

- An **adverse event** is a physical injury caused by medical care. It may be the result of substandard care (e.g., incorrect medication administered), or it may be a known risk of care (e.g., pulmonary embolism following surgery).

- A **sentinel event** is an event that leads to patient death or serious harm, such as wrong-site surgeries or suicides in care.

- A **near-miss** is an action that could have caused injury to a patient but did not. For example, if a nurse is preparing to administer a medication to the wrong patient but stops after checking the patient's ID bracelet.

No matter how minor a mistake may seem at the time of occurrence, it is important to report it quickly and accurately using the proper channels. The purpose of the **incident report** is to identify what problem occurred as well as any consequences of the incident. They are not intended to place blame but rather to document the event and track the occurrence of similar events. It is important to word the documentation as objectively and honestly as possible because these reports can be used in court if the incident turns into a lawsuit.

Most medical offices—and particularly large settings like hospitals—will have dedicated reporting systems that operate as part of a larger risk management strategy. **Risk management** is the process of analyzing how these events happen and building processes to prevent them from happening again.

A **conflict of interest** may arise in a medical office when a health care provider's professional responsibilities to a patient have been or could be compromised by other outside factors. Examples of possible conflicts of interest include:

- a physician referring a patient to a lab in which the physician has a financial interest

- a health care provider treating their own family members

- an arrangement between a physician and a pharmaceutical company that affects how prescriptions are written

If there is a question about whether a conflict exists, the medical assistant should discuss it with a supervisor and not get involved in the potential conflict.

Health care fraud is an intentional act of deceit, deception, or misrepresentation of services. Examples of fraud are changing claims forms for higher payments or billing for procedures that were not performed. **Health care abuse** is reckless conduct inconsistent with acceptable practices that result in unnecessary charges to the patient or insurance company. An example of abuse would be a physician performing unnecessary tests just to receive addi-

DID YOU KNOW?

The medical assistant should not notify the patient of an error—that is the responsibility of the physician unless it is delegated to someone else, such as the office manager.

tional payment. The primary difference between fraud and abuse is the ability to prove the physician's intent to deceive the insurer. If a medical assistant suspects fraud or abuse, it is important to document and report it to a supervisor or government agency, depending on the circumstances.

REVIEW QUESTIONS

25. A wrong-site surgery is considered which type of incident?

_____

26. What is the purpose of an incident report?

_____

27. What type of misconduct occurs if a physician refers all of their patients who need X-rays to an imaging center that he owns?

_____

28. Should the CMA notify the patient if an error has occurred?

_____

29. What is the key difference between health care fraud and health care abuse?

_____

ANSWER KEY

1. During the incubation period, the infectious organism establishes a presence in the host, but the host does not show any symptoms.

2. Influenza is caused by a virus.

3. A reservoir is where the infectious organism lives (e.g., on people, animals, or in a certain environment).

4. When an infected person sneezes or coughs, infectious agents trapped in the moisture are expelled and enter the respiratory system of a new host.

5. Organisms carry the infectious agent between hosts.

6. Sterilization kills all infectious agents, including bacterial spores. Cleaning and disinfection only kill some infectious agents.

7. When performing a surgical scrub, hands, wrists, and forearms should be cleansed for 10 minutes.

8. Part of the sterile field includes the hands and anterior trunk from the neck to the waist.

9. Each item should be opened per the package's instructions and checked for breaks or moisture.

10. Chemical sterilization (also known as cold sterilization) involves soaking heat-sensitive equipment in closed containers with strong chemical agents.

11. Health care workers should remove fluid-resistant gowns before leaving a patient's room.

12. When hands are visibly soiled, use soap and water for hand hygiene.

13. A patient on airborne precautions should be placed in a private, closed-door room with a negative-pressure air system.

14. In the event of a needlestick, used needles should immediately be placed in puncture-resistant containers. CMAs should recap needles using a mechanical device or a one-handed technique.

15. An exposure control plan explains the steps employees should take if they have been exposed to blood-borne pathogens.

16. According to safety data sheets (SDSs), flammable hazards are signified by the color red.

17. Sharps, like used needles, lancets, capillary tubes, and microscope slides, should be disposed of in a biohazard sharps container.

18. Blood and body fluids like urine can be disposed of in a drain, toilet, or utility sink.

19. In the event of a fire, the oxygen tank should be turned off.

20. Radiation exposure is monitored with a film badge.

21. A *Danger* sign is one of the warning signs used to warn staff and patients about potential dangers in the workplace. The *Danger* sign indicates an immediate hazard that could result in death or serious injury.

22. An automated external defibrillator (AED) is a common piece of emergency medical equipment used to restart a normal cardiac rhythm in patients with specific dysrhythmias.

23. During an emergency, the CMA should be familiar with exit routes, alert providers to emergency, provide immediate assistance, and help direct other office personnel.

24. Suction equipment is used to clear a patient's airway.

25. A wrong-site surgery is an example of a sentinel event.

26. An incident report is intended to objectively document the event and its consequences, and track the occurrence of similar events.

27. This type of misconduct is a conflict of interest.

28. No, the physician or delegated manager should notify the patient of an error.

29. Health care fraud is an intentional act of deceit, deception, or misrepresentation of services. Health care abuse is reckless conduct inconsistent with acceptable practices that results in unnecessary charges to the patient or insurance company.

3 ANATOMY AND PHYSIOLOGY

An understanding of human anatomy and physiology is vital to the work of a medical assistant. Tasks such as taking vital signs, documenting care, and collecting specimens all require a strong foundational knowledge of body systems and disease. For the medical assisting exam, candidates should focus on reviewing the structure and function of each body system as well as the underlying pathophysiology of common medical conditions.

The Biological Hierarchy

The biological hierarchy is a systematic breakdown of the structures of the human body organized from smallest to largest (or largest to smallest). The human body is made up of small units called cells. A **cell** is a microscopic, self-replicating, structural, and functional unit of the body that performs many different jobs. The cell is made up of many smaller units that are sometimes considered to be part of the biological hierarchy, including cytoplasm, organelles, nuclei, and a membrane that separates the cell contents from their surroundings.

Tissues compose the next-largest group of structures in the body. They are a collection of cells that all perform a similar function. The human body has four basic types of tissue:

- **Connective tissues**—which include bones, ligaments, and cartilage—support, separate, or connect the body's various organs and tissues.

- **Epithelial tissues** are thin layers of cells that line blood vessels, body cavities, and some organs.

- **Muscular tissues** contain contractile units that pull on connective tissues to create movement.

- **Nervous tissues** make up the peripheral nervous systems that transmit impulses throughout the body.

After tissues, **organs** are the next-largest structure in the biological hierarchy. Organs are a collection of tissues within the body that share a similar function. For example, the esophagus is an organ whose primary function is carrying food and liquids from the mouth to the stomach.

Organ systems, a group of organs that work together to perform a similar function, rank above organs as the next-largest structure on the biological hierarchy. The esophagus is part of the digestive organ system, which is the entire group of organs in the body that processes food from start to finish.

Finally, an **organism** is the total collection of all the parts of the biological hierarchy working together to form a living being; it is the largest structure in the biological hierarchy.

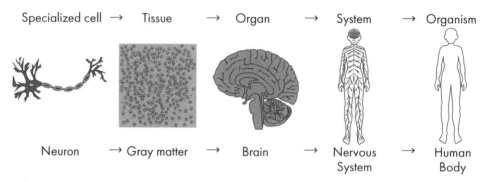

Figure 3.1. Biological Hierarchy

REVIEW QUESTIONS

1. What are tissues?

2. What type of tissue is cartilage?

3. What is the name for a group of organs that work together to perform a function?

Directional Terminology

When discussing anatomy and physiology, specific terms are used to refer to directions. Directional terms include the following:

- inferior: away from the head
- superior: closer to the head
- anterior: toward the front
- posterior: toward the back
- ventral: toward the front
- dorsal: toward the back
- medial: toward the midline of the body

- lateral: farther from the midline of the body
- proximal: closer to the trunk
- distal: away from the trunk

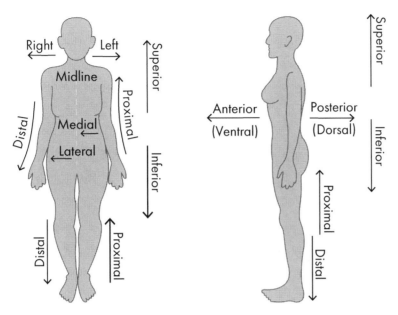

Figure 3.2. Directional Terminology

REVIEW QUESTIONS

4. What term describes "toward the back"?

_____

5. If a wound is described as superior-medial on the abdomen, where is it located?

_____

Body Cavities and Planes

The internal structure of the human body is organized into compartments called **cavities**, which are separated by membranes. There are two main cavities in the human body: the **dorsal cavity** and the **ventral cavity** (both named for their relative positions).

The dorsal cavity is further divided into the **cranial cavity**, which holds the brain, and the **spinal cavity**, which surrounds the spine. The two sections of the dorsal cavity are continuous. Both sections are lined by the **meninges**, a three-layered membrane that protects the brain and spinal cord.

The ventral cavity houses most of the body's organs. It can be further divided into smaller cavities. The **thoracic cavity** holds the heart and lungs, the **abdominal cavity** holds the digestive organs and kidneys, and the **pelvic cavity** holds the bladder and reproductive organs. Both the abdominal and pelvic cavities are enclosed by a membrane called the **peritoneum**.

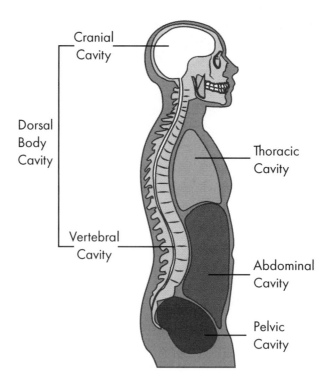

Figure 3.3. Body Cavities

The human body is divided by three imaginary planes.

- The **transverse plane** divides the body into a top and bottom half.
- The **frontal** (or coronal) **plane** divides the body into a front and back half.
- The **sagittal plane** divides the body into a right and left half.

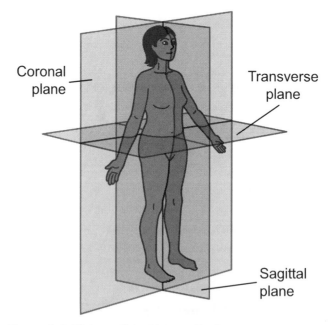

Figure 3.4. Planes of the Human Body

The Cardiovascular System

STRUCTURE AND FUNCTION OF THE CARDIOVASCULAR SYSTEM

The **cardiovascular system** circulates **blood**, which carries nutrients, wastes, hormones, and other important substances dissolved or suspended in liquid plasma. Two of the most important components of blood are **white blood cells**, which fight infections, and **red blood cells**, which transport oxygen. Red blood cells contain **hemoglobin**, a large molecule that includes iron atoms, which binds to oxygen.

Blood is circulated by a muscular organ called the **heart**. The human heart has four chambers, the right and left **atria** and the right and left **ventricles**, as shown in Figure 3.5. Each chamber is isolated by valves that prevent the backflow of blood once it has passed through. The **tricuspid** and **mitral valves** separate atria from ventricles, and the **pulmonary** and **aortic valves** regulate the movement of blood out of the heart into the arteries. The pumping action of the heart is regulated primarily by two neurological **nodes**, the **sinoatrial** and the **atrioventricular** nodes, whose electrical activity sets the rhythm of the heart.

The heart includes several layers of tissue:

- **pericardium:** the outermost protective layer of the heart that contains a lubricative liquid
- **epicardium:** the deepest layer of the pericardium that envelops the heart muscle
- **myocardium:** the heart muscle
- **endocardium:** the innermost, smooth layer of the heart walls

Blood leaves the heart and travels throughout the body in blood vessels, which decrease in diameter as they move away from the heart and toward the tissues and organs. Blood exits the heart through **arteries**, which become **arterioles** and then **capillaries**, the smallest branch of the circulatory system in which gas exchange from blood to tissues occurs. Deoxygenated blood travels back to the heart through **veins**.

The circulatory system includes two closed loops. In the **pulmonary loop**, deoxygenated blood leaves the heart and travels to the lungs, where it loses carbon dioxide and becomes rich in oxygen. The oxygenated blood then returns to the heart, which pumps it through the systemic loop. The **systemic**

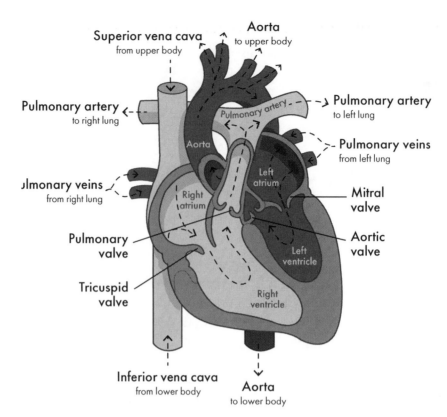

Figure 3.5. The Heart

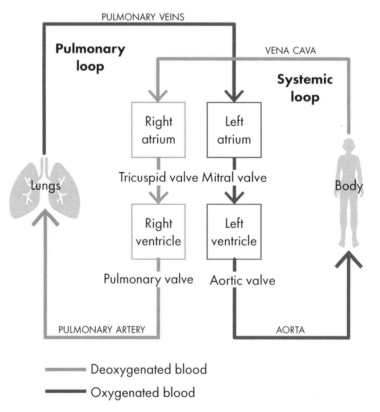

Figure 3.6. Path of Blood Flow Through the Cardiovascular System

loop delivers oxygen to the rest of the body and returns deoxygenated blood to the heart.

PATHOLOGIES OF THE CARDIOVASCULAR SYSTEM

Hypertension is increased blood pressure, usually above 140/80 mm Hg. Hypertension usually has no symptoms, but it has been linked to heart disease and stroke. **Hypotension** is decreased blood pressure, usually below 90/60 mm Hg.

Ischemia is reduced or restricted blood flow to tissues, and **infarction** is the death of tissue caused by restricted blood flow and the subsequent lack of oxygen. Causes of ischemia include:

- occlusion of blood vessels by an **embolus** (a mass made of fat, bacteria, or other materials) or a **thrombus** (blood clot; also called a thromboembolism)
- narrowed blood vessel (e.g., aneurysm or atherosclerosis)
- trauma

A **myocardial infarction** (MI; also called a heart attack) is an occlusion of the coronary arteries, which supply blood to the heart. The resulting death of cardiac tissue may lead to dysrhythmias, reduced cardiac output, or cardiac arrest. Patients with MI require immediate medical intervention to restore blood flow to the coronary arteries.

Atherosclerosis is a progressive condition in which **plaque** (composed of fat, white blood cells, and other waste) builds up in the arteries. The presence of advanced atherosclerosis places patients at a high risk for several cardiovascular conditions.

- Arteries may become **stenotic**, or narrowed, limiting blood flow to specific areas of the body (e.g., carotid stenosis).
- When a plaque **ruptures**, the plaque and the clot that forms around it (superimposed thrombus) can quickly lead to complete occlusion of the artery (e.g., MI).
- The clots or loosened plaque released by a rupture may also move through the bloodstream and occlude smaller vessels (e.g., ischemic stroke).
- Atherosclerosis is also a cause of **aneurysms** (widened arteries), which weaken arterial walls, increasing the risk of arterial dissection or rupture (e.g., abdominal aortic aneurysm [AAA]).

Dysrhythmias are abnormal heart rhythms.

- **Bradycardia** is a heart rate < 60 bpm.
- **Atrial fibrillation (A-fib)** is a rapid, irregular contraction of the atria. During A-fib, the heart cannot adequately empty, which causes

DID YOU KNOW?

Common symptoms of MI include pain or pressure in the chest, jaw, or arm; sweating; nausea/vomiting; and pallor. Some patients, especially women or people with diabetes, may present without chest pain.

blood to pool and clots to form. These clots can break off and travel to the heart or brain, causing a heart attack or stroke.

- **Atrioventricular (AV) block** is the disruption of electrical signals between the atria and ventricles. The electrical impulse may be delayed (first degree), intermittent (second degree), or completely blocked (third degree).

- During **ventricular fibrillation (V-fib)** the ventricles contract rapidly (300 – 400 bpm) with no organized rhythm, and there is no cardiac output.

- **Ventricular tachycardia (V-tach)** is tachycardia originating in the ventricles with 3 consecutive ventricular beats occurring at a rate less than 100 bpm. V-tach may be short and asymptomatic, or it may precede V-fib and cardiac arrest.

- **Pulseless electrical activity (PEA)** is an organized rhythm in which the heart does not contract with enough force to create a pulse. PEA is a non-shockable rhythm with a poor survival rate.

- **Asystole**, also called a "flat line," occurs when there is no electrical or mechanical activity within the heart. Like PEA, asystole is a non-shockable rhythm with a poor survival rate.

Heart failure occurs when either one or both of the ventricles in the heart cannot efficiently pump blood. Because the heart is unable to pump effectively, blood and fluid back up into the lungs (causing pulmonary congestion), or the fluid builds up peripherally (causing edema of the lower extremities). Heart failure is most commonly categorized into left-sided heart failure or right-sided heart failure, although both sides of the heart can fail at the same time.

Hemophilia is a recessive X-chromosome–linked bleeding disorder characterized by the lack of coagulation factors. **Sickle cell disease** is an inherited form of hemolytic anemia that causes deformities in the shape of the RBCs.

DID YOU KNOW?

V-fib and V-tach are the two shockable rhythms, meaning they can be corrected using an AED.

REVIEW QUESTIONS

8. How would a blood pressure of 82/45 mm Hg be classified?

_____

9. What is the difference between ischemia and infarction?

_____

10. Why do people with A-fib have a higher risk of stroke?

_____

11. What intervention is expected if a patient's cardiac rhythm is V-tach?

_____

12. Which arteries are affected by a myocardial infarction?

_____

The Respiratory System
Structure and Function of the Respiratory System

The **respiratory system** is responsible for the exchange of gases between the human body and the environment. **Oxygen** is brought into the body for use in glucose metabolism, and the **carbon dioxide** created by glucose metabolism is expelled. Gas exchange takes place in the **lungs**. Humans have two lungs, a right and a left, and the right lung is slightly larger than the left. The right lung has three **lobes**, and the left has two. The lungs are surrounded by a thick membrane called the **pleura**.

Respiration begins with **pulmonary ventilation**, or breathing. The first stage of breathing is **inhalation**. During this process, the thoracic cavity expands and the diaphragm muscle contracts, which decreases the pressure in the lungs, pulling in air from the atmosphere. Air is drawn in through the nose and mouth, then into the throat, where cilia and mucus filter out particles before the air enters the **trachea**.

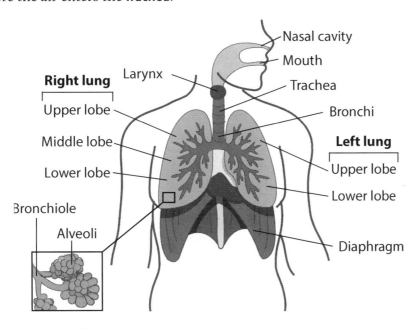

Figure 3.7. The Respiratory System

Once it passes through the trachea, the air passes through either the left or right **bronchi**, which are divisions of the trachea that direct air into the left or right lung. These bronchi are further divided into smaller **bronchioles**, which branch throughout the lungs and become increasingly small.

Eventually, air enters the **alveoli**—tiny air sacs located at the ends of the smallest bronchioles. The alveoli have very thin membranes, only one cell thick, and are the location of gas exchange with the blood: oxygen diffuses into the blood while carbon dioxide is diffused out.

Carbon dioxide is then expelled from the lungs during **exhalation**, the second stage of breathing. During exhalation, the diaphragm relaxes and the thoracic cavity contracts, causing air to leave the body, as the lung pressure is now greater than the atmospheric pressure.

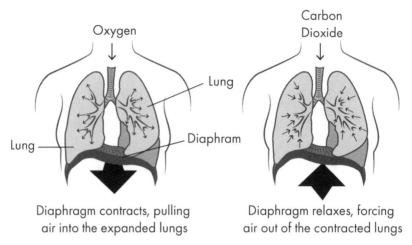

Figure 3.8. The Breathing Process

PATHOLOGIES OF THE RESPIRATORY SYSTEM

Lung diseases that result in the continual restriction of airflow are known as **chronic obstructive pulmonary disease (COPD)**. These include **emphysema**, which is the destruction of lung tissues, and **asthma**, in which the airways are compromised due to a dysfunctional immune response. The main causes of COPD are smoking and air pollution, and genetic factors can also influence the severity of the disease.

The respiratory system is also prone to **respiratory tract infections**, with upper respiratory tract infections affecting air inputs in the nose and throat, and lower respiratory tract infections affecting the lungs and their immediate pulmonary inputs. Viral infections of the respiratory system include **influenza** and the **common cold**; bacterial infections include **tuberculosis** and **pertussis** (whooping cough). **Pneumonia**, the inflammation of the lungs that affects alveoli, can be caused by bacteria, viruses, fungi, or parasites. It is often seen in people whose respiratory system has been weakened by other conditions.

Lung cancer is the second-most common type of cancer diagnosed in the United States. (Breast cancer is the most common.) Symptoms of lung cancer include cough, chest pain, and wheezing. Lung cancer is most often caused by smoking, but it can develop in nonsmokers as well.

Disruptions to the respiratory system can result in abnormal breathing patterns.

- **apnea:** not breathing.

- **hyperventilation:** increase in rate or volume of breaths, which causes excessive elimination of CO_2.
- **agonal breathing:** irregular gasping breaths accompanied by involuntary twitching or jerking. Agonal breathing is associated with severe hypoxia and is a sign the patient requires immediate medical treatment.
- **Biot's breathing:** alternating rapid respirations and apnea. Causes include stroke, trauma, and opioid use.
- **Cheyne-Stokes breathing:** deep breathing alternating with apnea or a faster rate of breathing; associated with left heart failure or sleep apnea.
- **Kussmaul breathing:** type of hyperventilation characterized by deep, labored breathing that is associated with metabolic acidosis (particularly diabetic ketoacidosis).

REVIEW QUESTIONS

13. Where does gas exchange take place in the lungs?

_____

14. A patient with diabetes is hyperventilating, with a deep, labored breathing pattern. What type of breathing might this be?

_____

15. Which term describes the absence of breathing?

_____

16. What are the main causes of COPD?

_____

17. What is a pulmonary embolism?

_____

The Nervous System

STRUCTURE AND FUNCTION OF THE NERVOUS SYSTEM

The **nervous system** coordinates the processes and actions of the human body. **Nerve cells**, or **neurons**, communicate through electrical impulses and allow the body to process and respond to stimuli. Neurons have a nucleus and transmit electrical impulses through their axons and dendrites. The **axon** is the stemlike structure, often covered in a fatty insulating substance called **myelin**, that carries information to other neurons throughout the body. Myelin is produced by **Schwann cells**, which also play an important role in nerve regeneration. **Dendrites** receive information from other neurons.

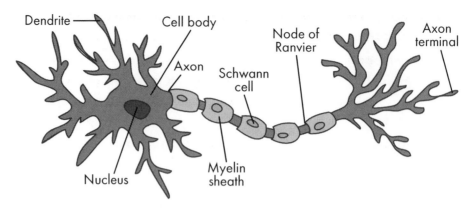

Figure 3.9. The Structure of a Neuron

The nervous system is broken down into two parts: the **central nervous system (CNS)** and the **peripheral nervous system (PNS)**. The CNS is made up of the brain and spinal cord. The brain acts as the control center for the body and is responsible for nearly all the body's processes and actions. The spinal cord relays information between the brain and the peripheral nervous system; it also coordinates many reflexes. The spinal cord is protected by the vertebral column, a structure of bones that enclose the delicate nervous tissue. The PNS is the collection of nerves that connect the central nervous system to the rest of the body.

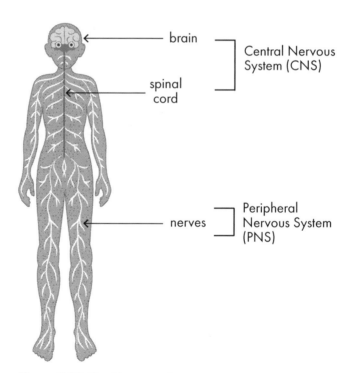

Figure 3.10. The Nervous System

The functions of the nervous system are broken down into the autonomic nervous system and the somatic nervous system. The **autonomic nervous system** controls involuntary actions that occur in the body, such as respiration, heartbeat, digestive processes, and more. The **somatic nervous system** is responsible for the body's ability to control skeletal muscles and voluntary movement as well as the involuntary reflexes associated with skeletal muscles.

The autonomic nervous system is further broken down into the sympathetic nervous system and the parasympathetic nervous system. The **sympathetic nervous system** is responsible for the body's reaction to stress and induces a "fight-or-flight" response to stimuli. For instance, if an individual is frightened, the sympathetic nervous system increases the person's heart rate and blood pressure to prepare them to either fight or flee.

In contrast, the **parasympathetic nervous system** is stimulated by the body's need for rest or recovery. The parasympathetic nervous system responds by decreasing heart rate, blood pressure, and muscular activation when a person is getting ready for activities such as sleeping or digesting food. For example, the body activates the parasympathetic nervous system after eating a large meal, which is why people then feel sluggish.

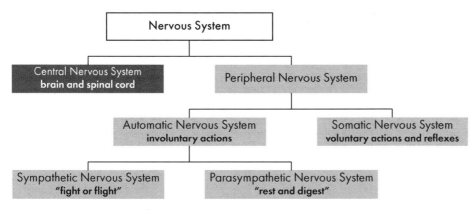

Figure 3.11. Divisions of the Nervous System

PATHOLOGIES OF THE NERVOUS SYSTEM

A **stroke**, or **cardiovascular accident (CVA)**, occurs when blood flow to brain tissue is disrupted. An **ischemic stroke** is the result of a blockage (embolus) in the vasculature of the brain. A **hemorrhagic stroke** is bleeding in the brain, often caused by a ruptured aneurysm.

The nervous system can be affected by a number of degenerative diseases that result from the gradual breakdown of nervous tissue. These include:

- **Parkinson's disease:** caused by cell death in the basal ganglia; characterized by gradual loss of motor function
- **multiple sclerosis (MS):** caused by damage to the myelin sheath; characterized by muscle spasms and weakness, numbness, loss of coordination, and blindness

- **amyotrophic lateral sclerosis (ALS):** caused by the death of neurons that control voluntary muscle movement; characterized by muscle stiffness, twitches, and weakness
- **Alzheimer's disease:** caused by damaged neurons in the cerebral cortex; characterized by memory loss, confusion, mood swings, and problems with language

The nervous system is also susceptible to infections, some of which can be life threatening. **Meningitis** is inflammation of the meninges, the protective membrane that surrounds the brain and spinal cord, and **encephalitis** is inflammation of the brain. Both conditions can be caused by viral or bacterial pathogens.

Epileptic seizures are brief episodes caused by disturbed or overactive nerve cell activity in the brain. Seizures range widely in severity and may include confusion, convulsions, and loss of consciousness. They have many causes, including tumors, infections, head injuries, and medications.

REVIEW QUESTIONS

18. What type of stroke is caused by a blockage (embolus) in the vasculature of the brain?

19. What types of signs and symptoms may be seen during an epileptic seizure?

20. What functions is the autonomic nervous system responsible for?

The Skeletal System

STRUCTURE AND FUNCTION OF THE SKELETAL SYSTEM

The skeletal system is made up of over 200 different **bones**, a stiff connective tissue in the human body with many functions, including:

- protecting internal organs
- synthesizing blood cells
- storing necessary minerals
- providing the muscular system with leverage to create movement

Bones are covered with a thin layer of vascular connective tissue called the **periosteum**, which serves as a point of muscle attachment, supplies blood to the bone, and contains nerve endings. **Osseous tissue** is the primary tissue that makes up bone. There are two types of osseous tissue: cortical (compact) bone and cancellous (spongy) bone. **Cortical bone** is the dense, solid material that surrounds the bone and gives it hardness and strength. It is usually concentrated in the middle part of the bone.

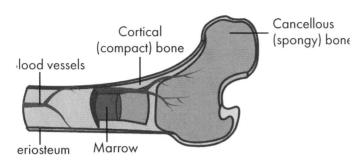

Figure 3.12. Structure of Bone

Cancellous bone is less dense, more porous, and softer. It is located at the ends of long bones, where it does not bear a structural load. Instead it is a site of the bone's blood production and metabolic activity, as it stores both blood vessels and **bone marrow. Red bone marrow** is responsible for producing red blood cells, platelets, and white blood cells. **Yellow bone marrow** is composed mostly of fat tissue and can be converted to red bone marrow in response to extreme blood loss in the body.

TABLE 3.1. Types of Bones		
Name	**Shape**	**Example**
Long bones	longer than they are wide	femur, humerus
Short bones	wider than they are long	clavicle, carpals
Flat bones	wide and flat	skull, pelvis
Irregular bones	irregularly shaped	vertebrae, jaw

The hundreds of bones in the body make up the human **skeleton**. The **axial skeleton** contains eighty bones and has three major subdivisions: the **skull**, which contains the cranium and facial bones; the **thorax**, which includes the sternum and twelve pairs of ribs; and the **vertebral column**, which contains the body's thirty-three vertebrae. These eighty bones function together to support and protect many of the body's vital organs, including the brain, lungs, heart, and spinal cord. The **appendicular skeleton**'s 126 bones make up the body's appendages. The main function of the appendicular skeleton is locomotion.

Various connective tissues join the parts of the skeleton together to other systems, as shown in the table on the next page.

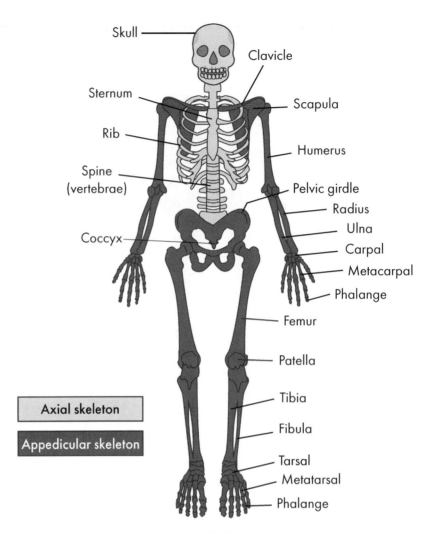

Figure 3.13. The Axial and Appendicular Skeletons

TABLE 3.2. Connective Tissue in the Skeletal System

Tissue	Function
Ligament	Joins bone to bone.
Tendon	Joins bones to muscles.
Cartilage	Cushions bones in joints. Provides structural integrity for many body parts (e.g., the ears and nose), maintains open pathways (e.g., the trachea and bronchi).

JOINTS

The point at which a bone is attached to another bone is called a joint. There are three basic types of joints:

- **Fibrous joints** connect bones that do not move.

- **Cartilaginous joints** connect bones with cartilage and allow limited movement.
- **Synovial joints** allow for a range of motion and are covered by articular cartilage that protects the bones.

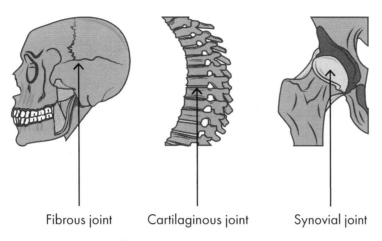

Fibrous joint   Cartilaginous joint   Synovial joint

Figure 3.14. Types of Joints

Synovial joints are classified based on their structure and the type of movement they allow. There are many types of synovial joints; the most important are discussed in Table 3.3.

TABLE 3.3. Types of Synovial Joints		
Name	**Movement**	**Found In**
Hinge joint	movement through one plane of motion as flexion/extension	elbows, knees, fingers
Ball-and-socket joint	range of motion through multiple planes and rotation about an axis	hips, shoulders
Saddle joint	movement through multiple planes, but cannot rotate about an axis	thumbs
Gliding joint	sliding movement in the plane of the bones' surfaces	vertebrae, small bones in the wrists and ankles
Condyloid joint	movement through two planes as flexion/extension and abduction/adduction, but cannot rotate about an axis	wrists
Pivot joint	only movement is rotation about an axis	elbows, neck

PATHOLOGIES OF THE SKELETAL SYSTEM

Arthritis is inflammation in joints that leads to swelling, pain, and reduced range of motion. There are many different kinds of arthritis. The most common is **osteoarthritis**, which is caused by the wearing down of cartilage in the joints due to age or injury. **Rheumatoid arthritis** and **psoriatic arthritis** are both types of inflammation at the joint caused by chronic autoimmune disorder, which can lead to excessive joint degradation.

Osteoporosis refers to poor bone mineral density due to the loss or lack of the production of calcium content and bone cells, which leads to bone brittleness. It is most common in postmenopausal women.

Postural deviations that cause excessive curvatures of the spine can have painful ramifications for the human body. These include **lordosis** (an excessive anterior curvature of the natural S-shape of the spine), **kyphosis** (an excessive posterior curvature of the natural S-shape of the spine), and **scoliosis** (an excessive lateral curvature of the spine).

Bone cancers include Ewing's sarcoma and osteosarcoma. In addition, white blood cell cancers, such as myeloma and leukemia, start in bone marrow. **Osteomyelitis** is an infection in the bone that can occur directly (after a traumatic bone injury) or indirectly (via the vascular system or other infected tissues).

REVIEW QUESTIONS

21. What is the function of cartilage?

_____

22. What is the purpose of bone marrow?

_____

23. What is lordosis?

_____

The Muscular System

The primary function of the muscular system is movement. Muscles contract and relax, resulting in motion. This includes both voluntary motion, such as walking, as well as involuntary motion that keeps the body systems, such as circulation, respiration, and digestion, running. Other functions of the muscular system include overall stability and protection of the spine as well as posture.

MUSCLE CELL STRUCTURE

The main structural unit of a muscle is the **sarcomere**. Sarcomeres are composed of a series of **muscle fibers**, which are elongated individual cells that stretch from one end of the muscle to the other. Within each fiber are hundreds of **myofibrils**, long strands within the cells that contain alternating layers of thin filaments made of the protein **actin** and thick filaments made of the protein **myosin**. Each of these proteins plays a role in muscle contraction and relaxation. During muscle contractions, myosin pulls the thin filaments of actin to the center of the sarcomere, causing the entire sarcomere to shorten, or contract, creating movement.

Skeletal muscles are activated by special neurons called **motor neurons**. Together, a motor neuron and its associated skeletal muscle fibers are called a **motor unit**. These motor neurons are located within the spinal cord and branch out to the muscles to send the nervous impulses for muscular contraction. The **neuromuscular junction** is the site at which the motor neuron and muscle fibers join to form a chemical synapse for nervous transmission to muscle.

TYPES OF MUSCLES

The muscular system consists of three types of muscle: cardiac, visceral, and skeletal. **Cardiac muscle** is only found in the heart and contracts involuntarily, creating the heartbeat and pumping blood. **Visceral muscles** are found in many of the body's essential organs, including the stomach and intestines. They slowly contract and relax to move nutrients, blood, and other substances throughout the body. Visceral muscles are also known as **smooth muscles** because, unlike cardiac and skeletal muscle, this tissue is not composed of sarcomeres with alternating thick and thin filaments. Visceral muscle movement is involuntary.

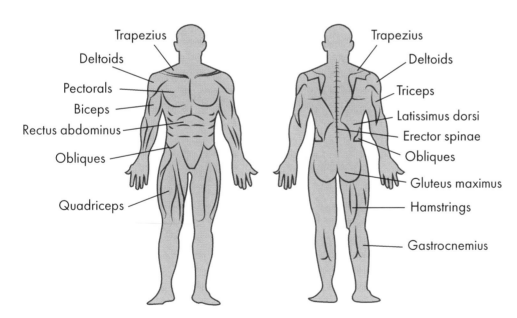

Figure 3.15. Major Muscles of the Body

Skeletal muscle is responsible for voluntary movement and, as the name suggests, is inextricably linked to the skeletal system. Skeletal muscles can engage in several types of muscle actions:

- **concentric**: muscular contraction in which the length of the muscle is shortening to lift the resistance (upward curl of bicep)
- **eccentric**: muscular contraction in which the muscle is resisting a force as it lengthens (downward curl of bicep)
- **isometric**: muscular contraction in which the resistance and force are even and no movement is taking place (holding an object)

PATHOLOGIES OF THE MUSCULAR SYSTEM

Injuries to muscle can impede movement and cause pain. When muscle fibers are overstretched, the resulting **muscle strain** can cause pain, stiffness, and bruising. Muscle **cramps** are involuntary muscle contractions (or **spasms**) that cause intense pain.

Muscle fibers can also be weakened by diseases, as with **muscular dystrophy (MD)**. MD is a genetically inherited condition that results in progressive muscle wasting, which limits movement and can cause respiratory and cardiovascular difficulties.

Rhabdomyolysis is the rapid breakdown of dead muscle tissue. It is usually caused by crush injuries, overexertion (particularly in extreme heat), and a variety of drugs and toxins (particularly statins, which are prescribed to lower cholesterol levels).

REVIEW QUESTIONS

24. What are the functions of the muscular system?

_____

25. What movement would an eccentric muscle action cause?

_____

26. What are the possible causes of rhabdomyolysis?

The Immune System

STRUCTURE AND FUNCTION OF THE IMMUNE SYSTEM

The human immune system protects the body against bacteria and viruses that cause disease. The system is composed of two parts, the innate system and the adaptive system. The **innate immune system** includes nonspecific defenses that work against a wide range of infectious agents. This system includes both physical barriers that keep out foreign particles and organisms along with cells that attack invaders. The second part of the immune system is the **adaptive immune system**, which "learns" to respond only to specific invaders.

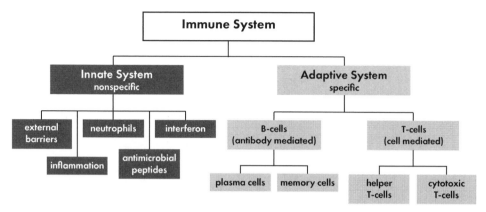

Figure 3.16. Divisions of the Immune System

Barriers to entry are the first line of defense in the immune system:

- The skin leaves few openings for an infection-causing agent to enter.

- Native bacteria outcompete invaders in openings.

- The urethra flushes out invaders with the outflow of urine.

- Mucus and earwax trap pathogens before they can replicate and cause infection.

However, pathogens can breach these barriers and enter the body, where they attempt to replicate and cause an infection. When this occurs, the body mounts a number of nonspecific responses. The body's initial response is **inflammation**, which increases blood flow to the infected area. This increase in blood flow increases the presence of white blood cells, also called **leukocytes**. (The types of white blood cells are discussed in Table 3.4.) Other innate responses include **antimicrobial peptides**, which destroy bacteria by interfering with the functions of their membranes or DNA, and **interferon**, which causes nearby cells to increase their defenses.

The adaptive immune system relies on molecules called **antigens** that appear on the surface of pathogens to which the system has previously been exposed. Antigens are displayed on the surface of cells by the major **histocompatibility complex (MHC)**.

In the cell-mediated response, **T-cells** destroy any cell that displays an antigen. In the antibody-mediated response, **B-cells** are activated by antigens. These B-cells produce plasma cells, which in turn release antibodies. **Antibodies** will bind only to specific antigens and destroy the infected cell. **Memory B-cells** are created during infection, allowing the immune system to respond more quickly if the infection appears again.

TABLE 3.4. Types of White Blood Cells

Type of Cell	Name of Cell	Role	Innate or Adaptive	Prevalence
Granulocytes	neutrophil	first responders that quickly migrate to the site of infections to destroy bacterial invaders	innate	very common
	eosinophil	attack multicellular parasites	innate	rare
	basophil	large cell responsible for inflammatory reactions, including allergies	innate	very rare
Lymphocytes	B-cells	respond to antigens by releasing antibodies	adaptive	common
	T-cells	respond to antigens by destroying invaders and infected cells	adaptive	
	natural killer cells	destroy virus-infected cells and tumor cells	innate and adaptive	
Monocytes	macro-phage	engulf and destroy microbes, foreign substances, and cancer cells	innate and adaptive	rare

PATHOLOGIES OF THE IMMUNE SYSTEM

The immune system of individuals with an **autoimmune disease** will attack healthy tissues. Autoimmune diseases (and the tissues they attack) include:

- psoriasis (skin)
- rheumatoid arthritis (joints)
- multiple sclerosis (nerve cells)
- lupus (kidneys, lungs, and skin)

The immune system may also overreact to harmless particles, a condition known as an **allergy**. Allergic reactions can be mild, resulting in watery eyes and a runny nose, but they can also include life-threatening swelling and respiratory obstruction.

Some infections will attack the immune system itself. **Human immunodeficiency virus (HIV)** attacks helper T-cells, eventually causing **acquired immunodeficiency syndrome (AIDS)**, which allows opportunistic infections to overrun the body. The immune system can also be weakened by previous infections or lifestyle factors such as smoking and alcohol consumption.

Cancers of the immune system include **lymphoma** and **leukemia**, which are caused by irregular growth of cells in lymph and bone marrow. Both white and red blood cells can become cancerous, but it is more common for the cancer to occur in white blood cells. Leukemia is the most common type of cancer to occur in children.

REVIEW QUESTIONS

27. How is the nonspecific immune system different from the adaptive immune system?

28. What are two cancers of the immune system?

29. How do allergic reactions present?

The Digestive System

STRUCTURE AND FUNCTION OF THE DIGESTIVE SYSTEM

The **digestive system** is responsible for the breakdown and absorption of food necessary to power the body. The digestive system starts at the **mouth**, which allows for the consumption and mastication of nutrients via an opening in the face. It contains the muscular **tongue** to move food and uses the liquid **saliva** to assist in the breakdown of food.

The chewed and lubricated food travels from the mouth through the **esophagus** via **peristalsis**, the contraction of smooth muscles. The esophagus leads to the **stomach**, the organ of the digestive tract found in the abdominal cavity that mixes food with powerful acidic liquid for further digestion. Once the stomach has created an acidic bolus of digested food known as **chyme**, it travels to the **small intestine**, where a significant amount of nutrient absorption takes place. The tubelike small intestine contains millions of fingerlike projections known as **villi** and microvilli to increase the surface area available for the absorption of nutrients found in food.

The small intestine then transports food to the **large intestine**. The large intestine is similarly tubelike but is larger in diameter than the small intestine. It assists in water absorption, further nutrient absorption, waste collection, and the production of feces for excretion. At the end of the large intestine are the **rectum** and the **anus**, which are responsible for the storage of feces and removal of feces, respectively. The anus is the opening at the opposite end of the digestive tract as the mouth.

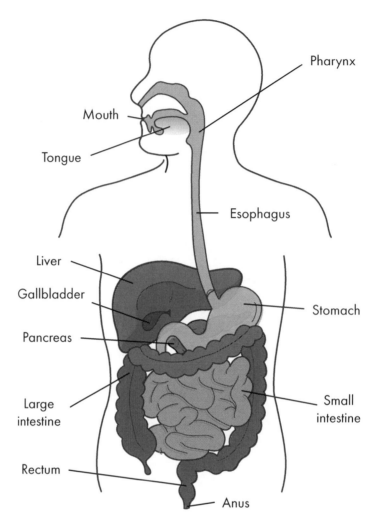

Figure 3.17. The Digestive System

Along the digestive tract are several muscular rings, known as **sphincters**, which regulate the movement of food through the tract and prevent reflux of material into the previous cavity. These include:

- upper esophageal sphincter: between the pharynx and esophagus
- lower esophageal sphincter: between the esophagus and stomach
- pyloric sphincter: between the stomach and small intestine
- ileocecal sphincter: between the small intestine and large intestine
- anus: between the rectum and the outside of the body

The digestive system also includes accessory organs that aid in digestion:

- **salivary glands:** produce saliva, which begins the process of breaking down starches and fats

- **liver:** produces bile, which helps break down fat in the small intestine
- **gallbladder:** stores bile
- **pancreas:** produces digestive enzymes and pancreatic juice, which neutralizes the acidity of chyme

PATHOLOGIES OF THE DIGESTIVE SYSTEM

The digestive system is prone to several illnesses of varying severity. Commonly, gastrointestinal distress is caused by an acute infection (bacterial or viral) affecting the lining of the digestive system. A resulting immune response triggers the body, as an adaptive measure, to void the contents of the digestive system in order to purge the infection.

Chronic GI disorders include **irritable bowel syndrome** (the causes of which are largely unknown) and **Crohn's disease**, an inflammatory bowel disorder that occurs when the immune system attacks the digestive system.

A number of different cancers can arise in the digestive system, including colon and rectal cancer, liver cancer, pancreatic cancer, esophageal cancer, and stomach cancer. Of these, colon cancer is the most common. People over 50 are recommended to get regular colonoscopies to screen for colon cancer, which has few symptoms in its early stages.

REVIEW QUESTIONS

30. Which anatomical feature prevents the movement of stomach contents into the esophagus?

_____

31. What is the purpose of salivary glands in digestion?

_____

32. What screening is important to rule out the most common digestive system cancer?

_____

The Urinary System

STRUCTURE AND FUNCTION OF THE URINARY SYSTEM

The **urinary system** excretes water and waste from the body and is crucial for maintaining the balance of water and salt in the blood (also called electrolyte balance). Because many organs function as part of both the reproductive and urinary systems, the two are sometimes referred to collectively as the **genitourinary system**.

The main organs of the urinary system are the **kidneys**, which perform several important functions:

- filter waste from the blood
- maintain the electrolyte balance in the blood
- regulate blood volume, pressure, and pH

The kidneys also function as an endocrine organ and release several important hormones, including **renin**, which regulates blood pressure. The kidney is divided into two regions: the **renal cortex**, which is the outermost layer, and the **renal medulla**, which is the inner layer.

The functional unit of the kidney is the **nephron**, which is a series of looping tubes that filter the blood. The resulting waste includes **urea**, a byproduct of protein catabolism, and **uric acid**, a byproduct of nucleic acid metabolism. Together, these waste products are excreted from the body in **urine**.

Filtration begins in a network of capillaries called a **glomerulus**, which is located in the renal cortex of each kidney. This waste is then funneled into **collecting ducts** in the renal medulla. From the collecting ducts, urine passes through the **renal pelvis** and then through two long tubes called **ureters**. The two ureters drain into the **urinary bladder**, which holds up to 1 liter of liquid. Urine exits the bladder through the **urethra**. In males, the urethra goes through the penis and also carries semen. In females, the much-shorter urethra ends just above the vaginal opening.

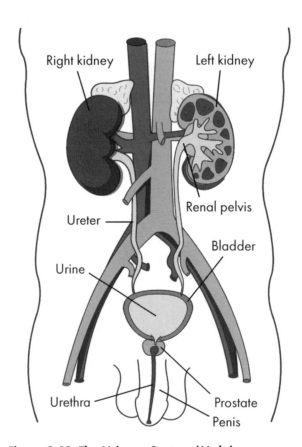

Figure 3.18. The Urinary System (Male)

PATHOLOGIES OF THE URINARY SYSTEM

Urinary tract infections (UTIs) occur when bacteria infects the kidneys, bladder, or urethra. They can occur in men or women but are more common in women. **Pyelonephritis**, infection of the kidneys, occurs when bacteria reach the kidney via the lower urinary tract or the bloodstream.

Chronic kidney disease, in which the kidneys do not function properly for at least three months, can be caused by a number of factors, including diabetes, autoimmune diseases, infections, and drug abuse. People with chronic kidney disease may need **dialysis**, during which a machine performs the task of the kidneys and removes waste from the blood.

Renal calculi (kidney stones) are hardened mineral deposits that form in the kidneys. They are usually asymptomatic but will cause debilitating pain and urinary symptoms once they pass into the urinary tract.

Urinary system cancers include bladder cancer and kidney cancer.

REVIEW QUESTIONS

33. What are the functions of the kidneys?

_____

34. Why do people with chronic kidney disease require dialysis?

_____

35. What are renal calculi?

_____

The Reproductive System
THE MALE REPRODUCTIVE SYSTEM

The **male reproductive system** produces **sperm**, or male gametes, and passes them to the female reproductive system. Sperm are produced during spermatogenesis in the **testes** (also called testicles), which are housed in a sac-like external structure called the **scrotum**. The scrotum contracts and relaxes to move the testes closer to or farther from the body. This process keeps the testes at the appropriate temperature for sperm production, which is slightly lower than regular body temperature.

Mature sperm are stored in the **epididymis**. During sexual stimulation, sperm travel from the epididymis through a long, thin tube called the **vas deferens**. Along the way, the sperm are joined by fluids from three glands:

- The **seminal vesicles** secrete a fluid composed of various proteins, sugars, and enzymes.
- The **prostate** contributes an alkaline fluid that counteracts the acidity of the vaginal tract.

- The **Cowper's gland** secretes a protein-rich fluid that acts as a lubricant.

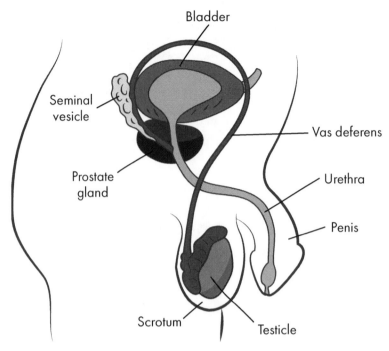

Figure 3.19. The Male Reproductive System

The mix of fluids and sperm, called **semen**, travels through the **urethra** and exits the body through the **penis**, which becomes rigid during sexual arousal.

The main hormone associated with the male reproductive system is **testosterone**, which is released by the testes (and in the adrenal glands in much smaller amounts). Testosterone is responsible for the development of the male reproductive system and male secondary sexual characteristics, including muscle development and facial hair growth.

THE FEMALE REPRODUCTIVE SYSTEM

The female reproductive system produces **eggs**, or female gametes, and gestates the fetus during pregnancy. Eggs are produced in the **ovaries** and travel through the **fallopian tubes** to the **uterus**, which is a muscular organ that houses the fetus during pregnancy. The uterine cavity is lined with a layer of blood-rich tissue called the **endometrium**. If no pregnancy occurs, the endometrium is shed monthly during **menstruation**.

Fertilization occurs when the egg absorbs the sperm; it usually takes place in the fallopian tubes but may happen in the uterus itself. After fertilization the new zygote implants itself in the endometrium, where it will grow and develop over 38 weeks (roughly nine months). During gestation, the developing fetus acquires nutrients and passes waste through the **placenta**. This temporary organ is attached to the wall of the uterus and is connected to the baby by the **umbilical cord**.

CHECK YOUR UNDERSTANDING

What type of muscle is most likely found in the myometrium of the uterus?

When the fetus is mature, powerful muscle contractions occur in the **myometrium**, the muscular layer next to the endometrium. These contractions push the fetus through an opening called the **cervix** into the **vagina**, from which the fetus exits the body. The placenta and umbilical cords are also expelled through the vagina shortly after birth.

The female reproductive cycle is controlled by a number of different hormones. **Estrogen**, produced by the ovaries, stimulates Graafian follicles, which contain immature egg cells. The pituitary gland then releases **luteinizing hormone**, which causes the egg to be released into the fallopian tubes during ovulation. During pregnancy, estrogen and **progesterone** are released in high levels to help with fetal growth and to prevent further ovulation.

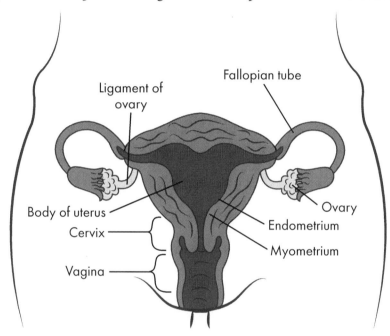

Figure 3.20. The Female Reproductive System

Pathologies of the Reproductive System

Sexually transmitted infections (STIs) include **chlamydia**, **gonorrhea**, **human papillomavirus (HPV)**, and **genital herpes**. Both chlamydia and gonorrhea are bacterial infections that have few symptoms in men but can cause burning, itching, and discharge in women. HPV and genital herpes are both viral infections that lead to warts and open sores, respectively. HPV has also been linked to the development of cervical cancer.

When untreated, bacterial infections in the female reproductive system can lead to **pelvic inflammatory disease (PID)**. Symptoms of PID include abdominal pain, fever, and vaginal discharge. PID is one of the most common causes of infertility.

Endometriosis is a condition in which endometrial tissue, which usually lines the inside of the uterus, grows outside the uterus. Symptoms include pain, irregular or painful menstruation, and infertility.

Cancers of the female reproductive system include ovarian cancer, cervical cancer, and uterine cancer. **Prostate cancer** is a common but slow-growing cancer of the male reproductive system. It is most common in patients over 50.

REVIEW QUESTIONS

36. What symptoms does endometriosis cause?

_____

37. Which virus may cause cervical cancer?

_____

38. What are the symptoms of chlamydia and gonorrhea?

_____

The Endocrine System

STRUCTURE AND FUNCTION OF THE ENDOCRINE SYSTEM

The endocrine system is made up of **glands** that regulate numerous processes throughout the body by secreting chemical messengers called **hormones**. These hormones regulate a wide variety of bodily processes, including metabolism, growth and development, sexual reproduction, the sleep-wake cycle, and hunger.

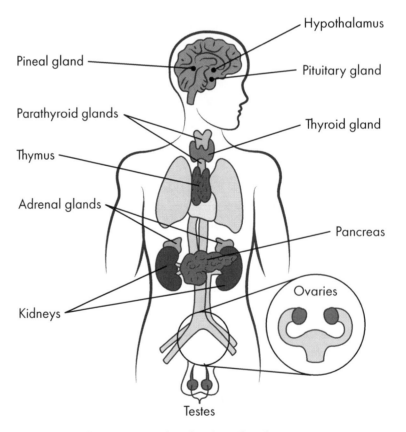

Figure 3.21. The Location of Endocrine Glands

The **hypothalamus** is a gland that plays a central role in the endocrine system by connecting it to the nervous system. Input from the nervous system reaches the hypothalamus, causing it to release hormones from the **pituitary gland**. These hormones in turn regulate the release of hormones from many of the other endocrine glands.

TABLE 3.5. Endocrine Glands and Their Functions

Gland	Regulates	Hormones Produced
Hypothalamus	pituitary function and metabolic processes including body temperature, hunger, thirst, and circadian rhythms	thyrotropin-releasing hormone (TRH), dopamine, growth hormone–releasing hormone (GHRH), gonadotropin-releasing hormone (GnRH), oxytocin, vasopressin
Pituitary gland	growth, blood pressure, reabsorption of water by the kidneys, temperature, pain relief, and some reproductive functions related to pregnancy and childbirth	human growth hormone (HGH), thyroid-stimulating hormone (TSH), prolactin (PRL), luteinizing hormone (LH), follicle-stimulating hormone (FSH), oxytocin, antidiuretic hormone (ADH)
Pineal gland	circadian rhythms (the sleep-wake cycle)	melatonin
Thyroid gland	energy use and protein synthesis	thyroxine (T_4), triiodothyronine (T_3), calcitonin
Parathyroid	calcium and phosphate levels	parathyroid hormone (PTH)
Adrenal glands	fight-or-flight response and regulation of salt and blood volume	epinephrine, norepinephrine, cortisol, androgens
Pancreas	blood sugar levels and metabolism	insulin, glucagon, somatostatin
Testes	maturation of sex organs, and secondary sex characteristics	androgens (e.g., testosterone)
Ovaries	maturation of sex organs, secondary sex characteristics, pregnancy, childbirth, and lactation	progesterone, estrogen
Placenta	gestation and childbirth	progesterone, estrogen, human chorionic gonadotropin, human placental lactogen (hPL)

Many important hormones can be broken down into either anabolic hormones or catabolic hormones. **Anabolic hormones** are associated with the regulation of growth and development; these include testosterone, estrogen, insulin, and human growth hormone. **Human growth hormone** is released by the pituitary gland and regulates muscle and bone development. Another example of an anabolic hormone is an **insulin-like growth factor (IGF)**, which is synthesized in the liver and aids in tissue growth and many other functions. **Catabolic hormones** help regulate the breakdown of substances into smaller molecules. For example, the breakdown of muscle glycogen for energy via the release of **glucagon** is a catabolic process.

PATHOLOGIES OF THE ENDOCRINE SYSTEM

Disruption of hormone production in specific endocrine glands can lead to disease. Overactive or underactive glands can lead to conditions like **hypothyroidism**, which is characterized by a slow metabolism, and **hyperparathyroidism**, which can lead to osteoporosis. **Adrenal insufficiency** (Addison's disease) is the chronic underproduction of steroids.

Diabetes mellitus is a metabolic disorder that affects the body's ability to produce and use **insulin**, a hormone that regulates cellular uptake of glucose (sugar).

- Uncontrolled diabetes can lead to high blood glucose levels (**hyperglycemia**) or low blood glucose levels (**hypoglycemia**).

- **Type 1 diabetes** is an acute-onset autoimmune disease predominant in children, teens, and adults under 30. Beta cells in the pancreas are destroyed and are unable to produce sufficient amounts of insulin, causing blood glucose to rise.

- **Type 2 diabetes** is a gradual-onset disease predominant in adults under 40, but it can develop in individuals of all ages. The person develops insulin resistance, which prevents the cellular uptake of glucose and causes blood glucose to rise. Type 2 diabetes accounts for 90% of all diabetes diagnoses in the United States.

- Diabetes requires long-term management with insulin or oral hypoglycemic drugs.

Thyroid cancer is relatively common but has few or no symptoms. In addition, benign (noncancerous) tumors on the thyroid and other endocrine glands can damage the functioning of a wide variety of bodily systems.

REVIEW QUESTIONS

39. What organ does not function properly in Type I diabetes?

40. What condition is caused by the chronic underproduction of steroids?

The Integumentary System

Structure and Function of the Integumentary System

The **integumentary system** refers to the skin (the largest organ in the body) and related structures, including the hair and nails. Skin is composed of three layers. The **epidermis** is the outermost layer of the skin. This waterproof layer contains no blood vessels and acts mainly to protect the body. Under the epidermis lies the **dermis**, which consists of dense connective tissue that allows skin to stretch and flex. The dermis is home to blood vessels, glands, and hair follicles. The **hypodermis** is a layer of fat below the dermis that stores energy (in the form of fat) and acts as a cushion for the body. The hypodermis is sometimes called the **subcutaneous layer**.

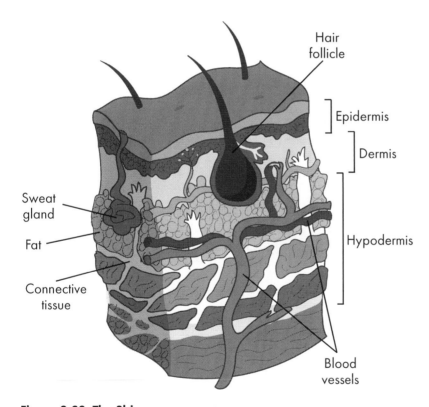

Figure 3.22. The Skin

The skin has several important roles. It acts as a barrier to protect the body from injury, the intrusion of foreign particles, and the loss of water and nutrients. It is also important for **thermoregulation**. Blood vessels near the surface of the skin can dilate, allowing for higher blood flow and the release of heat. They can also constrict to reduce the amount of blood that travels near the surface of the skin, which helps conserve heat. In addition, the skin produces **vitamin D** when exposed to sunlight.

Because the skin covers the whole body, it plays a vital role in allowing organisms to interact with the environment. It is home to nerve endings that sense temperature, pressure, and pain, and it also houses glands that help maintain homeostasis. **Eccrine glands**, which are located primarily in the palms of the hands and soles of the feet (and to a lesser degree in other areas of the body), release the water and salt mixture (sodium chloride, NaCl) called **sweat**. These glands help the body maintain the appropriate salt-water balance. Sweat can also contain small amounts of other substances the body needs to expel, including alcohol, lactic acid, and urea.

Apocrine glands, which are located primarily in the armpit and groin, release an oily substance that contains pheromones. They are also sensitive to adrenaline and are responsible for most of the sweating that occurs due to stress, fear, anxiety, or pain. Apocrine glands are largely inactive until puberty.

PATHOLOGIES OF THE INTEGUMENTARY SYSTEM

Psoriasis is an autoimmune condition that causes inflammation in the skin, resulting in red, flaking patches on the skin. **Eczema** (atopic dermatitis) is a red, itchy rash that usually occurs in children but can occur in adults as well.

Skin cancers can be categorized as melanoma or nonmelanoma cancers. **Melanoma** cancers appear as irregular, dark patches on the skin and are more difficult to treat than nonmelanoma cancers.

CHECK YOUR UNDERSTANDING

Why would flushing—the reddening of the skin caused by dilating blood vessels—be associated with fever?

REVIEW QUESTIONS

42. What is the outermost layer of the skin called?

43. What is the function of the hypodermis?

44. What type of cancer typically appears as irregular, dark patches on the skin?

ANSWER KEY

1. Tissues are a collection of cells that all perform a similar function.

2. Cartilage, bones, and ligaments are all types of connective tissue.

3. An organ system is a group of organs that work together to perform a function.

4. The terms posterior or dorsal both describe "toward the back."

5. A wound described as superior-medial on the abdomen would be located in the middle of the upper abdomen.

6. The thoracic cavity holds the heart and lungs.

7. The meninges are a three-layered membrane that protects the brain and spinal cord.

8. A blood pressure of 82/45 mm Hg indicates hypotension.

9. Ischemia is reduced or restricted blood flow to tissues and can be reversed with quick intervention; infarction is the death of tissue caused by restricted blood flow and the subsequent lack of oxygen.

10. If blood pools in the atrium and forms clots, these clots can break off and travel to the heart or brain. This leads to heart attack or stroke.

11. A patient with V-tach would be defibrillated, as this is a shockable rhythm.

12. Patients with myocardial infarction require immediate medical intervention to restore blood flow to the coronary arteries.

13. The alveoli are the location of gas exchange with the blood.

14. Kussmaul breathing is a type of hyperventilation characterized by deep, labored breathing. It is associated with diabetic ketoacidosis.

15. Apnea describes the absence of breathing.

16. Smoking and air pollution are the main causes of COPD, and genetic factors can influence the severity of the disease.

17. A pulmonary embolism is a blood clot (usually originating in the legs) that travels to the lungs, causing chest pain, shortness of breath, and low blood oxygen levels.

18. An ischemic stroke is caused by a blockage.

19. Some signs and symptoms of an epileptic seizure include confusion, convulsions, and loss of consciousness.

20. The autonomic nervous system controls involuntary actions that occur in the body, like respiration, heartbeat, and digestive processes.

21. Cartilage provides structure for certain body parts, such as the ears, nose, trachea, and bronchi. It also cushions bones in joints.

22. Red bone marrow is responsible for producing red blood cells, platelets, and white blood cells.

23. Lordosis is a postural deviation that causes an excessive anterior curvature of the natural S-shape of the spine.

24. The muscular system provides movement and overall stability and protection of the spine as well as posture.

25. An eccentric action results in muscular contraction in which the muscle is resisting a force as it lengthens (downward curl of bicep).

26. Rhabdomyolysis may be caused by crush injuries, overexertion (particularly in extreme heat), and a variety of toxins and drugs (particularly statins, used to treat high cholesterol).

27. The nonspecific immune system defenses work against a wide range of infectious agents, while the adaptive immune system responds to specific infectious agents it has encountered before.

28. Cancers of the immune system include lymphoma and leukemia, which are caused by irregular growth of cells in lymph and bone marrow.

29. Allergic reactions can be mild, presenting as watery eyes and a runny nose, but they can also include life-threatening swelling and respiratory obstruction.

30. The lower esophageal sphincter prevents reflux of stomach material into the esophagus.

31. Salivary glands produce saliva, which begins the process of breaking down starches and fats.

32. Colonoscopies are recommended for adults over 50 to screen for colon cancer.

33. Kidneys work to filter waste from the blood; maintain the electrolyte balance in the blood; and regulate blood volume, pressure, and pH.

34. People with chronic kidney disease may need dialysis, during which a machine performs the task of the kidneys and removes waste from the blood.

35. Renal calculi are also called kidney stones. They are hardened mineral deposits that may cause pain and urinary symptoms if they pass into the urinary tract.

36. When endometrial tissue grows outside the uterus, it can cause symptoms including pain, irregular or painful menstruation, and infertility.

37. Human papillomavirus (HPV) has been linked to cervical cancer.

38. Men may experience few or no symptoms of chlamydia and gonorrhea, but these STIs can cause burning, itching, and discharge in women.

39. In Type I diabetes, the pancreas does not function properly.

40. Adrenal insufficiency (Addison's disease) is the chronic underproduction of steroids.

41. The parathyroid regulates calcium and phosphate; these levels will be altered if the parathyroid does not function properly.

42. The outermost layer of the skin is the epidermis.

43. The hypodermis is a layer of fat below the dermis that stores energy (in the form of fat) and acts as a cushion for the body.

44. Melanoma cancers typically appear as irregular, dark patches on the skin.

4 PROCEDURES AND EXAMINATIONS

Medical assistants are authorized to perform or assist with a wide range of procedures and examinations. The supplies and techniques needed for procedures most likely to appear on the exam are discussed here.

Physical Examination Techniques

Patient examination is the process of examining the body and includes listening to the heart and lungs; looking in the eyes and ears; checking reflexes; assessing the abdomen; and measuring weight, height, and vital signs. Physical examination of the patient can be done using several techniques.

- **Observation**, or inspection, is a visual review of the patient's body, looking for abnormalities, skin color and condition, and symmetry.

- **Palpation** is the use of hands and fingertips to feel for positions and sizes of organs; masses, lumps, or other abnormalities; skin moisture and temperature; and joint flexibility.

- **Percussion** involves tapping parts of the body and using the sound produced to gauge the density of structures.

- **Auscultation** is using a stethoscope on different parts of the body to listen for abnormalities.

- **Manipulation** is the passive movement of the patient's joints to assess extent of movement.

- **Mensuration** is the measurement of height and weight.

Medical Examination Positions

The CMA should position the patient appropriately for different types of exams. These positions are discussed in the table below.

TABLE 4.1. Medical Examination Positions

Position	Description	Image
Supine	Patient lies on their back with arms to the sides. Supine positions are used during many surgical procedures, while performing an ECG, and for obtaining orthostatic blood pressure.	
Dorsal recumbent	Patient lies on their back with knees bent and feet flat on the table. Dorsal recumbent positions are used for gynecological exams.	
Lithotomy	Patient lies on their back with buttocks on the edge of the lower end of the table, legs elevated, and feet in stirrups. Lithotomy position is used for gynecological exams, childbirth, and some surgeries.	
Sims'	Patient lies on their left side with the left leg flexed, left arm resting behind the body, right leg flexed, and right arm at the chest. Sims' position is used for taking the temperature rectally, rectal examinations, and administering enemas.	

Position	Description	Image
Prone	Patient lies on their stomach. Prone position is used to examine the spine and for chiropractic procedures.	
Fowler's	Patient lies face up with their upper body elevated at 45 to 60 degrees. Fowler's position is used in barium swallow procedures, nasopharyngeal feedings, and respiratory distress.	
Semi-Fowler's	Same as Fowler's position, except the upper body is only elevated between 30 and 45 degrees. Semi-Fowler's position is used for nasogastric feedings, X-rays, and respiratory distress.	

REVIEW QUESTIONS

3. What position should a patient be placed in for a barium swallow procedure?

_____

4. The physician requests that a patient be placed in a prone position. How would you tell the patient to lie?

_____

5. What is the lithotomy position used for?

_____

Pediatric Exam Procedures

The medical assistant's role in a pediatric physical exam is to obtain infants' and children's height, weight, head circumference, temperature, pulse, and respiration, and then document the measurements on the patient chart. The patient's height, weight, and head circumference are plotted on a **growth chart** to gauge whether the child is growing appropriately.

Infants should be weighed completely undressed on a pediatric scale. Head circumference can be obtained with a tape measure. Height can be measured by laying the infant on the examination table in the supine position, marking the examination paper at the infant's head and feet (with legs straight), and then having a parent hold the infant while the CMA measures the distance between the two marks. Parents should hold fussy patients to keep them calm while the CMA takes the pulse and RR to ensure accurate measurements.

REVIEW QUESTIONS

6. Which pediatric measurements are plotted on a growth chart?

_____

7. What is the proper method to measure an infant's height?

_____

Obstetrical-Gynecological Exam Procedures

In an obstetrical-gynecological (ob-gyn) office, the medical assistant's role in the exam is to set up the exam room for procedures, obtain vitals (height, weight, blood pressure, pulse, respiration), and take the patient's history. The CMA should be familiar with the supplies needed for specific ob-gyn procedures.

A **pelvic exam** is a visual and physical exam of the reproductive organs, including the vulva, vagina, cervix, and uterus. The pelvic exam may include a Papanicolaou exam, commonly known as a **Pap smear**, during which cells are collected from the cervix to test for cervical cancer and HPV (human papillomavirus). Both exams are performed by the physician or a nurse practitioner. The supplies for pelvic exams and Pap smears are:

- speculum
- examination gloves
- cervical spatula
- cytobrush
- liquid-based cytology container
- lubricating jelly
- examination light
- examination gown
- towelette
- plastic lab bag

The liquid-based cytology container should be filled out with the patient's name, date of birth, medical record number, and date of last menstrual cycle.

The procedures carried out during a **prenatal exam** will vary with the stage of pregnancy. Either transvaginal or standard ultrasound may be used.

A fetal Doppler monitor can be used to measure the fetus's heart rate, and the patient's cervix may be examined. During a **postnatal exam**, the patient's healing and mental health are assessed.

The supplies for prenatal and postnatal exams include:

- gloves
- lubricating jelly
- examination gown
- towelette
- fetal Doppler monitor

REVIEW QUESTIONS

8. What supplies should be in the room for a prenatal exam?

9. What should be marked on the cytology container for a Pap smear specimen?

Procedures

CMAs may be asked to perform several basic procedures on a patient, including irrigations, dressing changes, and staple or suture removal. The steps to follow during patient procedures include:

- identifying the patient with two identifiers such as full name and date of birth
- washing hands before and after the procedures
- when performing procedures, explaining the process to the patient step by step and asking if they have any questions
- continuing to reassure the patient during procedures; this helps keep them calm and is an opportunity to gain their respect and trust
- documenting the procedure when finished, including what was done, how long it took, and how the patient responded

REVIEW QUESTIONS

10. What should be confirmed before beginning any procedure?

11. What should be documented after a procedure?

Eye Irrigation

Eye irrigation is performed when a patient's eye is irritated or damaged in an accident involving a chemical, sand, debris, or other irritant. The CMA should gather the necessary supplies.

- ophthalmic solution eyewash
- anesthetic eye drops
- basin
- paper drape

The patient should lie on the exam table with the affected side down and the paper drape under their head. The CMA should then apply two anesthetic eye drops in the affected eye. The CMA then places the basin under the patient's head near the affected eye, gently opens the eyelid, and slowly drops the ophthalmic solution into the lower and upper eyelids. Then the medical assistant should have the patient move their eye up and down and from side to side. The eye should be irrigated for 15 minutes. After irrigation, the CMA checks the patient's visual acuity. The procedures and the patient's tolerance should be documented. The CMA should give the patient educational material on eye irrigation and signs and symptoms to look for.

REVIEW QUESTIONS

12. What supplies are required for an eye irrigation?

_____

13. How long should an eye be irrigated for?

_____

Ear Irrigation

Ear irrigation is performed when a patient has excess wax (cerumen) in the ears or a child's tympanostomy tube becomes loose and is about to fall out of the ear. The supplies needed to irrigate an ear are:

- two basins
- warm water
- hydrogen peroxide
- paper drape
- Debrox (solution to soften the earwax)
- wax removal ear syringe

The patient should lie on the exam table in the Fowler's position, with a paper drape over the shoulder on the side of the ear to be irrigated. The CMA should apply two to five drops of Debrox in the ear to be irrigated. (For adults, pull the pinna of the ear up and back; for children, pull the pinna down and back.) Warm water and four to five capfuls of hydrogen peroxide are added to a basin. (The CMA should make sure the water is warm; cold water can give the patient a headache and cause dizziness.)

The medical assistant should have the patient take the other basin, hold it under the ear, and tilt their head to the side. The CMA should pull the warm water into the ear syringe and irrigate the ear, making sure to point the tip of the syringe toward the back of the ear canal. No more than 500 mL of water should be used. Ask the patient if they feel any pain while the ear is being irrigated. If they do, stop and inform the physician. The results of the procedure and the patient's tolerance should be documented. The CMA should offer the patient educational material on ear irrigation and signs and symptoms to look for.

Figure 4.1. Ear Irrigation

REVIEW QUESTIONS

14. How should the patient be positioned for an ear irrigation?

_____

15. A patient reports pain during an ear irrigation. What should the CMA do?

_____

Wound Care

When a patient has a wound or sore, the CMA might have to change the dressing. There are several methods of **dressing changes**, such as wet to dry, wet to wet, and sterile dressing. The physician's order will specify which dressing method to use. The supplies needed are:

- rolled gauze (Kling)
- tape
- two pairs of gloves
- scissors
- two or three pieces of 4-inch-square gauze and/or nonstick Telfa pads
- normal saline

The CMA will put on gloves and remove the old dressing, being careful not to pull the patient's skin. The area should be cleaned with normal saline and patted dry with a square of gauze. Then the medical assistant should change their gloves and take another square of gauze or a nonstick Telfa pad and place it over the wound. The area should be wrapped with Kling to secure the gauze in place. The gauze should be wrapped in spirals starting farthest from the heart to completely cover the dressing. Tape can be used to secure the Kling if necessary. The procedure and patient's tolerance should be documented. The CMA should give the patient educational material on dressing changes and signs and symptoms to look for.

Ostomies are openings that allow drainage from organs (e.g., bladder, intestine) outside the body. The opening on the skin's surface is called a **stoma**. Ostomies typically empty into an **ostomy bag** that can be opened at the bottom to be drained into the toilet. The ostomy bag is changed every 2 – 7 days.

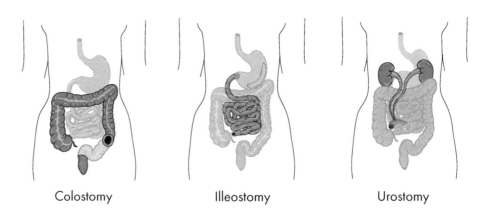

Colostomy   Illeostomy   Urostomy

Figure 4.2. Types of Ostomies

16. After the CMA removes the old dressing and cleanses the wound area, what should they do?

_____

17. How often should an ostomy bag be changed?

_____

18. How should the CMA determine what type of dressing is required when changing dressings?

_____

Suture or Staple Removal

Suture or **staple removal** is performed on patients who have had a previous injury or surgical incision closed. Before removal of sutures or staples, the CMA should verify how many sutures or staples were placed and when. The supplies for a suture removal are:

- suture removal kit
- bandages
- gloves
- mupirocin (Bactroban) ointment

To remove sutures, the CMA should put on gloves, open the suture removal kit, and take out the forceps and the suture scissors. Next, grasp the knot of the suture with the forceps and use the suture scissors to cut right under the knot. The forceps can be used to pull out the suture. Repeat for the remaining sutures. Count the sutures to make sure all have been removed. Mupirocin (Bactroban) ointment should be applied to the area before covering with a bandage. The CMA should document the procedure, including how many sutures were removed and the patient's tolerance. The CMA should also give the patient educational material on suture removal and signs and symptoms to look for.

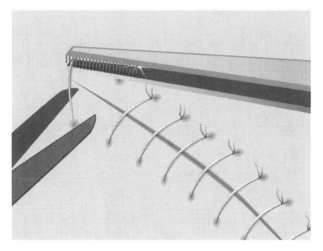

Figure 4.3. Suture Removal

HELPFUL HINT:

Sutures and staples are usually removed within 7 – 10 days.

For staple removal, the CMA will need:

- staple removal kit
- tape, gloves
- scissors
- nonstick Telfa pad
- wound-closure strips

To remove staples, the CMA should put on gloves, open the staple removal kit, and remove the staple extractor. The CMA should then place the staple extractor under the staple, close the handle, and gently move the staple side to side to remove. This process should be repeated for each staple. Once all staples are removed, the CMA should inspect the area and count the staples to make sure they have all been removed. Cut the wound-closure strips and apply them across the incision (strips help the site heal better with less scarring). Place a nonstick Telfa pad over the incision and tape it in place. Document the procedures, including how many staples were removed and the patient's tolerance. Give the patient educational material on staple removal and signs and symptoms to look for.

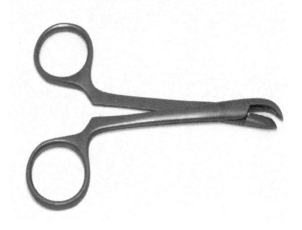

Figure 4.4. Medical Staple Remover

REVIEW QUESTIONS

19. The patient asks when sutures are to be removed. What should the CMA tell the patient?

_____

20. What is used to dress a site after staples are removed?

_____

21. During staple removal, how should the CMA confirm that all the staples have been removed?

_____

Surgical Assisting

Medical assistants may assist providers before, during, and after surgery. While CMAs may assist during more complex surgeries, the exam will focus on the CMA's role during minor procedures such as suturing, irrigating wounds, and removal of specimens for pathology analysis. The medical assistant should know how to do the following:

- prepare the patient
- set up and maintain the sterile field (surgical asepsis is covered in chapter 2, "Safety and Infection Control")
- provide instruments and medications as requested
- dress surgical wounds

PREPARING FOR SURGERY

Preparations for surgery will vary based on the type of surgery. For most minor procedures, the CMA may prepare the appropriate consent forms, collect pre-op specimens for testing (e.g., urine or blood), and gather the materials needed to perform the procedure.

To prepare the room, the CMA should drape the instrument tray to create a sterile field and arrange the needed materials on the tray. Once sterile instruments have been removed from packaging, they are generally considered sterile for 1 hour; if they are left out for longer before the surgery begins, they should be replaced. Once opened, sterile instruments should not be left unattended.

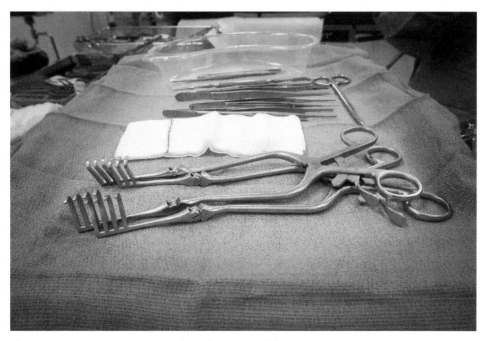

Figure 4.5. Mayo Instrument Stand Prepared for Surgery

To prepare patients for surgery, the medical assistant should first ask the patient to undress and put on a gown. The patient should then be appropriately positioned for the surgery. Next, the CMA should clean the patient's skin thoroughly with antiseptic. The patient will then need to be covered with a **drape** to create a sterile field. The size of the drape and the size of the opening (fenestration) will be selected based on the type of surgery.

SURGICAL INSTRUMENTS

To assist during surgery the medical assistant should be familiar with the **instruments** that will be used during the procedures. There are hundreds of medical instruments, many of which are referred to by different names that vary by location and provider. The medical assistant exam will not test your knowledge of all these instruments. Instead, you should be familiar with the general types of instruments and their uses. Some of the most commonly used surgical instruments are described below.

- **Scalpels** are sharp-edged instruments used to make incisions or cut tissue. They are available with varying blade shapes and in a range of sizes. They may be disposable or reusable with a detaching **handle**.

- **Punches** are used to cut out small areas of tissue for biopsy.

- **Curettes** are loops of metal attached to long handles used to collect tissue samples.

- Many types of **scissors** are available with specialized handles and blades designed to cut specific materials.

- **Forceps** are used to hold tissue or surgical materials.

- **Retractors** hold incisions open or move tissue aside to allow the surgeon access.

- **Speculums** are inserted into cavities to hold them open.

- **Probes** are used to search tissue or clear obstructions.

- **Dilators** are used to stretch an opening to allow larger instruments to pass through.

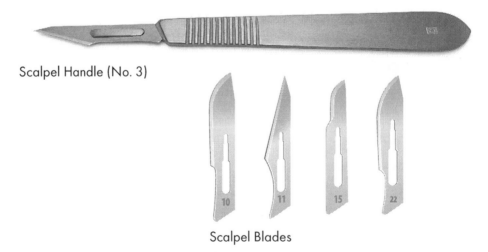

Scalpel Handle (No. 3)

Scalpel Blades

Figure 4.6. Surgical Instruments

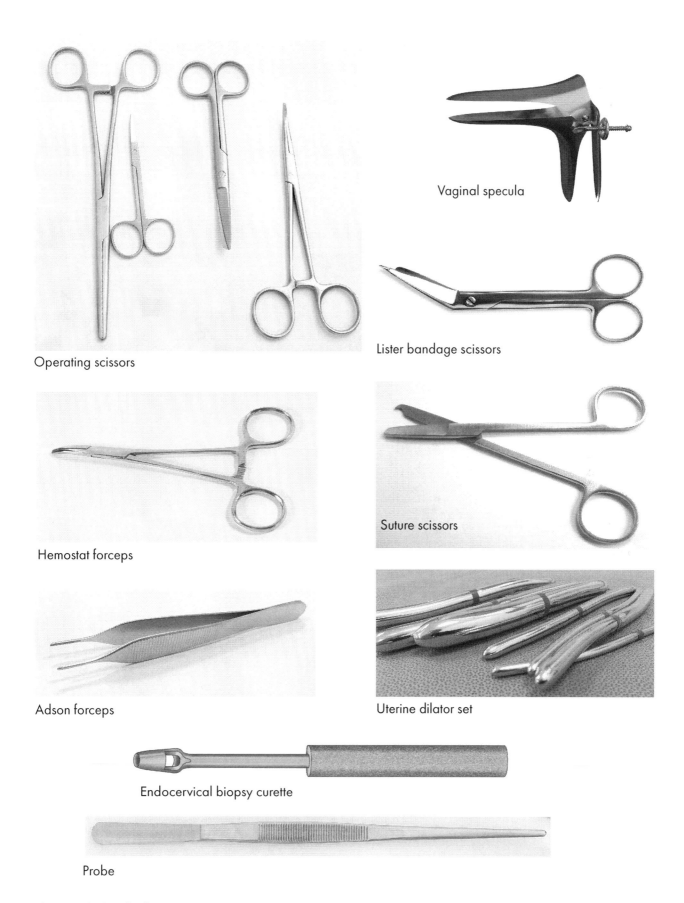

Operating scissors

Vaginal specula

Lister bandage scissors

Hemostat forceps

Suture scissors

Adson forceps

Uterine dilator set

Endocervical biopsy curette

Probe

Figure 4.6. Surgical Instruments

22. How long are instruments considered sterile after opening?

_____

23. What are dilators used for?

_____

24. What is used to reduce pain and numb areas during minor procedures?

_____

25. How should instruments be held to promote safety?

_____

26. What distinctive feature do Lister Bandage Scissors have?

_____

Cardiovascular Tests

ELECTROCARDIOGRAPHY (ECG)

An **electrocardiogram (ECG)** is a noninvasive diagnostic tool that records the heart's electrical activity. This diagnostic test can help determine a patient's cardiac rhythm and rate. It can also help diagnose electrolyte imbalances, heart attacks, and other damage to the heart. The readout from the ECG, often called an ECG strip, is a continuous waveform whose shape corresponds to each stage in the cardiac cycle. A normal heart rhythm and rate is called **normal sinus rhythm.**

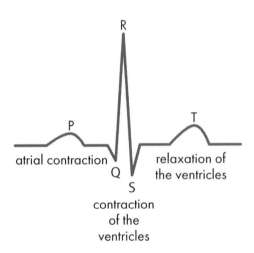

Figure 4.7. Waveforms and Intervals on an ECG

- **P wave:** right and left atrial contraction and depolarization

- **QRS complex:** contraction of the ventricles

- **T wave:** relaxation of the ventricles and repolarization

A **12-lead ECG** is performed by placing ten electrodes in specific locations on the patient's chest, arms, and legs. In order for the leads to stick to the skin, the patient's skin has to be clean and dry. If there is excess chest hair, it is sometimes necessary to shave the area to keep the lead on the skin. Patients, especially those with breasts, should be offered a cover for the chest once electrode lead placement is done. The patient should be reclined or supine and instructed to not talk or move during the procedure.

TABLE 4.2. 12-Lead ECG Electrode Placement

Electrode	Placement
V1	fourth intercostal space to the right of the sternum
V2	fourth intercostal space to the left of the sternum
V3	midway between V2 and V4
V4	fifth intercostal space at the midclavicular line
V5	anterior axillary line at the same level as V4
V6	midaxillary line at the same level as V4 and V5
RA	between right shoulder and right wrist
LA	between left shoulder and left wrist
RL	above right ankle and below the torso
LL	above left ankle and below the torso

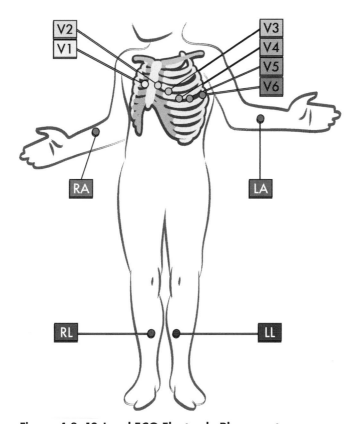

Figure 4.8. 12-Lead ECG Electrode Placement

Medical assistants do not interpret ECG strips or diagnose patients. However, they should be able to identify abnormal ECG strips and communicate to the provider what is abnormal about the strip. When reading an

ECG strip, the CMA should look for abnormalities in heart rate or rhythm (the shape of the waves).

- The normal number of heartbeats per minute is 60 – 100. A slow heart rate (**bradycardia**) is < 60 bpm. A rapid heart rate (**tachycardia**) is > 100 bpm.

- A **regular rhythm** has a constant rate. An **irregular rhythm** has a variable rate.

- The most significant finding of an ECG is the presence of **ST elevation** or **ST depression**. These rhythms are indicators of myocardial infarctions, a life-threatening blockage in the coronary arteries that requires immediate treatment.

- Other indicators of myocardial infarction include the presence of a **Q wave** and a **T wave inversion**. (Normal T waves are upright.)

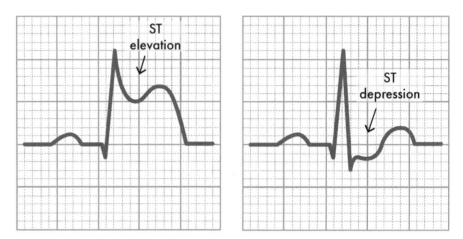

Figure 4.9. ST Elevation and ST Depression

ECG strips for common rhythms are shown below, along with descriptions of their important features.

Normal sinus rhythm: normal, regular cardiac rhythm (60 – 100 bpm)

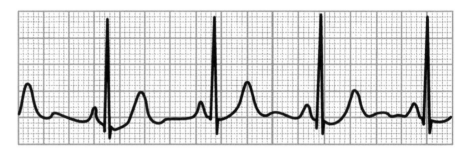

Figure 4.10. Normal Sinus Rhythm

Atrial fibrillation: an irregular rhythm with erratic or absent P waves

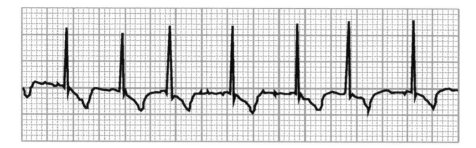

Figure 4.11. Atrial Fibrillation

Atrial flutter: regular or irregular rhythm with no P waves; looks like sawtooth waves

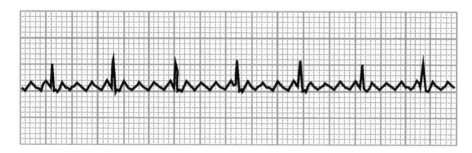

Figure 4.12. Atrial Flutter

Supraventricular tachycardia: regular rhythm with a rate of 150 – 250 bpm; P and T waves merge

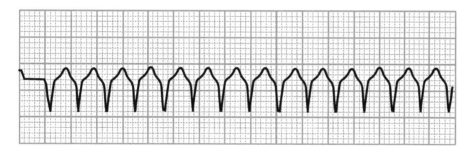

Figure 4.13. Ventricular Tachycardia

Ventricular fibrillation: irregular rhythm and no measurable rate; looks like a wavy line

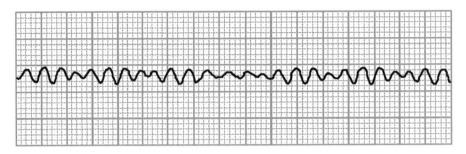

Figure 4.14. Ventricular Fibrillation

Asystole: no heart rate or rhythm

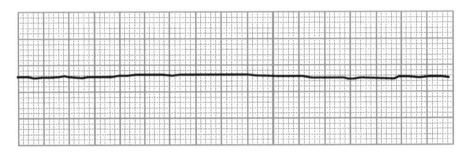

Figure 4.15. Asystole

Artifacts are ECG changes that result from interference or external factors rather than cardiac activity. They have several causes. Internal or patient-based causes include patient movement, muscle tremor, seizures, and breathing (often called a wandering baseline). External causes are interference from other electrical devices, and cable and electrode malfunction (insufficient gel, incorrect or loose lead placement).

HOLTER MONITORS

A **Holter monitor** is a wearable device that allows for a longer period of cardiac rhythm analysis (from 24 hours to a few weeks). The device provides a continuous monitor of the patient's electrical activity—the patient does not have to press a button to activate this recording. This device can help detect dysrhythmias that may be occurring while the patient is not at the hospital.

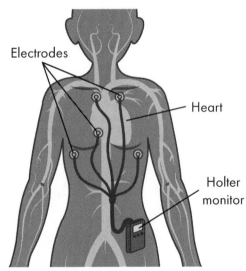

Figure 4.16. Holter Monitor

After the test is complete, the physician will review the readout from the monitor to determine if treatment is needed.

CARDIAC STRESS TEST

A **cardiac stress test** is used to observe how the heart reacts to stress. It allows the provider to check for signs of discomfort or pain during the test that can be correlated with the ECG. There are two types of stress tests: exercise and chemical.

- On an **exercise stress test**, the patient is placed on a treadmill while wearing ECG leads.

- With a **chemical stress test**, the patient (who may not be healthy enough to be tested on a treadmill) will receive a medication through their IV to make their heart work harder. This patient is also monitored with an ECG during the test.

A normal healthy heart should be able to handle the "stress" without showing any changes on an ECG that suggest injury or ischemia. In an unhealthy heart, a positive stress test will show ECG changes that suggest injury or ischemia to the heart muscle.

REVIEW QUESTIONS

27. What does the QRS complex on an ECG represent?

_____

28. Where should the V4 electrode be placed?

_____

29. A patient's ECG shows significant artifacts. What should the CMA do to correct the issue?

_____

30. The CMA obtains an ECG on a patient and identifies ST elevation. What should the CMA do?

_____

31. Why would a chemical stress test be done rather than an exercise stress test?

_____

Vision Tests

COLOR

Some people can have color vision deficiencies or **color blindness** that make it difficult to detect differences in color. The most common form is red-green color blindness, but people can also have blue-yellow color blindness or complete color blindness (meaning they cannot see color). In a color blindness test, patients are asked to identify numbers and shapes made of dots that are surrounded by dots of another color. Patients who cannot differentiate between the two colors will not be able to see the number or shape.

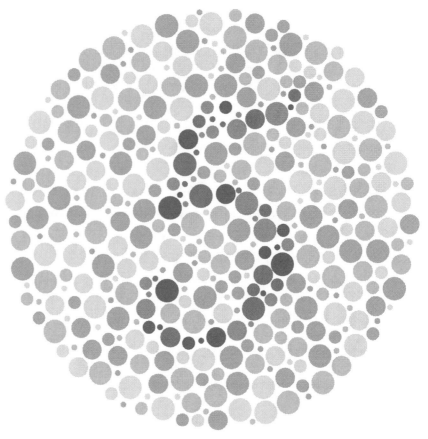

Figure 4.17. Color Blindness Test

DID YOU KNOW?

Eyesight is recorded as OU (both eyes), OD (right eye), OS (left eye). You can remember this by: y**OU** look with **BOTH** eyes; the **RIGHT** meds will not **OD**; the only one **LEFT** is **OS**.

ACUITY AND DISTANCE

The **Snellen test** evaluates visual acuity, or how clear a patient's vision is at a distance. The patient covers one eye and reads from the Snellen eye chart from the top to the bottom. The lowest row that the patient can read correctly is their vision in that eye. The test is repeated with the other eye and then with both eyes uncovered.

Results are recorded as a fraction, such as 20/20 or 20/60. A visual acuity of 20/80 means that the patient can read at a distance of 20 feet what a person with average vision can read at 80 feet. An acuity of 20/40 vision is required to drive. A person with 20/200 vision is legally blind.

An **E chart** also checks visual acuity similarly to the Snellen test. It is used for young children, patients who cannot read, or patients who do not use the Latin alphabet.

Figure 4.18. Snellen Eye Chart

1	20/200
2	20/100
3	20/70
4	20/50
5	20/40
6	20/30
7	20/25
8	20/20
9	
10	
11	

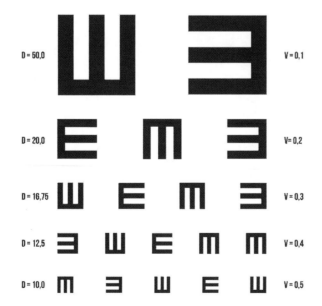

Figure 4.19. E Chart

A **Jaeger card** measures visual acuity at a normal reading distance, 14 inches from the eyes. The patient keeps both eyes open and reads the smallest sentence they can without squinting.

OCULAR PRESSURE (TONOMETRY)

Ocular pressure is the measure of pressure inside the patient's eye. After numbing eye drops are applied, a tonometer is gently touched to the surface of the eye to check the ocular pressure. Elevated pressure can lead to glaucoma, eventually leading to loss of vision.

VISUAL FIELD TESTS

Visual field tests check for peripheral vision loss and blind spots in each eye. The patient will cover one eye and look straight ahead with the other eye while answering questions about different images or light sources.

REVIEW QUESTIONS

32. How is a patient prepared for an ocular pressure test?

_____

33. A patient is blind in the left eye. How should their eyesight be recorded?

_____

34. What conditions can be caused by elevated ocular pressure?

Audiometric (Hearing) Tests

PURE TONE AUDIOMETRY

Pure tone audiometry measures the patient's hearing threshold (the quietest sound they can hear). Patients wear headphones, and a beep or tone is played into one ear at a time at varying volumes. The patient is asked to raise their hand when they hear the tone. This test can only be used with patients who can understand directions and cooperate.

SPEECH AND WORD RECOGNITION

Speech and word recognition tests measure how well a patient can listen to and repeat words. An example of a speech recognition test is called the **speech reception threshold (SRT)**. This test can only be performed on older children and adults who can talk. It helps to measure the extent of a patient's hearing loss. Similar to the pure tone audiometry test, the patient is given headphones to listen with. However, instead of tones, in the SRT the patient is asked to listen to and repeat words that are being said at differing volumes.

TYMPANOMETRY

Tympanometry tests for abnormalities in the middle ear behind the tympanic membrane (eardrum). During tympanometry, a tube is placed in the outer ear that changes the air pressure in the ear. A tone is then played into the ear, and the movement of the eardrum is recorded on a tympanogram. An abnormal response of the eardrum under different pressures can indicate infection, ruptured tympanic membranes, malfunctioning eustachian tubes, or other issues.

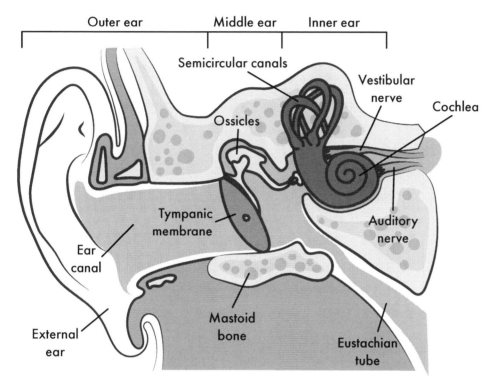

Figure 4.20. Anatomy of the Ear

REVIEW QUESTIONS

35. What device is used for a pure tone audiometry test?

36. What must a patient be able to do for an SRT test?

37. What does a tympanometry test assess?

Allergy Tests

An allergy skin test allows providers to check for many different allergies at once. The tests are usually done on the forearms for adults and on the back for children, although high-volume tests may be done on an adult patient's back. For both locations, the area should be thoroughly cleaned and then labeled with numbers or the names of the potential allergens to be applied.

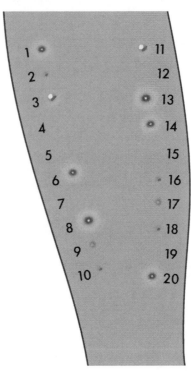

Figure 4.21. Allergy Scratch Test on Forearm

DID YOU KNOW?

Patients should be instructed to stop taking antihistamine medications 10 days before an allergy test.

In a **scratch test**, a small amount of allergen is applied to the surface of the skin and pricked with a lancet. In **intradermal skin testing**, a small amount of the allergen is injected just under the surface of the skin.

The site is then observed for 15 minutes to look for signs of a reaction, which includes a raised red bump and swelling around the scratch or injection site. CMAs who assist with allergy tests should look for signs of anaphylaxis, including difficulty breathing and a rapid heart rate, which would indicate that emergency treatment is needed.

A **radioallergosorbent test (RAST)** measures the number of antibodies for specific allergens in the patient's blood. The higher the number of antibodies, the more likely the patient is to have a severe allergic reaction.

REVIEW QUESTIONS

38. In what area of the patient is an allergy skin test performed?

_____

39. What medication must be avoided before allergy testing?

_____

Respiratory Tests

PULMONARY FUNCTION TESTS (PFT)

Pulmonary function tests (PFT) measure how well the lungs work. Measurements taken during a PFT may include:

- tidal volume (VT): amount of air inhaled or exhaled during normal breathing
- minute volume (MV): amount of air exhaled per minute
- vital capacity (VC): amount of air exhaled after taking a large inhalation
- functional residual capacity (FRC): amount of air left in the lungs after a normal exhale
- residual volume: amount of air left in the lungs after a large exhalation
- total lung capacity: amount of air in the lungs when full
- forced vital capacity (FVC): amount of air exhaled quickly after taking a large inhalation
- peak expiratory flow rate (PEFR): the fastest rate that air can be exhaled from the lungs

SPIROMETRY

The most common PFT is **spirometry**. During the test, the patient's nose is clipped, and they are asked to breathe into the spirometer mouthpiece to obtain the values described above. There may be additional tests, such as post-bronchodilator spirometry. This involves the patient inhaling a medication and then repeating spirometry to see if their values improve.

Before the test, the patient should be instructed to avoid smoking, exercise, caffeine, and overeating. The provider should instruct patients when and how to use their breathing medications before the test. The patient should wear loose-fitting clothing; tight clothes may be too restrictive and affect test results.

PEAK FLOW RATE

While spirometer testing is done at a clinic or hospital, a **peak flow measurement** can be done at home daily to check how well a patient's asthma is being controlled. This test may detect narrowing of the patient's airways even before they begin to have symptoms of wheezing or shortness of breath and can alert a patient on when they should seek medical attention.

A **peak flow meter (PFM)** is a handheld device that measures **peak expiratory flow rate (PEFR)**. The patient blows into the mouthpiece of the device and will need to record at least three separate readings each time. With these readings, patients will be able to tell if they are in a green, yellow, or red zone.

- Green: 80 – 100% of the patient's highest peak flow. The patient's current asthma treatment is working, no new medications or activity restrictions are needed.

- Yellow: 50 – 80% of the patient's peak flow. This means the patient's airways are narrowing some and can result in mild cough, shortness of breath, fatigue, trouble with exercise or sleeping.

- Red: < 50% of the patient's peak flow. This means severe narrowing of the patient's airways, and emergent medical attention is needed.

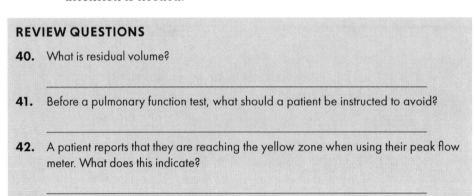

REVIEW QUESTIONS

40. What is residual volume?

_____

41. Before a pulmonary function test, what should a patient be instructed to avoid?

_____

42. A patient reports that they are reaching the yellow zone when using their peak flow meter. What does this indicate?

_____

ANSWER KEY

1. The health care provider uses observation to check for abnormalities, skin color and condition, and symmetry.

2. A stethoscope is used for auscultation.

3. For a barium swallow procedure, patients should be placed in Fowler's position.

4. The patient should be instructed to lie on their stomach.

5. The lithotomy position is used for gynecological exams, childbirth, and some surgeries.

6. A growth chart plots the height, weight, and head circumference of pediatric patients.

7. Height can be measured by laying the infant on the examination table in the supine position, marking the examination paper at the infant's head and feet (with legs straight), and then measuring the distance between the two marks.

8. Both prenatal and postnatal exams require gloves, lubricating jelly, examination gown, towelette, and a fetal Doppler monitor.

9. The cytology container should be marked with the patient's name, date of birth, medical record number, and date of last menstrual cycle.

10. Before beginning any procedure, confirm the patient's identity by using two identifiers such as full name and date of birth.

11. After a procedure, document what procedure was done, how long it took, and how the patient responded.

12. Before performing an eye irrigation, the CMA will need ophthalmic solution eyewash, anesthetic eye drops, basin, and a paper drape.

13. The eye should be irrigated for 15 minutes.

14. The patient should be placed in the Fowler's position for an ear irrigation.

15. If a patient reports pain, the CMA should stop the procedure and notify the physician.

16. The CMA should remove soiled gloves and perform hand hygiene, before putting on a clean pair of gloves.

17. An ostomy bag should be changed every 2 – 7 days.

18. The CMA should refer to the physician's order to determine which dressing method to use.

19. Sutures are usually removed in 7 – 10 days.

20. Wound-closure strips are placed and covered with a nonstick Telfa pad that is held in place with tape.

21. The CMA should count the staples that have been removed.

22. Once sterile instruments have been removed from packaging, they are considered to be sterile for 1 hour.

23. Dilators are used to stretch an opening to allow larger instruments to pass through.

24. An anesthetic may be used, either subcutaneously injected or as a spray.

25. Instruments should always be held carefully by the tip and handed to the physician so the handle can be easily grasped. Scalpels should always be handled with the blade side pointed downward.

26. Lister Bandage Scissors have one blunt edge for sliding under dressings.

27. The QRS complex on an ECG represents contraction of the ventricles.

28. The V4 electrode is placed on the fifth intercostal space at the midclavicular line.

29. The CMA should ensure there is no interference from another device and check for cable and electrode malfunction (insufficient gel, incorrect or loose lead placement).

30. The CMA should notify the physician immediately because ST elevation is a medical emergency.

31. Chemical stress tests are used for patients who may not be healthy enough to tolerate being tested on the treadmill.

32. The patient is given numbing eye drops prior to the test.

33. The code used for the right eye is OD.

34. Elevated ocular pressure can lead to glaucoma and eventual loss of vision.

35. A pure tone audiometry test uses headphones.

36. The patient must be able to speak.

37. A tympanometry tests for abnormal responses of the eardrum, which can indicate infection, ruptured tympanic membranes, malfunctioning eustachian tubes, or other issues.

38. The tests are usually done on the forearms for adults and on the back for children, although high-volume tests may be done on an adult patient's back.

39. Antihistamines must be discontinued for 10 days before allergy testing.

40. Residual volume is the amount of air left in the lungs after a large exhalation.

41. The patient should be instructed to avoid smoking, exercise, caffeine, and overeating.

42. This means the patient's airways are narrowing some and can result in mild cough, shortness of breath, fatigue, and trouble with exercise or sleeping. The physician should be notified of these results.

5 COLLECTING AND PROCESSING SPECIMENS

Blood tests, urinalysis, and stool samples are often necessary to determine a patient's diagnosis. Medical assistants may be responsible for performing these tests or ensuring specimens are collected properly. They are also responsible for documenting the tests they have performed and providing the results to the practitioner to review in a timely manner.

Venipuncture

Venipuncture (vein puncture), frequently referred to as a blood draw or phlebotomy, is the process of puncturing the skin to collect blood from a vein into an attached vial or tube. Venipuncture can be done using an evacuated tube system (most common) or a winged infusion blood collection set (also called a butterfly), which is used for small veins, usually in pediatric and elderly patients.

For most samples, blood is collected and stored in **evacuated tubes**. Once connected to the venipuncture needle, the vacuum in the tube pulls blood from the vein into the tube.

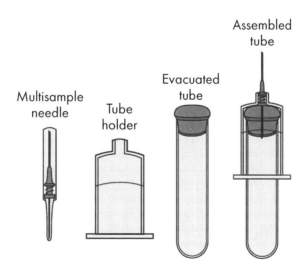

Figure 5.1. Components of an Evacuated Tube System

Tube additives are added to the evacuated tubes for different blood tests. The additives determine which tube should be filled first to avoid damage to the blood sample or contamination of the other tubes. The colored caps of the tube correspond to the additive inside. It is important to never mix a blood sample from one tube with another tube. Below is the recommended order of draw.

TABLE 5.1. Evacuated Tube Additives and Order of Draw				
Order of Draw	**Type of Collection**	**Commonly Used For . . .**	**Color**	**Additive**
1	blood cultures	blood cultures	yellow	**sodium polyanethol sulfonate (SPS)**, an anticoagulant that reduces damage to bacteria
2	sodium citrate tubes	coagulation tests	light blue	**sodium citrate**, an anticoagulant
3	serum tubes	chemistry tests (e.g., metabolic panel, lipid panel)	red	**silica**, a clot activator
			red and gray; gold	**serum separator tube (SST)** with silica and separator gel
			orange	**rapid serum tube (RST)** with **thrombin**, a fast-acting anticoagulant
4	heparin tubes	stat chemistry tests	dark green	**heparin**, an anticoagulant
			light green; green and gray	**plasma separator tube (PST)** with heparin and gel separator
5	EDTA tubes	hematology tests (e.g., CBC, blood bank testing)	lavender; pink	**EDTA**, an anticoagulant
			pearl/ white	**plasma preparation tube (PPT)** with EDTA and gel separator

Order of Draw	Type of Collection	Commonly Used For ...	Color	Additive
6	sodium fluoride or potassium oxalate	glucose tests, ethanol tests	gray	**sodium fluoride**, an antiglycolytic agent, or **potassium oxalate**, an anticoagulant
7	acid-citrate-dextrose (ACD)	DNA testing, transplant compatibility	yellow	**acid-citrate-dextrose (ACD)**, an anticoagulant (acid citrate) and RBC preservative (dextrose)
N/A	trace element–free tubes	toxicology, trace element tests	royal blue	free of trace element contamination and may contain other additives (drawn in order of additives)

A **winged infusion** blood collection set (or **butterfly**) consists of a 0.5 – 0.75 inch (1.3 – 1.9 cm) needle with plastic extension "wings" connected to a 5 – 12 inch (12.7 – 30.5 cm) tubing. The tubing can be attached to a syringe or an evacuated tube holder.

The process for drawing blood is described below.

1. Wash hands, then put on non-sterile gloves.
2. Confirm patient identity with TWO identifiers.
3. Obtain patient consent.
4. Verify the testing requirements (e.g., has the patient fasted as asked?).
5. Select site for draw.

Blood is usually drawn from the area anterior to the elbow. The **median cubital vein** is most commonly used, but other veins, including the cephalic and basilic, may be used if the median cubital vein is not accessible. Blood may also be drawn from the veins in the back of the hand or from veins in the forearm. Blood should NOT be drawn from the wrist, feet, or ankles or from sites with obvious infection or bruising. Blood draws should also not be done on the same side as a patient's mastectomy or fistula placement.

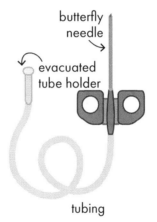

butterfly needle

evacuated tube holder

tubing

Figure 5.2. Winged Infusion Set Attached to an Evacuated Tube Holder

HELPFUL HINT:

Simplified Order of Draw:

1	cultures	yellow
2	citrate	light blue
3	serum	red/orange
4	heparin	green
5	EDTA	lavender/pink
6	fluoride	gray

DID YOU KNOW?

The first draw from a butterfly should be discarded because air in the tubing will cause the first evacuated tube to be underfilled.

DID YOU KNOW?

When a patient holds out their arm or rolls up their sleeve for a blood draw, they are giving implied consent.

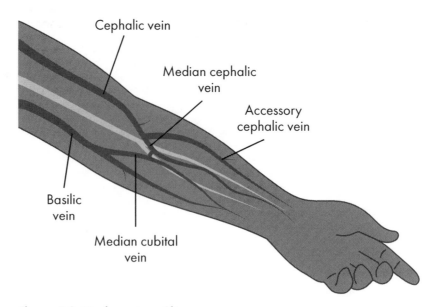

Figure 5.3. Venipuncture Sites

6. Apply tourniquet.

Tourniquets are elastic bands wrapped around the arm that restrict the flow of blood through veins out of the arm, causing the veins to expand and making them easier to puncture. Apply a tourniquet to the arm 2 – 4 inches ABOVE the site of the intended blood draw. This will help make veins more prominent and easier to select. Do not leave the tourniquet on for more than 1 – 2 minutes.

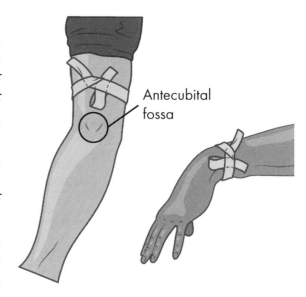

Figure 5.4. Tourniquet Placement for Venipuncture (Antecubital Fossa and Hand)

7. Cleanse site.

Cleanse site with 70% isopropyl alcohol swab. Start at the intended site and then clean in concentric circles away from the center. Let skin air-dry for 30 seconds. If the area is touched after cleansing, it must be cleansed again.

8. Select needle.

Choose the appropriate needle size for the patient and type of blood draw. Needle diameter is given by its gauge number: smaller-diameter needles have higher gauge numbers.

- 20-gauge multisample: large-volume tubes, adults with normal-sized veins

- 21-gauge multisample: standard venipuncture needle for patient with normal-sized veins
- 22-gauge multisample syringe: older children, adults with small or "difficult" veins
- 23-gauge butterfly: infants and children, hand veins of adults
- 25-gauge butterfly: premature/neonate scalp veins
- Anchor vein by placing thumb a few cm below site.

9. Enter skin with needle at 15 – 30-degree angle.

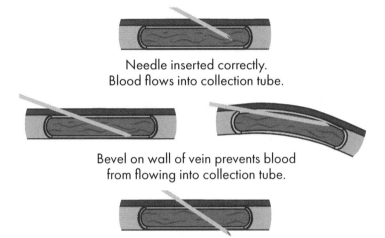

Needle inserted correctly.
Blood flows into collection tube.

Bevel on wall of vein prevents blood
from flowing into collection tube.

Needle inserted too far.
Blood does not flow into collection tube.

Needle partially inserted into vein.
Blood moves into surrounding tissue, causing bruising.

Figure 5.5. Needle Placement in Vein for Venipuncture

10. Remove tourniquet after blood flow has been established.
11. Fill and remove tubes.
12. When draw is complete, place 2 × 2 gauze over site and remove needle. The needle should be disposed of properly in a sharps container.
13. Apply pressure to site, then tape gauze in place.
14. Label tubes with patient's first and last name, ID number, date/time of collection, and the CMA's initials.

REVIEW QUESTIONS

1. What information must be confirmed with the patient before the CMA can begin venipuncture?

Dermal Puncture

A **capillary sample** or **dermal puncture** is done to draw a small amount of blood from the capillaries by cutting or puncturing the skin. They are used when only a few drops of blood are needed, such as an infant heel stick or point-of-care glucose testing on adult fingertips (sometimes called a finger stick). The process of acquiring a capillary sample is described below.

1. Wash hands, then put on non-sterile gloves.
2. Confirm patient identity with TWO identifiers.
3. Select site.

Infant heel sticks are done on the outer sides of the infant's heel. Old puncture sites should not be reused. Adult finger sticks are usually done on the medial or lateral side of the middle or ring finger. The CMA should never perform a finger stick on the nail or middle of the finger pad. As with venipuncture, areas with infection or bruising should be avoided.

4. Select lancet.

The skin is punctured using a small needle called a **lancet**. The length of lancets ranges from 0.85 mm (used for infant heel sticks) to 2.2 mm.

5. Warm site with appropriate warming device if needed to increase blood flow.
6. Clean site in the same manner as used for venipuncture.
7. Puncture skin while pressing firmly on the finger and then discard lancet in sharps container.

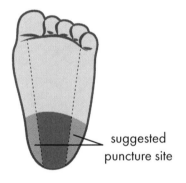

suggested puncture site

Figure 5.6. Location of Infant Heel Stick

Figure 5.7. Location of Finger Stick

8. Wipe away first drop of blood with gauze to prevent contamination.

9. Fill tubes or other collection devices in order of draw.

The CMA should hold the punctured finger or heel over a collection container and gently massage to encourage blood flow. If the blood is not sufficient, the CMA should take advantage of gravity by pointing the site down and applying a small amount of pressure above the site.

10. Place gauze and pressure over puncture site.

11. Apply bandage after rechecking site.

12. Label specimen containers.

REVIEW QUESTIONS

6. What is a lancet used for?

_____

7. Where should a lancet be disposed of after using?

_____

8. Where should a capillary sample be obtained from an infant?

_____

Urine Specimen

Urine is assessed for various reasons and can be tested in the medical office or sent to off-site laboratories. Analysis of urine occurs by physical, chemical, and microscopic means. The urine is assessed for color, clarity, pH, specific gravity, glucose, ketones, nitrites, white blood cells, and red blood cells. A typical urine specimen should include 30 – 50 mL of urine collected in a dry, clean container.

Urine can be collected at random times or at a specific time. **Random** urine samples are not taken at a scheduled time. Drug screenings are often intentionally randomized. Patients are notified that they have 4 – 6 hours to come to the lab and provide a urine sample.

A **first morning** urine sample is collected before the patient takes in any fluid so that the urine is more concentrated. It is usually collected after 8 hours of sleep, but it may be collected after any 8-hour period during which the patient did not urinate.

A **timed** urinalysis can span 2 – 72 hours. (A 24-hour specimen is the most common.) Timed tests are usually done when the substance being tested for is excreted at differing rates throughout the day (e.g., testosterone or creatinine). Urine is collected over the given time period and added to a large collection container. The patient should discard their first morning urine and start collecting urine after that.

HELPFUL HINT

Important Considerations for Timed Urine Collection:

- Patients should void at the beginning of the sample time period to empty the bladder. This urine should not be collected.

- Some timed urine tests require patients to refrigerate the collection container or to follow a certain diet during the timed period.

A **postprandial** test is a timed urine test for glucose done 2 hours after the patient eats. A **fasting** urinalysis tests for glucose after at least 8 hours of fasting. It is usually done first thing in the morning to make it easier on the patient. The patient should discard their first morning urine and collect the second voided urine sample after the fasting period has ended.

Different collection methods are appropriate for different tests being performed.

- A **regular voided sample** can be collected by the patient without any special preparations.

- A **midstream sample** is collected after the patient has voided a small amount of urine to flush material away from the urinary opening.

- **Double voiding** requires the patient to discard their first morning urine and wait a set amount of time (usually 30 minutes) to collect a sample.

- For a **clean-catch** urine sample, the patient should clean the opening to the urethra with an antiseptic wipe and void half of the urine into the toilet. The remaining urine is then collected in a sterile container.

Urinary collection bags are used to collect urine samples from pediatric patients. The adhesive bag is sealed around the baby's genitals and removed once enough urine has been collected.

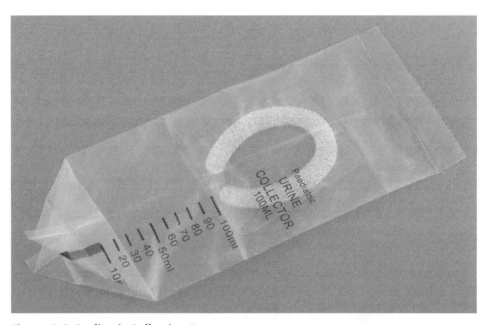

Figure 5.8. Pediatric Collection Bag

- **Catheterized** urine samples are collected with a catheter (a tube that is passed through the urethra into the bladder).

9. How should a patient be instructed to collect a clean-catch urine sample?

10. How is a double voided urine sample collected?

11. When is a postprandial urine sample collected?

12. What should patients be instructed to do with each urine sample collected during a 24-hour timed urine sample?

13. What type of collection device is used to collect a urine sample from a 6-month-old patient?

Fecal Specimen

A **stool** (or **feces**) **specimen** is collected to evaluate for conditions affecting the digestive tract, including infection, parasites, cancer, bleeding, and nutrient absorption deficiency. Fecal specimens are usually collected by the patient and returned to the provider. The medical assistant should be prepared to explain to the patient how to collect the sample.

Instructions for the patient are as follows:

- Collect stool in a dry, clean container provided by the physician's office.
- The stool should not come in contact with water, urine, or toilet paper.
- Samples should come from three different bowel movements.
- Patients should stop taking NSAIDs, aspirin, or steroids 1 week before sample collection.
- Patients should stop taking vitamin C and iron 3 days before sample collection.
- A high-fiber diet can help stimulate a bowel movement.
- Stool samples should not be collected from patients who are menstruating, who have actively bleeding hemorrhoids, or who have a urinary tract infection.

Figure 5.9. Stool Sample Collection Devices

REVIEW QUESTIONS

14. What are common reasons to test a fecal specimen?

_____

15. How should a stool sample be collected?

_____

16. What medications should patients be told to avoid before collecting a stool sample?

_____

Sputum Specimen

Sputum is the thick mucus produced by the lungs when an infection or inflammatory process is present. It is collected by having a patient deeply cough to produce sputum into a designated sterile container. This mucus is examined by the lab to identify bacteria. If bacteria are detected, the sputum can be cultured to find which antibiotic will best treat the infection.

Instructions for the patient are as follows:

- Do not use antibacterial mouthwash before giving the sample.
- Drink lots of water before providing the sample.
- If done at home, sputum samples should be collected first thing in the morning.

REVIEW QUESTIONS

17. At what time of day should a patient be instructed to collect a sputum sample?

_____

18. What should NOT be used prior to providing a sputum sample?

_____

Swabs

A **swab** is a small amount of absorbent material on a long, thin stick. Swabs are used to collect biological material for testing and cultures from several locations. They are sterile products, and when taking a swab, the CMA should ensure that swabs are not contaminated.

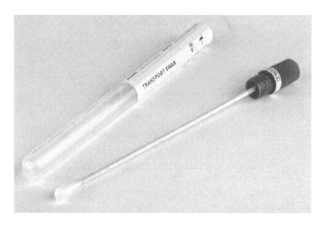

Figure 5.10. Swab with Collection Tube

- The **throat swab** is done to check the back of the throat or pharynx for bacterial infections such as strep throat.
- A **genital swab** is used to test for sexually transmitted infections.
- A **wound culture swab** uses a designated swab to evaluate draining as well as infected wounds or surgical wounds for bacteria.
- **Nasopharyngeal swabs** test for respiratory infections, including flu, RSV (an infant respiratory infection), and COVID-19.

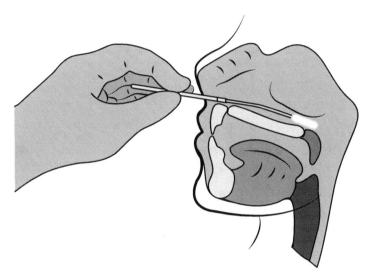

Figure 5.11. Nasopharyngeal Swab Collection

The steps for collecting a swab are as follows:

1. Wash hands and put on gloves.
2. Open package and remove sterile swab.
3. Moisten swab using sterile sodium chloride as needed.
4. Gently pass swab over area for collection.
5. Place swab into collection tube and close.
6. Label sample.
7. Discard gloves and swab packaging.

REVIEW QUESTIONS

19. What care should be taken when handling swabs for specimen collection?

_____

20. What type of swab should be used to collect a sample to test for COVID-19?

_____

21. What is a genital swab used to test for?

_____

Labeling, Storing, and Tracking Specimens

The collection, testing, and transportation of specimens should always be carefully documented. All specimens should be properly labeled with the time of collection and TWO patient identifiers. Patient identifiers include:

- patient's full name (last, first) or medical record number
- date of birth
- matching specimen barcode label

After collection, specimens should be appropriately preserved. For example, urine samples should be refrigerated after collection and may need to be packed with frozen gel packs for pickup by outside laboratories.

Some specimens require "fixation" using a **fixative**. The most commonly used chemical fixative is **formaldehyde**, which is usually combined with water to form a solution called **formalin**.

Formaldehyde stops a specimen from decaying, keeping it as close to its original state as possible. Generally, formaldehyde is used to preserve tissue samples that are being sent to histology for diagnosis, such as a core biopsy of a cyst or an organ. Formaldehyde can be toxic if it is inhaled or comes into contact with skin. It is also very flammable. It is important to be cautious around it.

To preserve as much of the tissue sample as possible, fixation should be done immediately after the tissue is obtained.

To preserve a specimen in formaldehyde:

1. Make sure the area is well ventilated.
2. Put on protective equipment, including a face shield, an apron or lab coat, and gloves. If the solution is less than 10% formaldehyde, use regular exam gloves as protection. If the concentration is greater than 10%, medium- or heavy-weight gloves made from a waterproof material such as rubber are needed.
3. Cover the workstation with a waterproof barrier.
4. The formalin solution should be added to the container (unless a prefilled container is used) in an amount that is at least 15 times the volume of the tissue sample to be preserved. The container should be large enough to accommodate the fixative solution and the tissue sample, with an allowance for the initial swelling of the tissue sample that will occur during fixation.
5. Place the tissue sample in the container.
6. Close the container, making sure the lid is on tight enough to prevent leakage.

7. Label the container with the patient's name and date of birth and date and time of sample collection.

8. Store the sample to be sent to the lab at room temperature away from any fire or heat source.

REVIEW QUESTIONS

22. What are considered appropriate patient identifiers?

_____

23. How much formalin solution should be used to preserve a tissue sample?

_____

24. How should urine samples be stored after collection?

_____

25. A tissue sample needs to be stored in 20% formalin. What personal protective equipment is required to safely handle this?

_____

26. How should a sample placed in formalin be stored?

_____

Sources of Contamination

The medical assistant should be aware of possible sources of contamination that may compromise biological specimens. These sources should be avoided or mitigated to avoid false laboratory results or retesting. Possible sources of contamination are listed in the following table.

TABLE 5.2. Possible Sources of Specimen Contamination

Source	Example
Environment	airborne contaminants
	exposure to light or extreme temperatures
Container	non-sterile container
	non-compatible container that leaches into sample
Collection tools	contaminated swabs or other collection devices
Health care providers	improper hand hygiene
	not cleaning area before collecting specimen

REVIEW QUESTIONS

27. What action can health care providers take to ensure that specimens do not get contaminated?

_____

Examining Specimens

In a physician's office laboratory, a certified medical assistant may do simple one-step tests. These tests are referred to as waived tests because a regulating agency determines them to be low-complexity tests. Medical assistants are also responsible for monitoring the equipment in the lab to make sure they are producing accurate results.

One of the lab procedures a medical assistant may be responsible for is **inoculating** a culture. This is when a bacteria or other microorganism is introduced into or onto a culture media, such as wiping a swab of bacteria onto a petri dish. The petri dish is then labeled and stored in an **incubator** to wait for the results of the test. A medical assistant monitors the temperature readings and inspects the petri dishes inside the incubator for any signs of bacterial growth. Incubators must maintain a steady temperature and humidity level in order to grow the microbiological cultures introduced to the sterile petri dishes.

A **centrifuge** is a machine used to spin specimen tubes quickly to separate liquids with different weights, most commonly to separate blood cells from plasma cells. After spinning a blood sample in a centrifuge for 10 – 15 minutes, the plasma in the sample should rise to the top of the tube, and the red blood cells should be drawn down to the bottom of the tube. It is important to ensure that the centrifuge is properly balanced before the test is run, or the machine may be damaged.

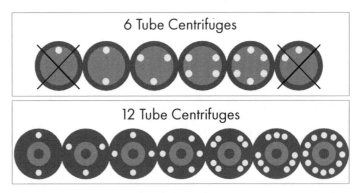

Figure 5.12. Balancing a Centrifuge

Microscopes allow for examination of objects that are too small to see with the naked eye. A medical assistant may be responsible for preparing a specimen the provider will examine using the microscope. Preparation involves creating a **microbiologic slide**, the vehicle used for holding a specimen so it can be examined under a microscope. Usually, the specimens that are evaluated in a physician's office lab require quick action not possible with an outside lab.

The specimen may also need to be evaluated quickly because it will become too compromised to be accurate if there is a delay.

For a **wet mount**, the specimen is placed onto a drop of water on a microscopic slide and then topped with a coverslip. Wet mounts allow the provider to examine bacteria that normally move or live in a liquid environment. For example, for a vaginal wet mount test, the provider examines vaginal discharge for infections that cause vaginitis.

REVIEW QUESTIONS

29. What is the machine used to separate blood cells from plasma cells called?

_____

30. Why must centrifuges be balanced?

_____

31. How is a wet mount microscope slide prepared?

_____

32. What is the CMA's responsibility in inoculating a culture?

_____

33. How long should a blood sample be spun in a centrifuge?

_____

Laboratory Quality Control and Assurance

Quality control processes exist to identify, reduce, and correct laboratory errors. These standardized procedures help prevent inaccurate results or the need for specimen recollection. **Testing protocols** outline specific steps on how to safely perform each test. **Testing records** and **performance logs** document daily work. All quality control activities should be documented in **quality control logs**.

Daily equipment maintenance is an important quality control measure.

- **Calibration** involves maintenance of an instrument so that it provides results within an acceptable range.

- Daily control testing should be performed before patient care every day to confirm the equipment is working correctly.

- Monitor temperature controls: certain specimen collections and chemicals must be kept at specific temperatures to ensure accuracy. There is usually a temperature log for each storage environment in the quality control records.

- Reagent storage: reagents are stored according to manufacturer's instructions.

34. What is the purpose of quality control processes?

35. What is the purpose of calibration?

36. A refrigerator is used to store urine samples. What should be checked and logged each day to ensure samples are accurate?

Laboratory Panels

Common laboratory panels and tests are described below. The CMA should be able to differentiate between normal and abnormal test results.

Urine can be used to test for a wide variety of conditions, including infections, metabolic disorders (e.g., diabetes), organ dysfunction, and cancers, as well as pregnancy. Urinalysis includes three main components:

- Urine is **physically** inspected for color, amount, clarity, and odor.
- A **chemical** test (usually using a dipstick) detects bacteria, protein, or blood in the urine. It also tests values such as specific gravity and pH.
- A **microscopic** analysis reveals the presence and number of particles viewable under a microscope, such as microorganisms, cells, crystals, and casts.

TABLE 5.3. Urinalysis Dipstick Testing

Testing for	Purpose	Normal Reading or Range
Leukocytes	Presence of WBCs indicates infection.	negative
Nitrate	Nitrates indicate infection by gram-negative bacteria.	negative
Urobilinogen	Urobilinogen indicates liver disease.	0.2 – 1 mg
Protein	Protein may indicate kidney disease or eclampsia.	negative
pH	Decreased (acidic) pH may indicate systemic acidosis or diabetes mellitus; increased (alkali) pH may indicate systemic alkalosis or UTI.	4.5 – 8
Blood	Blood in urine may indicate infection, kidney stones, or coagulation disorders.	negative
Specific gravity	This measures the concentration of urine, which can be affected by kidney or metabolic disorders.	1.010 – 1.025

Testing for	Purpose	Normal Reading or Range
Ketone	Ketones are produced during fat metabolism; their presence may indicate diabetes, hyperglycemia, starvation, alcoholism, or eclampsia.	negative
Bilirubin	Bilirubin is produced during the breakdown of heme; its presence may indicate liver disease.	negative
Glucose	Glucose in urine indicates hyperglycemia.	0 – 15 mg/dL

Hematology samples are usually collected using venipuncture and are analyzed to determine the number and type of blood cells present in the sample.

TABLE 5.4. Hematology Studies

Complete Blood Count (CBC)		
Testing for	Purpose	Normal Reading or Range
White blood cells (WBCs)	number of WBCs in blood; an increased number of WBCs can be an indication of inflammation or infection	4,500 – 10,000 cells/mcL
Red blood cells (RBCs)	carry oxygen throughout the body and filter carbon dioxide	men: 5 – 6 million cells/mcL women: 4 – 5 million cells/mcL
Hemoglobin (HgB)	protein that holds oxygen in the blood	men: 13.8 – 17.2 g/dL women: 12.1 – 15.1 g/dL
Hematocrit (Hct)	percentage of the blood composed of red blood cells	men: 41% – 50% women: 36% – 44%
Red blood cell indices	mean corpuscular volume (MCV): average size of the red blood cells mean corpuscular hemoglobin (MCH): average amount of hemoglobin per RBC mean corpuscular hemoglobin concentration (MCHC): average concentration of hemoglobin in RBCs	MCV: 80 – 95 fL MCH: 27.5 – 33.2 pg MCHC: 334 – 355 g/L
Platelets	play a role in the body's clotting process	150,000 – 450,000 cells/mcL

COAGULATION Studies

Prothrombin time (PT)	tests how long it takes blood to clot	10 – 13 sec
International normalized ratio (INR)	determines the effectiveness of an anticoagulant in thinning blood	healthy adults: < 1.1 patients receiving anticoagulants: 2.0 – 3.0
Partial thromboplastin time (PTT)	assesses the body's ability to form blood clots	60 – 70 sec
Activated partial thromboplastin time (APTT)	measures the body's ability to form blood clots using an activator to speed up the clotting process	20 – 35 sec

OTHER Hematology Studies

Erythrocyte sedimentation rate (ESR or sed rate)	measures rate at which RBCs sediment (fall); increased ESR may indicate inflammation, anemia, or infection; decreased ESR may indicate heart failure or liver or kidney disease; ESR increases with age	men: 12 – 14 mm/h women: 18 – 21 mm/h
C-reactive protein (CRP)	blood test for inflammation (similar to ESR); elevated in inflammation, infection, sepsis, and heart disease	< 10 mg/L
Total cholesterol (LDL and HDL)	a steroid produced by the liver that is needed to build and maintain animal cell membranes and that has protective properties for the heart; goals for low-density lipoprotein (LDL) and high-density lipoprotein (HDL) levels are based on the patient's risk factors for cardiovascular disease	< 200 mg/dL LDL: < 100 mg/dL HDL (men): 40 – 50 mg/dL HDL (women): 50 – 59 mg/dL
Triglycerides	stores fat	< 150 mg/dL

Chemistry and **metabolic studies** assess the function of various organ systems, including the liver, kidneys, and thyroid. They are also used to assess blood sugar and hemoglobin A1C, a more reliable indicator of blood glucose levels.

TABLE 5.5. Chemistry and Metabolic Studies

Liver Function Tests

Albumin	a protein made in the liver; low levels may indicate liver damage	3.5 – 5.0 g/dL

Liver Function Tests

Alkaline phosphatase (ALP)	an enzyme found in the liver and bones; increased levels indicate liver damage	45 – 147 U/L
Alanine transaminase (ALT)	an enzyme in the liver that helps metabolize protein; increased levels indicate liver damage	7 – 55 U/L
Aspartate transaminase (AST)	an enzyme in the liver that helps metabolize alanine; increased levels indicate liver or muscle damage	8 – 48 U/L
Total protein	low levels of total protein may indicate liver damage	6.3 – 7.9 g/dL
Total bilirubin	produced during the breakdown of heme; increased levels indicate liver damage or anemia	0.1 – 1.2 mg/dL

Blood Sugar

glucose	measures glucose or blood sugar level	Normal value: 70 – 120 mg/dL (this can vary if the patient is fasting or has just eaten)
hemoglobin A1C	measures average blood sugar level for the past 2 – 3 months by checking the percent of hemoglobin that are coated in sugar	Normal levels of nondiabetics: < 5.7% > 6.5 indicates diabetes

Kidney Function Tests

BUN	by-product of ammonia metabolism; filtered by the kidneys; high levels can indicate insufficient kidney function	7 – 20 mg/dL
Creatinine	product of muscle metabolism; filtered by the kidneys; high levels can indicate insufficient kidney function	0.6 – 1.2 mg/dL
BUN-to-creatinine ratio	increased ratio indicates dehydration, AKI, or GI bleeding; decreased ratio indicates renal damage	10:1 – 20:1

continued on next page

TABLE 5.5. Chemistry and Metabolic Studies *(continued)*

Kidney Function Tests

GFR	volume of fluid filtered by the renal glomerular capillaries per unit of time; decreased GFR indicates decreased renal function	men: 100 – 130 mL/min/1.73 m^2 women: 90 – 120 mL/min/1.73 m^2 GFR < 60 mL/min/1.73 m^2 is common in adults > 70 years

Electrolytes

Potassium (K$^+$)	helps with muscle contraction and regulates water and acid-base balance	3.5 – 5.2 mEq/L
Sodium (Na$^+$)	maintains fluid balance and plays a major role in muscle and nerve function	135 – 145 mEq/L
Calcium (Ca^{2+})	plays an important role in skeletal function and structure, nerve function, muscle contraction, and cell communication	8.5 – 10.3 mg/dL
Chloride (Cl$^-$)	plays a major role in muscle and nerve function	98 – 107 mEq/L
Magnesium (Mg^{2+})	regulates muscle, nerve, and cardiac function	1.8 – 2.5 mg/dL

REVIEW QUESTIONS

37. A patient's total bilirubin levels are 6 mg/dL. What should the CMA do?

_____

38. What is the normal range for potassium?

_____

39. What does an elevated level of BUN indicate?

_____

40. What level of HDL is normal for women?

_____

41. A patient has an HgA1C level of 9. What condition does the patient have?

_____

Specialized Testing

Specialized testing can be done to confirm specific infections or identify other conditions, such as pregnancy. Some of the most common specialized tests are described in the table below.

TABLE 5.6. Specialized Laboratory Tests		
Test	**Description**	**Normal Result**
Mononucleosis test (Mono spot test)	Blood test that checks for Epstein–Barr virus antibodies.	negative
Rapid Group A Streptococcus test	Throat swab culture that checks for presence of Group A Streptococcus bacteria (which causes strep throat).	negative
hCG pregnancy test	This can be a blood or urine test to check for pregnancy. hCG is a hormone produced by the placenta.	Urine: positive or negative hCG QUALitative: positive or negative hCG QUANTitative: > 25 mIU/mL is considered positive for pregnancy; this number will increase during the pregnancy
H. pylori	Detects a stomach ulcer–causing bacteria in the stomach called **Helicobacter pylori (H. pylori** for short). It can be tested by blood antibody test, urea breath tests, stool antigen test, or a stomach biopsy.	negative
Influenza	Uses nasopharynx swab to test for the flu virus.	negative
Fecal occult blood (FOB)/ Guaiac testing	Tests for the presence of blood in the stool, even blood that cannot be seen by the naked eye.	negative (no blood in stool)
Purified protein derivative (PPD) skin test	Detects tuberculosis; the provider injects a small amount of PPD under the top layer of skin, and the patient returns 2 days later to have the area observed for a reaction.	negative (redness and swelling at injection site indicates a positive test result)

DID YOU KNOW?

The **H. pylori** breath test measures **C-urea**, which is produced by the bacteria. The patient blows into a specialized bag before drinking a solution of synthetic urea. After the drink, the patient waits 15 minutes and then blows into a second bag.

REVIEW QUESTIONS

42. A CMA is reading the result of a PPD skin test. The area has no redness or inflammation. How should the CMA record the result?

_____

43. What does the Mono spot test check for?

_____

44. Which test identifies blood in the stool?

_____

ANSWER KEY

1. The CMA will need to obtain two identifiers of patient identity, receive patient consent, and verify testing requirements.

2. A 22-gauge multisample syringe should be used with older children and adults with small or difficult veins.

3. The needle should be inserted at a 15 – 30-degree angle.

4. The order of draw recommended by CLSI is:

   1. blood cultures
   2. sodium citrate tubes
   3. serum tubes
   4. heparin tubes
   5. EDTA tubes
   6. sodium fluoride/potassium oxalate

   The CMA should draw (1) the citrate tube, then (2) the SST, and then (3) the PPT (an EDTA tube).

5. The tourniquet should be removed after blood flow has been established.

6. A lancet is a small needle used to pierce the skin for capillary blood collection.

7. The lancet should be disposed of properly in a sharps container after using.

8. Infant heel sticks should be performed on the outer side of an infant's heel.

9. The patient should clean the opening to the urethra with an antiseptic wipe and void half of the urine into the toilet. The remaining urine is then collected in a sterile container.

10. The patient discards their first morning urine and waits a set amount of time (usually 30 minutes) to collect a sample.

11. A postprandial test is a timed urine test for glucose done 2 hours after the patient eats.

12. For a 24-hour test, urine is collected over 24 hours and added to a large collection container. The patient should discard their first morning urine and start collecting urine after that.

13. Urinary collection bags are used to collect urine samples from pediatric patients.

14. A fecal specimen is collected to evaluate for conditions affecting the digestive tract, including infection, parasites, cancer, bleeding, and nutrient absorption deficiency.

15. The sample should be collected using the collection device provided by the medical office; the sample should not come in contact with water, urine, or toilet paper.

16. Patients should stop taking NSAIDs, aspirin, and steroids 1 week before sample collection. Vitamin C and iron should be avoided for 3 days prior.

17. Sputum samples done at home should be collected first thing in the morning.

18. Patients should not use antibacterial mouthwash before providing a sputum sample.

19. Swabs are sterile and should be handled to avoid contamination during specimen collection.

20. Nasopharyngeal swabs test for respiratory infections, including flu, RSV, and COVID-19.

21. A genital swab is used to test for sexually transmitted infections.

22. Patient identifiers include the patient's full name (last, first) or medical record number, date of birth, and matching specimen barcode label.

23. At least 15 times the volume of the tissue sample to be preserved should be used.

24. Urine samples require refrigeration after collection. Ice packs may be needed during transportation to lab.

25. Medium- or heavy-weight gloves made from a waterproof material like rubber are needed.

26. The sample should be stored at room temperature away from any fire or heat source to be sent to the lab.

27. Health care providers should practice proper hand hygiene and make sure to clean the area before collecting the specimen.

28. Contamination can result in false laboratory results and the need for retesting.

29. A centrifuge is a machine used to spin specimen tubes quickly to separate liquids with different weights, such as to separate blood cells from plasma cells.

30. It is important for the centrifuge to be properly balanced before any test is run, or the machine and specimens may be damaged.

31. The specimen is placed onto a drop of water on a microscopic slide and then topped with a coverslip.

32. A medical assistant monitors the temperature readings and inspects the petri dishes inside the incubator for any signs of bacterial growth.

33. A blood sample should be spun in a centrifuge for 10 – 15 minutes. At this point, the plasma in the sample should rise to the top of the tube, and the red blood cells should be drawn down to the bottom of the tube.

34. Quality control processes identify, reduce, and correct laboratory errors.

35. Calibration maintains an instrument so that it provides results within an acceptable range.

36. Certain specimens, such as urine samples, must be kept at specific temperatures to ensure accuracy. There is usually a temperature log for each storage environment in the quality control records.

37. The normal range for bilirubin is between 0.1 and 1.2 mg/dL. The CMA should notify the physician of the elevated level that may indicate liver damage or anemia.

38. The normal range for potassium is 3.5 – 5.2 mEq/L.

39. An elevated level of BUN can indicate insufficient kidney function.

40. High-density lipoprotein (HDL) is a steroid produced by the liver that is needed to build and maintain animal cell membranes and that has protective properties for the heart. The normal level of HDL for women is between 50 and 59 mg/dL.

41. Hemoglobin A1C (HgA1C) measures average blood sugar level by checking the percent of hemoglobin that are coated in sugar. An HgA1C level of 9 would indicate diabetes.

42. The result would be recorded as negative.

43. The Mononucleosis test (Mono spot test) is a blood test that checks for Epstein–Barr antibodies.

44. The fecal occult blood/guaiac test checks for the presence of blood in the stool, even blood that cannot be seen by the naked eye.

6 PHARMACOLOGY

Pharmacology

Pharmacology is the study of the origin, uses, preparation, and effects of drugs on the body systems. The majority of drugs act on the system in two ways:

- mimicking or suppressing normal physiological processes in the body
- inhibiting the growth of certain microbial or parasitic organisms

Drugs cannot change the fundamental physiological processes that occur in the body—they can only change the rate at which they occur. Drug action occurs when the drug binds to receptors on a protein molecule in the body to activate or block a physiological process.

- An **agonist** binds to receptors and stimulates activity. For example, nitroglycerin is an agonist that results in the activation of enzymes that dilate blood vessels. Endogenous agonists (e.g., serotonin, epinephrine) are the molecules produced by the body that naturally bind to receptor sites.

- An **antagonist** binds to a receptor to block activity. For example, ACE inhibitors block the angiotensin-converting enzyme (ACE), which normally causes blood vessels to constrict. The result is dilation in the blood vessels.

The **brand name** of a drug is the name it is given by the pharmaceutical company that funded its research and development. This company holds the drug's patent for up to 20 years after its initial development, but when the patent expires, other pharmaceutical companies can produce the drug.

DID YOU KNOW?

Prescribing information about available drugs, including dosage and side effects, is compiled in the *Physicians' Desk Reference*, also known as the *PDR*. This information is available online and is integrated into many health record systems.

A **generic drug** must have the same active ingredient, strength, and dosage form as the brand-name drug, but the inactive ingredients do not need to be the same. Many generic drugs cost less to produce because generic manufacturers do not need to recoup the cost of research and development.

For the FDA to approve a generic drug, it must be **therapeutically equivalent** to the brand name, meaning it produces the same clinical effect and has the same safety profile. Generally, generic drugs can be substituted for prescribed brand-name medications (and vice versa) when the substitution will save the patient money. In fact, many insurers and state regulations require this substitution.

> **REVIEW QUESTIONS**
>
> 1. How does an agonist activate a physiological process?
>
> _____
>
> 2. What characteristics must be shared between a brand-name drug and a generic equivalent?
>
> _____
>
> 3. Why are generic drugs often substituted for brand-name prescriptions?
>
> _____

Adverse Reactions

Adverse drug reaction is a broad term used to describe unwanted, uncomfortable, or dangerous effects resulting from taking a specific medication. Most adverse drug reactions are dose-related, but they can also be allergic or idiosyncratic (unexpected responses that are neither dose-related nor allergic responses). Adverse drug reactions are one of the leading causes of morbidity and mortality in health care. They can be classified by severity as follows:

- mild (e.g., drowsiness)
- moderate (e.g., hypertension)
- severe (e.g., abnormal heart rhythm)
- lethal (e.g., liver failure)

Allergic reactions may cause itching, rash, airway edema with difficulty breathing, or a drop in blood pressure. Severe allergic reactions can cause anaphylaxis, which is a life-threatening condition requiring emergent care. An idiosyncratic reaction can cause almost any sign or symptom, and such a reaction usually cannot be predicted.

Adverse drug reactions are classified into six types.

TABLE 6.1. Types of Adverse Drug Reactions

Type	Description	Example
A augmented	predictable reactions arising from the pharmacological effects of the drug; dependent on dose	diarrhea due to antibiotics; hypoglycemia due to insulin
B bizarre	unpredictable reactions; independent of dose	hypersensitivity (anaphylaxis) due to penicillin
C chronic	reactions caused by the cumulative dose (the dose taken over a long period of time)	osteoporosis with oral steroids
D delayed	reactions that occur after the drug is no longer being taken	teratogenic effects with anticonvulsants
E end of use	reactions caused by withdrawal from a drug	withdrawal syndrome with benzodiazepines
F failure	unexpected failure of the drug to work; often caused by dose or drug interactions	resistance to antimicrobials

REVIEW QUESTIONS

4. What is an adverse drug reaction?

_____

5. A patient reports diarrhea on the second day of taking antibiotics. What type of adverse drug reaction is this?

_____

6. When does a delayed adverse drug reaction occur?

_____

Classes of Drugs

A **drug class** is a group of related medications that have the same mechanism of action or are used to treat the same condition. Drugs within a single drug class usually have the same suffix, although the suffixes of older drugs may differ because grouping generic drugs by suffix is a relatively new concept.

→

CONTINUE

TABLE 6.2. Drug Classes

Drug Class (suffix)	Action (indications)	Example(s) generic name (brand name)
Cardiovascular System Drugs		
angiotensin II receptor blockers (A2RBs) (–artan)	relax blood vessels (hypertension)	losartan (Cozaar) valsartan (Diovan)
angiotensin-converting enzyme (ACE) inhibitors (–pril)	relax blood vessels (hypertension, heart failure)	lisinopril (Prinivil, Zestril) benazepril (Lotensin)
anticoagulants (blood thinners)	prevent coagulation and thrombus formation	rivaroxaban (Xarelto) warfarin (Coumadin)
calcium channel blockers (–pine)	relax blood vessels (hypertension, angina, dysrhythmias)	amlodipine (Norvasc) diltiazem (Cardizem)
HMG-CoA reductase inhibitors (–statin)	reduce cholesterol by inhibiting cholesterol production	atorvastatin (Lipitor) simvastatin (FloLipid, Zocor)
beta blockers (B1s) or beta-adrenergic blocking agents (–olol)	relax blood vessels (hypertension, angina, migraine anaphylaxis)	metoprolol (Lopressor) carvedilol (Coreg)
Respiratory System Drugs		
beta-2 agonists (-erol)	bronchodilators (COPD, asthma)	albuterol salmeterol
Nervous System Drugs		
anticonvulsants	prevent seizures	carbamazepine (Tegretol) topiramate (Topamax)
atypical antipsychotics	manage psychosis in mood disorders and schizophrenia	quetiapine fumarate (Seroquel) aripiprazole (Abilify)
barbiturates (–barbital)	depress the central nervous system (sedation, seizures)	butabarbital (Butisol Sodium) pentobarbital (Nembutal)
benzodiazepines (–pam)	reduce anxiety and relax muscles	alprazolam (Xanax) clonazepam (Klonopin)

Drug Class (suffix)	Action (indications)	Example(s) generic name (brand name)
Nervous System Drugs		
hypnotics	reduce anxiety and induce sleep	eszopiclone (Lunesta) zolpidem (Ambien)
local anesthetics (–caine)	block sensation in a small area	lidocaine (Xylocaine, Lidoderm) benzocaine
nonsteroidal anti-inflammatory drugs (NSAIDs)	reduce pain and inflammation	ibuprofen (Motrin, Advil) naproxen (Aleve, Naprosyn)
opioid pain relievers (–codone)	block pain signals in brain	oxycodone (Percocet, OxyContin) morphine (Astramorph, Duramorph)
Musculoskeletal System Drugs		
muscle relaxants	reduce muscle spasms	cyclobenzaprine (Flexeril) tizanidine (Zanaflex)
neuromuscular blockers (–nium)	paralyze skeletal muscles (intubation, surgery)	pancuronium (Pavulon) rocuronium (Zemuron)
Immune System Drugs		
antifungals (–azole)	inhibit growth of or kill fungi	fluconazole tioconazole
antivirals (–vir)	inhibit growth of or kill viruses	docosanol (Abreva) oseltamivir (Tamiflu)
corticosteroids (–olone, –sone)	reduce inflammation	dexamethasone (Decadron) prednisone (Sterapred)
histamine H1 antagonists/ antihistamines	block histamine receptors (allergies, nausea/ vomiting, motion sickness)	loratadine (Alavert, Claritin) cetirizine (Zyrtec)
immunosuppressants	suppress the immune system (cancer, autoimmune conditions)	adalimumab (Humira) methotrexate (Trexall)
Digestive System Drugs		
antiemetics	reduce nausea and vomiting	ondansetron (Zofran) prochlorperazine (Compro)

continued on next page

TABLE 6.2. Drug Classes (continued)

Drug Class (suffix)	Action (indications)	Example(s) generic name (brand name)
Digestive System Drugs		
histamine-2 blockers (–tidine)	reduce stomach acid (heartburn, GERD)	famotidine (Pepcid) ranitidine (Zantac)
proton pump inhibitors (–razole)		esomeprazole (Nexium) omeprazole (Prilosec)
Urinary System Drugs		
diuretics (potassium sparing: –actone; loop diuretics: –emide)	increase urine production (hypertension, edema)	hydrochlorothiazide (Microzide) furosemide (Lasix)
Reproductive System Drugs		
phosphodiesterase type 5 inhibitors (–afil)	relax blood vessels in the penis (erectile dysfunction)	sildenafil (Revatio, Viagra) tadalafil (Cialis)
Endocrine System Drugs		
antidiabetics	increase insulin and/or decrease glucose production (type 2 diabetes)	metformin (Fortamet, Glucophage) glipizide (Glucotrol)
Antibiotics		
penicillins (–cillin)	inhibit growth of or kill bacteria	amoxicillin (Augmentin) penicillin
macrolides (–thromycin)		azithromycin (Zithromax) clarithromycin
tetracyclines (–cycline)		doxycycline tetracycline
lincosamide		clindamycin (Cleocin)
cephalosporin		cefdinir cephalexin (Keflex)
fluoroquinolones (quinolones) (–floxacin)		ciprofloxacin levofloxacin (Levaquin)

Antibiotics

sulfonamide		trimethoprim-sulfamethoxazole (co-trimoxazole) (Bactrim)
aminoglycosides		gentamicin (Garamycin) tobramycin (Tobrex)

Antidepressants

dopamine/norepineph-rine-reuptake inhibitors	increase dopamine and norepinephrine levels	bupropion (Wellbutrin, Zyban)
selective serotonin reuptake inhibitors (SSRIs)	increase serotonin levels	sertraline (Zoloft) escitalopram (Lexapro)
serotonin-norepineph-rine reuptake inhibitors (SNRIs)	increase serotonin and norepineph-rine levels	duloxetine (Cymbalta) venlafaxine (Effexor)
tricyclic antidepressants	increase serotonin and norepineph-rine levels	amitriptyline (Amitid, Amitril, Elavil, Endep) nortriptyline (Pamelor)

REVIEW QUESTIONS

7. What are antiemetics used to treat nausea and vomiting?

_____

8. What drug class is bupropion (Wellbutrin)?

_____

9. What is the mechanism of action for tricyclic antidepressants?

_____

Common Medications

The CMA exam will cover many commonly prescribed medications, including their generic and brand names, indications, common side effects, and contra-indications. A list of the 50 most common drugs prescribed in the United States is in the table on the next page.

→
CONTINUE

TABLE 6.3. Fifty Most Commonly Prescribed Medications in the United States

Generic Name (Brand Name)	Drug Class	Adverse Effects and Contraindications
atorvastatin (Lipitor) simvastatin (FloLipid, Zocor) rosuvastatin (Crestor) pravastatin (Pravachol)	HMG-CoA reductase inhibitors (statin)	**ADR:** muscle/joint pain Interactions: grapefruit/grapefruit juice, some antibiotics (e.g., cyclosporine, clarithromycin), some antifungals (e.g., itraconazole) Pregnancy: Category X
levothyroxine (Synthroid)	synthetic hormone	**BBW:** weight reduction **ADR:** dysrhythmias, trouble breathing, headache, nervousness, irritability, weight loss Interactions: iron supplement, calcium supplement, antacids Counseling: take with water 30 minutes before eating
lisinopril (Prinivil, Zestril)	ACE inhibitor	**BBW:** fetal toxicity **ADR:** cough, hypotension, dizziness Interactions: other medications that lower BP
metformin (Fortamet, Glucophage) glipizide (Glucotrol)	antidiabetic	**ADR:** hypoglycemia, diarrhea, nausea, headache Interactions: alcohol, miconazole (glimepiride) Counseling: take with food (metformin); take 30 minutes before food (glipizide)
amlodipine (Amvaz, Norvasc)	calcium channel blocker	**ADR:** headache, edema, tiredness, dizziness Interactions: other drugs that lower BP
metoprolol (Toprol-XL, Lopressor) carvedilol (Coreg) atenolol (Tenormin)	beta blocker	**BBW:** abrupt discontinuation **ADR:** dizziness, fatigue, weight gain Interactions: other drugs that lower BP

Generic Name (Brand Name)	Drug Class	Adverse Effects and Contraindications
albuterol (Ventolin HFA, Proventil HFA, Combivent Respimat, DuoNeb, ProAir HFA)	bronchodilator	**ADR:** headache, fast heart rate, dizziness, sore throat, nasal congestion Interactions: beta blockers, digoxin, MAOIs, tricyclic anti-depressants
omeprazole (Prilosec) pantoprazole (Protonix)	proton pump inhibitor	**ADR:** headache, abdominal pain, nausea, diarrhea, vomiting Interactions: digoxin, clopi-dogrel, benzodiazepines, warfarin
losartan (Cozaar)	angiotensin II receptor blocker	**BBW:** fetal toxicity **ADR:** dizziness, headache, fatigue Interactions: potassium supple-ments, other drugs that lower BP Pregnancy: Category D
gabapentin (Gralise, Neurontin)	anticonvulsant (also indicated for neu-ropathy)	**ADR:** drowsiness, dizziness, edema, angioedema (pre-gabalin), suicidal thoughts, emotional changes Interactions: alcohol, other CNS depressants
acetaminophen; hydrocodone (Norco, Vicodin, Lortab) tramadol (Ultram) oxycodone (OxyContin)	opioid	**BBW:** addiction, misuse, and abuse; respiratory depression; accidental ingestion; neonatal opioid withdrawal syndrome; risk from use with other CNS depressants **ADR:** constipation, light-headedness, dizziness, nausea and vomiting Interactions: MAOIs, seroto-nergic drugs, alcohol, other CNS depressants Counseling: may impair the ability to perform potentially hazardous activities

continued on next page

Generic Name (Brand Name)	Drug Class	Adverse Effects and Contraindications
hydrochlorothiazide (Microzide) furosemide (Lasix)	diuretic	**ADR:** hypotension, weakness, dizziness, blurred vision Interactions: alcohol, other antihypertensive drugs, NSAIDs
sertraline (Zoloft) escitalopram (Lexapro) fluoxetine (Prozac) trazodone (Desyrel) citalopram (Celexa)	selective serotonin reuptake inhibitor (SSRI)	**BBW:** increased risk of suicidal thoughts/behaviors **ADR:** insomnia, headache, agitation, dizziness, drowsiness, dry mouth, nausea, vomiting Interactions: MAOIs
bupropion (Wellbutrin, Zyban)	dopamine/norepi-nephrine-reuptake inhibitor	
duloxetine (Cymbalta) venlafaxine (Effexor)	serotonin-norepi-nephrine reuptake inhibitor	
montelukast (Singulair)	bronchodilator	**BBW:** neuropsychiatric symptoms **ADR:** respiratory infection, fever, headache, sore throat, cough
fluticasone (Flonase, Flovent)	corticosteroid (nasal, oral inhalant)	ADR (nasal/oral inhalation): headache, nasal/throat irritation, nose bleed, cough, worsening of infections
amoxicillin (Augmentin)	antibiotic (penicillin)	**ADR:** diarrhea, nausea
acetaminophen (Tylenol)	analgesic, anti-pyretic	**BBW:** hepatotoxicity **ADR:** nausea and vomiting Contraindications: hepatic impairment
prednisone (Sterapred)	corticosteroid (oral tablet)	ADR (oral tablet): fluid retention, hyper/hypoglyce-mia, hypertension, changes in behavior/mood, weight gain, worsening of infections Interactions (oral tablet): anti-diabetics, anticoagulants, oral contraceptives, NSAIDs

Generic Name (Brand Name)	Drug Class	Adverse Effects and Contraindications
amphetamine and dextroamphetamine (Adderall) methylphenidate (Ritalin)	ADHD treatment	**BBW:** potential for abuse/dependence **ADR:** insomnia, headache, fast heart rate, mood changes, decreased appetite, vomiting, dry mouth Interactions: MAOIs
insulin glargine (Lantus)	insulin	**ADR:** hypoglycemia, injection site reactions Interactions: other insulin products
ibuprofen (Advil, Motrin) meloxicam (Mobic)	NSAID	**BBW:** cardiovascular thrombotic events, GI bleeding **ADR:** abdominal pain, diarrhea, upset stomach Pregnancy: Category D (> 30 weeks)
tamsulosin (Flomax)	alpha-1 blocker (indicated for BPH)	**ADR:** orthostatic hypotension, sexual disorder, dizziness, headache
alprazolam (Xanax) clonazepam (Klonopin)	benzodiazepine	**BBW:** risk of respiratory depression and death when used with opioids; risk of abuse/dependence **ADR:** drowsiness, sedation, fatigue, memory impairment Interactions: alcohol, other CNS depressants
potassium	supplement	**ADR:** nausea, vomiting, flatulence, abdominal pain/discomfort, and diarrhea Interactions: potassium-sparing diuretics
clopidogrel (Plavix) aspirin	anticoagulant	**BBW:** bleeding, abrupt discontinuation **ADR:** bleeding Interactions: omeprazole/esomeprazole (clopidogrel), NSAIDs

continued on next page

TABLE 6.3. Fifty Most Commonly Prescribed Medications in the United States (continued)

Generic Name (Brand Name)	Drug Class	Adverse Effects and Contraindications
ranitidine (Zantac)	histamine H2 antagonist	**ADR:** headache, constipation, diarrhea, nausea, vomiting Interactions: warfarin
cyclobenzaprine (Flexeril)	muscle relaxant	**BBW:** abrupt discontinuation (baclofen) **ADR:** drowsiness, dizziness, dry mouth, nausea and vomiting Interactions: alcohol, other CNS depressants, MAOIs, serotonergic drugs Contraindications: use of MAOIs (cyclobenzaprine)
azithromycin (Zithromax)	antibiotic (macrolide)	**ADR:** diarrhea, nausea Interactions: anticoagulants, antidiabetics
allopurinol (Lopurin, Zyloprim, Aloprim)	antigout	**ADR:** rash, nausea, vomiting, drowsiness Interactions: anticoagulants Counseling: may impair the ability to perform potentially hazardous activities
BBW: black box warning **ADR:** adverse drug reactions		

REVIEW QUESTIONS

10. Metformin is indicated for what condition?

_____

11. What is a concern with the antidepressant monoamine oxidase inhibitors (MAOIs)?

_____

12. What warnings should a patient be alerted to when taking clopidogrel (Plavix)?

_____

Storage of Drugs

In the medical office, medications must be stored and secured in accordance with all applicable laws. Medication storage cabinets and medication supply rooms must be kept locked. Most medications should be stored in a cool, dry place away from heat, light, and humidity. Pills and capsules in particular are easily damaged by heat and moisture.

It is important to instruct the patient to follow any storage instructions, such as refrigeration requirements, that are on the prescription label. Patients should also be reminded to store medications out of the reach of children or pets to prevent accidental ingestion of the medication.

The **expiration date** on medications, including nonprescription medications, should be noted to ensure that the drug is still safe and effective. The expiration date is usually expressed as a month and a year, and the medication is considered usable through the end of the given month. For example, if the expiration date on a drug is 7/22, the last day it should be taken is 07/31/2022.

It is also important to note when medications have been opened. Some medications lose effectiveness soon after they are opened and will have a **beyond-use date (BUD)** that gives the date the medication should be discarded.

REVIEW QUESTIONS

13. What common drugs require refrigeration?

14. The expiration date on a bottle of lisinopril 10 mg tablets is 3/22. When is the last day these tablets may be taken?

Medication Packaging

Medications can be packaged in a variety of ways depending on the medication form, intended use, shelf stability, and more. Some common forms of medication packaging are discussed below.

A **multidose vial** contains more than one dose of a liquid medication intended for injection. These vials usually include preservatives that prevent the growth of bacteria. The vial should be dated when opened, and discarded within 28 days (unless instructions on the vial state otherwise).

Figure 6.1. Multidose Vial

When possible, multidose vials should be used only for a single patient. When that is not possible (e.g., influenza vaccines), they should be stored in medication preparation areas. Multidose vials should be discarded if they are used in the patient treatment area to avoid contamination.

An **ampule** is a sealed container, usually made of glass, containing a sterile medication or powder to be made up in solution to be used for injection. The ampule must be broken at the neck in order to reconstitute or administer the medication. Because they must be broken for use, ampules are single use only.

Figure 6.2. Ampule

Unit dose packaging offers convenience and safety by supplying individual doses of medications in individual packets. The medication comes packaged in nonreusable containers, and patients get the exact dose they need. The packaging can take many forms, including blister cards, strips, pouches, sticks, vials, and prefilled syringes.

Prefilled cartridge needles contain accurate, premeasured doses of a medication. Since the medication is already prepared in the syringe, the chances of dosing and medication errors are reduced, as is the risk of microbial contamination. Some of these medications are prepared using a needle-free design or cartridge system, eliminating the potential for any needlestick injuries.

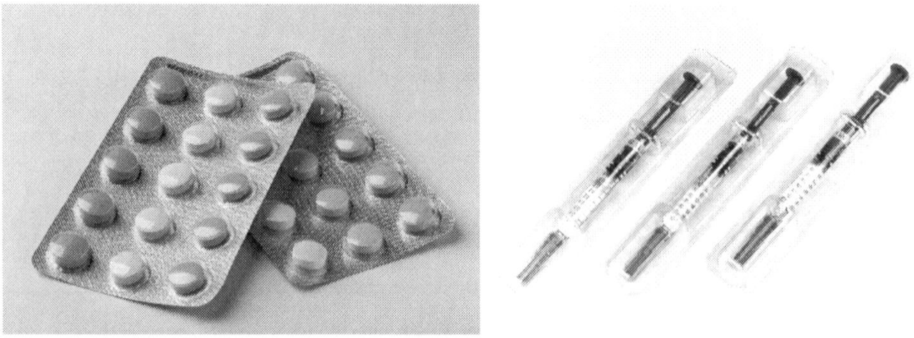

HELPFUL HINT:

When drawing up a medication from an ampule, the CMA should have a filter needle available to ensure that no glass shards are mixed with the medication.

Figure 6.3. Unit Dose Packages

Some medications must be stored in powdered form because they rapidly lose their effectiveness once they are mixed into a solution. These powdered medications are often supplied in vials to which a liquid (the diluent) will be added to **reconstitute** the medication before it can be administered.

Figure 6.4. Reconstituting Powdered Medication

When reconstituting injectable medications, the CMA must determine both the type and amount of diluent to be used. Sterile water and 0.9% NaCl are commonly used, but some medications require a special diluent.

REVIEW QUESTIONS

15. What type of needle is required when drawing up a medication from an ampule?

16. How is powdered medication reconstituted?

17. When should multidose vials be discarded?

Drug Dosage Units

The table below gives the common units seen when preparing and administering medications. The CMA should be able to convert dosages between units and calculate the amount of medication to be administered.

TABLE 6.4. Converting Between Units					
Into Metric			**Out Of Metric**		
If you know	**Multiply by**	**To get**	**If you know**	**Multiply by**	**To get**
Mass (Weight)					
ounces	28	grams	grams	0.035	ounces
pounds	0.45	kilograms	kilograms	2.2	pounds
Volume					
teaspoons	5	milliliters (CC)	milliliters (CC)	0.03	fluid ounces

continued on next page

TABLE 6.4. Converting Between Units (continued)

Into Metric			Out Of Metric		
If you know	Multiply by	To get	If you know	Multiply by	To get
Mass (Weight)					
tablespoons	15	milliliters (CC)	liters	2.1	pints
fluid ounces	30	milliliters (CC)	liters	1.06	quarts
cups	0.24	liters	liters	0.26	gallons
pints	0.47	liters			
quarts	0.95	liters			
gallons	3.8	liters			

Quick dosage calculations conversions are listed below:

- 1 mg = 1,000 mcg
- 1 gm (g) = 1,000 mg
- 1 L = 1,000 mL
- 1 mL = 1 cc
- 5 mL = 1 tsp
- 15 mL = 3 tsp = 1 tbsp
- 30 mL = 2 tbsp = 1 oz
- 8 oz = 1 cup
- 1 kg = 1,000 gm (g)
- 1 kg = 2.2 lb

The following method can be used to calculate the amount of a drug to administer.

$$x = \frac{DV}{H}$$

The following variables are used:

- x = amount to give
- D = desired dose or dose ordered
- H = dose on hand or dose on container
- V = vehicle (form and amount)

Vehicle (V) is the unit that "carries" the dose on hand. For example, a 150 mg tablet has a V of 1 because one tablet "carries" the 150 mg dose. A 200 mg/5 mL mixture has a vehicle of 5 because the 5 mL "carries" the dose of 200 mg.

Examples

1. Order: Tagamet 600 mg

Drug available: 300 mg tablet

$D = 600$ mg

$H = 300$ mg

$V = 1$

$x = \dfrac{DV}{H} = \dfrac{600(1)}{300} = 2$ tablets

2. Order: Dilantin 50 mg

Drug available: 125 mg/5 mL

$D = 50$ mg

$H = 125$ mg

$V = 5$

$\dfrac{DV}{H} = \dfrac{50(5)}{125} = \dfrac{250}{125} = 2$ mL

REVIEW QUESTIONS

18. If a patient weighs 233 lbs, what is his weight in kilograms?

_____

19. A physician prescribed a patient gabapentin 1200 mg 3 times per day. If the capsules are 300 mg each, how many capsules should the patient be instructed to take at each dose?

_____

20. A patient reports she gave her 6-year-old child a tablespoon of cough syrup. How would the CMA record this amount in milliliters?

_____

21. How many grams are in 1 kilogram?

_____

22. A patient unable to tolerate swallowing pills is ordered to take 300 mg of cefdinir oral suspension every 12 hours. The formula concentration is 125 mg/5 ml. How many milliliters should the patient take for one dose?

_____

Routes of Administration

The following routes are used to administer medications:

- **buccal** (BUC): placed between the cheek and gum via spray, gel, or tablet
- **inhalation** (INH): inhaled into the respiratory system via mist, spray, or mask

- **intradermal** (ID): injected into the dermal skin layer at a 15-degree angle via a 25- to 27-gauge needle
- **intramuscular** (IM): injected into the muscle at a 90-degree angle via an 18- to 23-gauge needle
- **intravenous** (IV): injected into a vein via an 18- to 22-gauge needle
- **ophthalmic**: placed in the eye via ointment or drops
- **oral** (PO): taken by mouth and swallowed via capsule, tablet, liquid, gel, or solution
- **otic**: placed in the ear via drops
- **parenteral**: any injected medication (SC, IM, ID, or IV)
- **rectal** (PR): placed in the rectum via applicator (cream or suppository)
- **subcutaneous** (SC): injected into the subcutaneous tissue at a 45- to 90-degree angle via a 22- to 25-gauge needle
- **sublingual** (SL): placed under the tongue via gel or tablets
- **topical** (TOP): placed on the skin via patch, ointment, cream, liquid, or spray
- **transdermal**: placed on the skin via patch
- **urethral**: placed in the urethra and bladder via catheter
- **vaginal** (PV): placed in the vagina via applicator (cream or suppository)
- **Z-track**: a specific IM injection method used to prevent the medication from irritating the subcutaneous tissue. The skin at the injection site is pulled to one side before injection. After injection, the skin is released, and the medication cannot seep into the subcutaneous layers.

REVIEW QUESTIONS

23. At what angle should a subcutaneous injection be given?

_____

24. What are the different types of parenteral injections?

_____

25. Where is a buccal medication administered?

_____

Intramuscular Injection

Intranasal Delivery

Intravenous Delivery

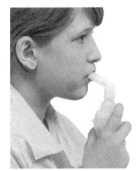

Inhalation

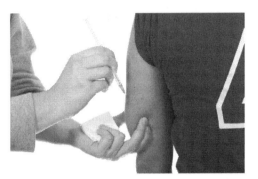

Subcutaneous Injection

Buccal Delivery

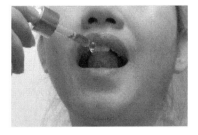

Sublingual Delivery

Figure 6.5. Routes of Administration

⟶
CONTINUE

Medication Administration and Documentation

The "six rights of medication administration" should be followed every time a patient is given any medication to prevent errors.

1. **Right patient:** The medical assistant must check the name on the provider's order and verify the patient's first and last names, along with a second identifier (e.g., birth date or medical records number).

2. **Right drug:** The medical assistant must check the drug label for expiration date and name three separate times: when taking the drug container out, after placing the medication in the dispenser (syringe or medication cup), and before returning the container to storage or disposing of it.

3. **Right route:** The medical assistant must check the provider's order for correct route.

4. **Right dose:** The medical assistant must check the provider's order for the right dose.

5. **Right time:** The medical assistant must check the provider's order for the right time to give the medication.

6. **Right documentation:** The medical assistant must record the medication administration in the patient's record, noting date, time, drug, route, dose, site, results, tolerance, and patient education.

Certain information must be documented and maintained for every prescription that is written. The provider will maintain these records within the patient's electronic health record, and the pharmacy will maintain the records for the prescriptions when they are filled. The documentation should include the following information:

- patient's full name and address
- patient's date of birth
- the date the prescription was written
- the name, strength, dosage form, and quantity of the drug dispensed
- any refill instructions from the prescriber
- the prescriber's name, address, and DEA number (where required)
- the complete directions for use of the drug (e.g., when to take it, how to take it, where to store it, foods that should be avoided, etc.)

A **medication error** is any health care action or decision that causes an unintended consequence. Whenever the technician commits or discovers a medication error, they must inform their supervisor immediately. Failure to inform supervisors of an error can be grounds for dismissal.

Sometimes, a medication error almost happens but ultimately does not. These events are called **near-misses**. Even though the error did not occur (and thus no patients were harmed), it is still considered an error and should be reported similarly.

REVIEW QUESTIONS

26. How is the patient's identity confirmed?

_____

27. What should be recorded in the medical record when administering a medication to a patient?

_____

28. A CMA accidentally gives the wrong dosage of medication to a patient. What should the CMA do FIRST?

_____

Immunizations

CHILDHOOD IMMUNIZATIONS

The childhood immunization schedule is recommended by public health officials for immunity against childhood diseases. Immunizations are only given to healthy infants and children, so the medical assistant should be sure that the patient does not have a fever or any active illness. If the patient is sick, the appointment should be rescheduled. The patient's health history should not show any allergies or past convulsions due to immunizations.

The parent should be advised on the benefits and risks of all immunizations prior to administration and be given a **vaccine information statement (VIS)**. These forms are produced by the CDC and provide important information about the risks and benefits of vaccines.

Most immunizations are given in a series. When more than one dose is required for immunity, the shot sequence is referred to as a primary series. The primary series requires a booster for the series to be complete and effective. Below are the most common vaccines and the diseases they prevent.

- DTaP (diphtheria, tetanus, and pertussis):
  - **Diphtheria** is an acute infectious disease caused by *Corynebacterium diphtheriae*, which is a gram-positive club-shaped bacillus. Symptoms of diphtheria include headache, fever, sore throat, and malaise.

- o **Tetanus** is caused by *Clostridium tetani*. Symptoms include stiff jaw, fever, and weakness.
- o **Pertussis**, also known as whooping cough, is an acute infectious disease caused by the gram-negative bacillus *Bordetella pertussis*. Symptoms include fever, dry cough, and sneezing.
- Hib: *Haemophilus Influenzae* **Type B** is caused by a nonmotile, gram-negative parasitic bacterium. Symptoms include sore throat, fever, cough, and muscle aches.
- MMR (measles, mumps, rubella):
  - o **Measles**, also called rubeola, is spread by direct contact, indirect contact, or droplet infection. Lasting around 10 days, it causes a red skin rash, runny nose, cough, and sore throat.
  - o **Mumps** is caused by an infectious organism that attacks the parotid and salivary glands, and is transmitted by direct contact or droplet infection.
  - o **Rubella**, also known as the German measles, is caused by a virus that leads to an upper respiratory infection. Other symptoms are fever, joint pain, and a fine red rash.
- HBV (hepatitis B virus): **Hepatitis B** is a highly contagious form of viral hepatitis, caused by the hepatitis B virus (HBV). It is transmitted by contact with contaminated saliva, semen, or blood. Symptoms include nausea, vomiting, fever, jaundice, and dark urine.
- VZV (varicella-zoster virus): Better known as chicken pox, **varicella** is a highly contagious viral illness that is spread by direct contact and droplet infection. Symptoms include an itchy rash, fever, headache, and general malaise.
- IPV (inactivated poliovirus): **Polio** is a serious disease that can lead to infantile paralysis (poliomyelitis). Symptoms include headache, nausea, vomiting, and rash. The vaccine contains inactivated polio virus (IPV).

ADULT IMMUNIZATIONS

While fewer in number, adult vaccines are also an important part of patient care. In addition, health care workers themselves need to get certain vaccines to help protect the vulnerable populations they interact with. Important adult immunizations and vaccines are listed below.

- Influenza vaccine: **Influenza** viruses are associated with approximately 36,000 deaths each year in the United States alone. The composition of the influenza vaccine changes from year to year based on predictions of which strains will be most prominent. Clinical researchers found that aging adults who receive this vaccine have less severe influenza illness and fewer complications, and the mortality rate is reduced.

- Pneumococcal vaccine: **Pneumococcal** infections cause around 40,000 deaths every year in the United States. The pneumococcal vaccine provides immunity to the *Streptococcus pneumoniae* organism. All adults over the age of 65 years should receive this vaccine, as should those who are considered high risk. The injection is given intramuscularly in the deltoid muscle.

- Herpes zoster vaccine: The **herpes zoster** virus vaccine can prevent shingles in people over 60. This injection reduces the occurrence of shingles, and for those who do develop shingles, it lessens illness severity.

- Tetanus vaccine: Most aging adults are not aware that they need to be immunized against *Clostridium tetani*, the bacteria that leads to tetanus. The **tetanus** vaccine is recommended every 10 years for adults and is usually available as tetanus-diphtheria toxoid (Td), given intramuscularly.

VACCINE RECORDKEEPING AND STORAGE

Before administering any vaccines, it is important to give the patient (or parent/legal guardian) copies of all pertinent vaccine information statements and make sure they understand the risks and benefits of the vaccine(s). The vaccination administration record should be completed after administration of the vaccine(s). The forms vary by state, but in general, all of the following information will be included on the vaccination administration record:

- type of vaccine given
- date the vaccine was given
- funding source of the vaccine given: F (federal), S (state), or P (private)
- route and site of administration on the patient
- lot number and manufacturer of the vaccine
- date on the VIS and the date it was given to the patient (or parent/legal guardian)
- signature (or initials) and title of the person who administered the vaccine

Patients (or their parents/legal guardians) often request vaccination records to fulfill requirements for attending school or playing sports. These records might also be requested by other agencies (e.g., health departments) in the event of a recall or problem with the vaccine. It is important that these records remain up to date, accurate, and complete.

Proper vaccine storage and handling is essential for ensuring that vaccines maintain their potency and effectiveness. Different vaccines require different storage temperatures, but most must be either refrigerated or frozen. Many vaccines also need to be protected from exposure to light. CMAs must be familiar with and adhere to all recommendations for the proper storage of vaccines.

TABLE 6.5. Vaccine Storage

Store in Refrigerator:	Store in Freezer:	Protect from Light:
36°F to 46°F (2°C to 8°C)	−58°F to 5°F (−50°C to −15°C)	
9vHPV		Afluria
diphtheria toxoid, tetanus toxoid, and pertussis (DT, DTaP, DTaP-HepB-IPV, DTap-IPV, DTap-IPV/Hib, Tdap, Td)		Bexsero
		FLUAD
		Fluarix
		Flublok
HepA		Flucelvax
HepB		FluLaval
HepA-HepB		Flumist
Hib	MMR	Gardasil 9
influenza (LAIV, IIV, RIV)	MMRV	Hiberix
meningococcal (MenACWY-D, Men-ACWY-CRM, MenB-4C, MenB-FHbp)	VAR	IPOL
	ZVL	M-M-R II
		Menveo
MMR		ProQuad
pneumococcal (PCV13 and PPSV23)		Rotarix
rotavirus (RV1 and RVS)		RotaTeq
RZV		Shingrix
		Varivax
		Zostavax

REVIEW QUESTIONS

29. A 3-year-old child is due for vaccinations. The CMA takes the temperature and finds that the child has a fever. What should the CMA do?

30. At what temperature should vaccinations be stored in the refrigerator?

_____

31. How often should adults receive a tetanus vaccination?

_____

32. What can happen if vaccines are not properly stored?

_____

33. What information is included in a vaccine information statement?

_____

ANSWER KEY

1. The agonist binds to receptors and stimulates activity.

2. A generic equivalent must have the same active ingredient, strength, and dosage form as the brand-name drug, but the inactive ingredients do not need to be the same.

3. Most generic drugs cost less than brand-name equivalents.

4. An adverse drug reaction is an unwanted, uncomfortable, or dangerous effect resulting from taking a specific medication.

5. Diarrhea from antibiotics is an augmented reaction, which means it is a predictable reaction resulting from the pharmacological effects of the drug.

6. A patient might experience a delayed adverse drug reaction after they have stopped taking the drug.

7. Antiemetics are used to treat nausea and vomiting.

8. Bupropion (Wellbutrin) is in the dopamine/norepinephrine-reuptake inhibitor class.

9. Tricyclic antidepressants increase serotonin and norepinephrine levels.

10. Metformin is an antidiabetic used to treat type 2 diabetes.

11. MAOIs are a class of antidepressants that are effective in treating mood disorders but are rarely used due to their potential for drug-drug interactions.

12. Patients should be warned that bleeding may occur if the medication is stopped abruptly.

13. Common drugs requiring refrigeration include regular insulin, reconstituted antibiotics, and some vaccines.

14. This expiration date indicates that the last day these tablets may be taken is 03/31/2022.

15. A filter needle must be used to ensure that no glass shards are mixed with the medication.

16. Medication stored in powdered form often needs to be reconstituted with a liquid, or diluent. The CMA must determine the most appropriate diluent, such as sterile water or 0.9% NaCl.

17. Multidose vials should be used only for a single patient, and should be discarded if they are used in the patient treatment area in order to avoid contamination.

18. To convert a patient's weight from pounds to kilograms, multiply by 0.45: 233 lbs × 0.45 = 104.85 kg.

19. The patient should be instructed to take 4 capsules 3 times per day.

    $D = 1200$ mg

    $H = 300$ mg

    $V = 1$

    $x = \dfrac{DV}{H} = \dfrac{1200(1)}{300} = 4$ capsules

20. The CMA should record the amount as 15 mL.

21. There are 1,000 grams in 1 kilogram.

22. The patient should take 2.1 milliliters.

    $\dfrac{DV}{H} = \dfrac{125(5)}{300} = \dfrac{625}{300} = 2.1$ mL

23. A subcutaneous injection should be given at a 45- to 90-degree angle.

24. The different types of parenteral injections are intramuscular, intradermal, subcutaneous, and intravenous.

25. A buccal medication is placed between the cheek and gum via spray, gel, or tablet.

26. Patients are identified by name and one other identifier, like birth date or medical records number.

27. When administering medication to a patient, the CMA should record the name of the medication, date and time of administration, route of administration, dose, site, results, tolerance, and patient education.

28. The CMA must inform their supervisor immediately.

29. The CMA should notify the physician. Only healthy children should receive scheduled vaccinations.

30. Vaccinations should be stored in the refrigerator at 36°F – 46°F (2°C – 8°C).

31. The tetanus vaccine is recommended every 10 years for adults.

32. Proper vaccine storage and handling is essential to ensure that vaccines maintain their potency and effectiveness.

33. The vaccine information statement provides information about the vaccine, including risk and benefits.

7 EMERGENCY MANAGEMENT

A **medical emergency** is an unexpected, life-threatening event. It can occur at any time, so it is important to be prepared and understand what to do. A medical assistant's role is to stay calm and follow the office's emergency management policy and protocol. The more prepared the CMA is for an emergency, the better the outcome will be for the patient. Knowing how to recognize common emergency situations and what to do can help ensure that the patient remains safe and the event does not escalate.

Some key points for the CMA to remember during an emergency are:

- Secure the scene and do not panic.
- Relocate nearby visitors and patients.
- Work with other members of the health care team to ensure that all necessary equipment is available.
- Know the location of the crash cart.
- Maintain cardiopulmonary resuscitation (CPR) certification and follow training.
- Do not attempt any intervention without the proper training.
- Be observant; the CMA may need to provide information about the event.
- Remember to complete all applicable documentation regarding the emergency.

Emergency Identification

In an emergency, the medical assistant may be the one delegated to perform the initial assessment of the patient. If the patient is actively presenting with an emergency, the initial assessment should be brief and focused on responsiveness, circulation, airway, and breathing. Unconscious patients should be aroused through speech and touch. If they remain unresponsive, the CMA should assess circulation. If the patient is pulseless, the CMA should follow CPR protocols. If the patient appears stable, a standard assessment should be performed.

Patients presenting with life-threatening symptoms will be **triaged** to determine their acuity (the level of care they will need). In most states, medical assistants are NOT allowed to triage patients, as it requires exercising clinical judgment. However, it is helpful for the CMA to understand how the process works in order to assist providers as needed.

When patients are triaged, the provider will assess the severity of their symptoms and determine how long they can wait for care. If multiple patients require attention, the triage process will also determine who should be seen first. Each office will have its own triage protocols, which are often color-coded, as explained below.

Standard (green): Standard patients are stable and should be seen by the provider within the normal time frame.

Urgent (yellow): Urgent patients should be assessed by the provider as soon as possible to determine a treatment plan.

- low pulse oximetry even with unlabored breathing
- high or low blood pressure
- infection symptoms lasting longer than a week despite treatment (in the very young and very old)
- significant medical history and new symptoms

Very Urgent (orange): The provider should be notified immediately. Very urgent patients should be assessed by the provider, who will determine if transfer to a higher level of care is needed.

- labored breathing, wheezing
- mental fogginess, confusion, difficulty speaking
- acute changes after an injury
- signs of infection after procedure
- acute, unrelieved pain

Immediate (red): Patients with life-threatening symptoms need immediate care. 911 should be called, and the patient should be prepared for transfer to the emergency department.

- airway compromise
- agonal breaths (gasping, labored breaths)
- chest pain
- uncontrolled bleeding
- signs of shock
- unresponsive or responsive only to painful stimuli

During and after an emergency, the CMA should document the event and provide information to emergency medical services (EMS). EMS will expect a chronological timeline of the events and what interventions or treatments were given. Medical assistants should be prepared to give the following information:

- patient's name, age, and pertinent medical history
- the concern or chief complaint
- current vital signs
- what was done to treat the concern
- patient's current condition
- patient's allergies

Anaphylactic Shock

Anaphylactic shock (or **anaphylaxis**) is a life-threatening, severe allergic reaction that causes widening of blood vessels and constriction of airways in the lungs. The most common causes of anaphylactic shock are food allergens, medications, and insect venom. Symptoms of anaphylactic shock include:

- respiratory distress (can be severe)
- swelling (edema) in face, lips, or tongue
- skin pallor or flushing
- low blood pressure
- weakness
- dizziness or fainting

- vomiting or diarrhea
- altered mental status
- anxiety or confusion

Patients receiving medications in the office may experience anaphylactic shock, so medical assistants should be familiar with its symptoms. Anaphylactic shock is treated with an epinephrine injection. The provider may choose to transfer the patient to an emergency department for further observation or if treatment is ineffective.

REVIEW QUESTIONS

4. During anaphylactic shock, what happens to the blood vessels and airway?

_____

5. What medication is used to treat anaphylactic shock?

_____

Asthmatic Attack

Asthma, an obstructive disease of the lungs, is characterized by long-term inflammation and constriction of the bronchial airways. Patients with asthma often experience exacerbations (called acute asthmatic attacks) triggered by lung irritants, exercise, stress, or allergies. Symptoms of an acute asthmatic attack include:

- wheezing
- frequent cough (productive or nonproductive)
- shortness of breath
- tightness in the chest
- severe exacerbations marked by:
  o rapid breathing
  o audible wheezing
  o anxiety
  o low oxygen levels

Treatment for an acute asthmatic attack aims to widen the airways of the lungs. Patients are given a bronchodilator such as albuterol or ipratropium through a mask or mouthpiece. They may also receive a corticosteroid. Patients should be monitored for dizziness and rapid heart rate following treatment.

Patients who do not respond to treatment are in **status asthmaticus**, a severe condition characterized by unmanageable asthma exacerbations with limited or no pauses between the exacerbations. These patients will require immediate transfer to an emergency department.

REVIEW QUESTIONS

6. What type of medicine is used to widen lung airways during an asthma attack?

_____

7. What symptoms characterize status asthmaticus?

_____

Bleeding

There are three types of bleeding: arterial, venous, and capillary.

Arterial bleeding occurs when an artery is damaged. Because arteries carry high volumes of blood at high pressure, arterial bleeding can be life-threatening and requires immediate intervention to prevent low blood pressure and other issues related to decrease in blood volume.

Arterial blood is bright red and "spurts" due to the pressure of the heart pumping. The blood is often moving too quickly for clotting to occur.

Venous bleeding occurs when a vein is damaged. Veins carry high volumes of blood, but they do not supply the same pressure as arteries, so although venous bleeding may be heavy, it is slower than arterial bleeding. The blood is also darker because it is deoxygenated.

Capillary bleeding occurs when the small blood vessels that create the network between veins and arteries are damaged. Capillary bleeding is often seen in wound beds or with skin abrasions. Bleeding from the capillaries is usually controlled easily.

The treatment for all types of bleeding is to apply direct pressure to the site.

1. Maintain standard precautions, including wearing gloves.
2. Apply pressure using sterile gauze. Pressure may be applied for up to 20 minutes depending on the type of bleed.
3. If the bleed is arterial, pressure may be applied above the site of bleeding (only if directed by the provider).
4. Continue to evaluate for symptoms of shock.
5. Assist with cleaning and dressing the wound once the bleeding has stopped.

HELPFUL HINT

Do not remove blood-soaked dressings, as this will interrupt the clotting process. Instead add gauze as necessary.

REVIEW QUESTIONS

8. What type of bleeding spurts or pulses from the wound?

_____

9. What is the first step to treating all types of bleeding wounds?

_____

Bone Fractures

A **fracture** is any break in a bone. Fractures are diagnosed via X-ray. Fractures can be open or closed. **Open fractures** include a break in the skin; the skin is intact with a **closed fracture**. Further classifications of fractures are made based on the configuration of the fracture.

- Non-displaced: Broken area of the bone remains in alignment; this is the optimal condition for reduction (setting) and healing.

- Displaced: Broken areas of bone are not aligned. Displacement may require manual or surgical reduction including hardware for fixation.

- Transverse: A horizontal break in a straight line across the bone that occurs from a force perpendicular to the break.

- Oblique: A diagonal break that occurs from a force higher or lower than the break.

- Spiral: A twisting break around the circumference of the bone that is common in sports injuries.

- Comminuted: The break is fragmented into three or more pieces. This is more common in people over 65 and those with brittle bones.

- Compression: The break is crushed or compressed, creating a wide, flattened appearance. Compression frequently occurs with crush injuries.

- Segmental: Two or more areas of the bone are fractured, creating a segmented area of "floating" bone.

If the patient has a suspected fracture, the CMA should immobilize the area. If it is an open fracture, any bleeding should be controlled. The CMA should keep the fractured area elevated if possible and prepare the patient for further diagnostic evaluation or transfer. It is important to monitor for symptoms of shock, especially with an open fracture.

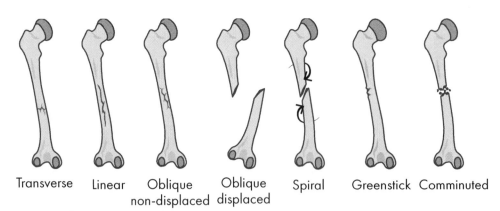

Transverse   Linear   Oblique   Oblique   Spiral   Greenstick Comminuted
                        non-displaced   displaced

Figure 7.1. Types of Fractures

Burns

Burns are trauma to the skin or underlying tissue caused by heat, radiation, electricity, or chemical exposure. Burns are classified by depth as first degree, second degree, and third degree.

- **Superficial** (first degree): Damage is limited to the epidermis and does not result in blisters (e.g., sunburn).

- **Partial-Thickness** (second degree): Damage includes the dermis and epidermis accompanied by severe pain.

- **Full-Thickness** (third degree): All layers of the skin are damaged, and there is likely underlying tissue damage. The patient may not feel pain in areas of significant nerve damage.

First-degree burns usually resolve on their own. Medical assistants should treat first-degree burns by cooling the area with a cold compress or running the burn under cold water. If needed, a dry nonstick dressing can be used.

When treating second- and third-degree burns, it is important that the CMA does not break any blisters, remove loose tissue on the burn, or remove material adhering to the burn. These actions can lead to infection and further damage. A sterile towel should be applied to the site, as well as sterile water or sterile normal saline. In the office setting, patients should be transferred to a higher level of care for further treatment and monitored for shock while awaiting transfer.

Cardiac and Respiratory Arrest

Cardiopulmonary (cardiac) arrest occurs when the heart stops beating, which causes blood flow to stop. The patient will have no pulse and either will not be breathing or will display labored breathing (agonal gasps). Immediate **cardiopulmonary resuscitation (CPR)** should be started for any patient in arrest.

Respiratory arrest occurs when breathing stops or is no longer effective at meeting the body's oxygen needs. Respiratory arrest often occurs with cardiac arrest but can occur alone as well. It will eventually lead to cardiac arrest.

Both cardiac and respiratory arrest are life-threatening conditions that require immediate treatment to preserve life and tissue function. The CMA should follow these steps:

1. Get help and contact 911.

2. Assess the patient and check for pulse (for no longer than 5 seconds). If the patient has a pulse, perform rescue breathing. If the patient has no pulse, begin performing CPR.

Rescue breathing:

- Use the head tilt–chin lift method to assess the airway.

- Ensure the patient's airway is clear.

- If an obstruction is visible, attempt to clear it. However, be careful to not obstruct the airway by pushing the object in deeper.

- Provide breaths at a rate of 10 – 12 breaths per minute.

- If a pulse oximeter is available, attach it to the patient to monitor oxygenation and pulse.

CPR:

- Perform chest compressions at a rate of 30 compressions to two breaths for a single rescuer, with a goal of 100 compressions a minute.

- Compressions should be 2 inches in depth.

- Allow full chest recoil.

- Use the head tilt–chin lift method to assess the airway after the first 30 compressions.

- Use the AED as necessary. Prepare for transfer to a higher level of care.

REVIEW QUESTIONS

14. How deep should chest compressions be during CPR?

_____

15. While giving rescue breathing, how many breaths should be provided to the patient per minute?

_____

16. In single-rescuer CPR, what is the ratio of chest compressions to breaths?

_____

Cerebrovascular Accident (CVA)

A **cerebrovascular accident (CVA)**, or stroke, occurs when the blood supply to the brain is disrupted due to damage in the brain's blood vessels. A **hemorrhagic stroke** occurs when a vessel ruptures in the brain. The blood that accumulates damages brain tissue and causes neurological impairment. An **ischemic stroke** occurs when arteries in the brain are blocked, leading to ischemia (reduced blood flow) and damage to brain tissue. The lack of blood flow can be caused by a thrombosis (blood clot) or an embolus (other materials, such as fat).

During a cerebrovascular event or stroke it is important to remember that response time is critical—the longer the CVA is untreated, the more damage will be done to the brain. Knowing the signs and symptoms of an event and treating it as soon as possible can improve patient outcomes. The CMA should be able to recognize the symptoms of a stroke and communicate this to the provider.

CMAs should use the acronym **FAST** from the American Stroke Association to evaluate symptoms.

- **F**ace drooping—Ask the patient to smile. Are there signs of asymmetry?
- **A**rm weakness—Does the patient have any weakness in their arms?
- **S**peech difficulty—Is their speech slurred or garbled?
- **T**ime to call 911—If the answer to any of these questions is yes, the CMA should call 911, remembering to note the symptoms and time of onset.

Patients may also present with confusion, vision changes, severe headache, dizziness, mobility issues, or breathing difficulties.

REVIEW QUESTIONS

17. What are the common symptoms of stroke?

_____

18. What type of stroke is caused by ruptured blood vessels in the brain?

_____

Cold Exposure

Cold exposure occurs when a person is exposed to cold temperatures for an extended period of time. Exposure to cold can lead to different outcomes based on the exposed area and the severity of the cold.

Frostbite is injury to the dermis and underlying tissue due to cold. The exposure to cold leads to cellular damage, impairment of the vascular system, and an inflammatory response. Frostbite most commonly affects fingers and toes. Skin may appear red, blue, or black, depending on the level of tissue damage.

Areas affected by frostbite should be assessed and gently rewarmed. The CMA should check skin tissue for sensation and note whether the skin that was exposed is hard, white, or black. The area should be gently rewarmed as instructed by the provider. Warming is usually done with lukewarm water between 98°F and 105°F. Medical assistants should always ensure that any cold-exposed tissue is clean and use only clean sterile dressings to bandage blistered or broken skin.

Chilblains are inflammatory responses that occur in the skin and small blood vessels as a result of repeated exposure to cold but not freezing temperatures. They are most commonly seen in women, underweight patients, and patients with Raynaud's disease. Chilblains are treated by gently warming the affected area with heating pads.

Hypothermia occurs when core body temperature drops below 95°F (35°C), causing a reduction in metabolic rate and respiratory, cardiac, and neurological functions. When body temperature drops below 86°F (30°C), the body is unable to maintain its core temperature. Symptoms of hypothermia include:

- shivering
- confusion
- speech changes
- extreme fatigue
- slow heart rate
- labored breathing

Patients with hypothermia should be insulated to prevent further heat loss and transferred to an emergency department.

REVIEW QUESTIONS

19. What part of the body is most commonly affected by frostbite?

_____

20. What type of dressing should be applied to broken or blistered skin damaged by frostbite?

_____

Concussion

A **concussion** is a short-lived and reversible change in mental status following trauma to the head. The change can last from several minutes to any time up to 6 hours. Patients may temporarily lose consciousness, but often they do not. Symptoms resulting from short-term injury are temporary and resolve within a few weeks. Common concussion symptoms include:

- headache or pressure
- mental fogginess
- fatigue
- speech changes
- dizziness
- tinnitus
- nausea and/or vomiting

Sometimes symptoms may be delayed and do not present for several days. Patients with concussions are usually advised to rest, avoid strenuous physical activity, and avoid activities that require concentration. Multiple concussions can cause progressive damage, including permanent injury. People who engage in contact sports are at a greater risk for concussion and should refrain from playing until all symptoms are resolved and the provider has cleared them.

REVIEW QUESTIONS

21. What are symptoms of a concussion?

22. When can athletes go back to playing sports after a concussion?

Diabetic Ketoacidosis (DKA)

Hyperglycemia (high blood sugar) occurs when serum glucose concentrations are elevated in response to a decrease in available insulin or to insulin resistance. The condition is most often associated with diabetes mellitus but can also be caused by medications (such as corticosteroids and amphetamines), infection, sepsis, and endocrine disorders.

Diabetic ketoacidosis (DKA) is a hyperglycemic state characterized by an insulin deficiency that stimulates the breakdown of adipose tissues (fat). This process results in the blood becoming too acidic. DKA develops quickly (less than 24 hours) and is most common in people with type 1 diabetes. It can also be caused by uncontrolled blood sugar from missed medication or from illness. Uncontrolled DKA can lead to coma and requires immediate treatment.

Symptoms of DKA include:

- dehydration and extreme thirst
- elevated blood glucose (blood sugar) levels
  - hyperglycemia: > 200 mg/dL
  - DKA: usually 350 – 800 mg/dL
- frequent urination
- ketones in the urine
- fruity breath
- extreme fatigue
- dry or flushed skin
- nausea and vomiting
- abdominal pain
- difficulty breathing
- confusion

Hyperglycemic patients require IV insulin and fluid and electrolyte replacement. The patient will most likely be transferred to a higher level of care.

REVIEW QUESTIONS

23. What pathophysiological process leads to DKA?

_____

24. What are the symptoms of DKA?

_____

Foreign Body Obstruction

Choking is caused by a foreign body obstructing the airway. Unaddressed choking will lead to loss of consciousness and cardiac arrest. If a patient begins choking, the CMA should alert the nearest provider and attempt to dislodge the obstruction until a provider is available. Never perform a blind sweep, as this may lodge the object farther in the airway.

If the patient is conscious, the Heimlich maneuver or abdominal thrusts should be used to dislodge the object. The CMA should perform five thrusts by applying pressure between the rib cage and navel. Between abdominal thrusts, the patient's consciousness should be quickly assessed. The CMA should perform abdominal thrusts until the object is dislodged or the patient becomes unconscious. If the patient should become unconscious, they should be lowered to the ground, and the CMA should continue abdominal thrusts until the patient is pulseless and requires CPR. For an infant with an obstructed airway, the CMA should switch between five back slaps and five abdominal thrusts.

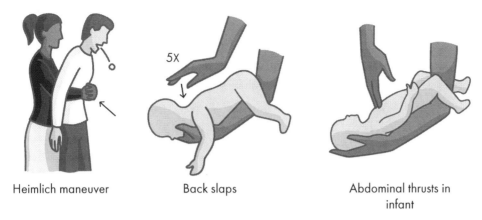

| Heimlich maneuver | Back slaps | Abdominal thrusts in infant |

Figure 7.2. Dislodging Foreign Bodies in Airway

REVIEW QUESTIONS

25. Why should a blind sweep NOT be done on a patient with a non-visible airway obstruction?

26. If an infant is choking, what should the CMA do?

Heat Exposure

Heat exposure occurs when the body is exposed to high temperatures for an extended period of time. Like exposure to cold, exposure to heat can present with varying symptoms based on the degree of exposure.

Heat cramps occur when physical exertion leads to a profuse loss of fluids and sodium through sweating. When fluids are replaced but sodium is not, the resulting electrolyte imbalance causes muscle cramps.

Heat exhaustion occurs when the body is exposed to high temperatures, leading to dehydration. It is not a result of the body's inability to regulate or maintain body temperature.

Heatstroke occurs when the body is unable to reduce excess heat, leading to an increased core temperature over 104°F (40°C). The resulting inflammatory process can cause multiple organ failure that, if not treated, leads to death. **Classic heatstroke** occurs as a result of prolonged exposure to high temperatures with no air-conditioning or access to fluids. **Exertional heatstroke** occurs when exercising in extreme heat.

General symptoms of heat exposure include:

- sweating
- rapid heartbeat

- fainting
- headache
- cramping
- nausea and vomiting

The medical assistant should rehydrate patients with heat exposure emergencies and assess their body temperature as the provider directs. Patients with heat stroke should be cooled using compresses applied to the neck, armpit, and groin. They may also need supplemental oxygen and cardiac monitoring. The provider will determine if the patient with heat exposure should be transferred to a higher level of care.

REVIEW QUESTIONS

27. Where should cool compresses be applied in a patient with heat stroke?

28. What happens to the heart rate during heat exposure?

Hyperventilation

Hyperventilation occurs when the patient's breathing becomes rapid and the body expels more carbon dioxide than it produces. Hyperventilation is often caused by anxiety or stress but can also be caused by cardiovascular or respiratory disorders. Hyperventilation accompanied by chest pain should be considered an acute emergency, and the CMA should follow office emergency protocols.

When **hyperventilation** is caused by anxiety, the CMA should help the patient relax to slow their breathing. The CMA should reassure the patient and have them try one of the following techniques to slow breathing:

- pursed lip breathing.
- breathe using their belly.
- breathe through their hands.
- intermittently hold their breath for 10 – 15 seconds.

REVIEW QUESTION

29. How can the CMA assist a patient who is hyperventilating to slow their breathing?

Insect and Animal Bites

Most **insect bites** are more of an annoyance than an emergency. However, some bites require further evaluation and treatment. Bites may be toxic (e.g., brown recluse spider), and some insects carry disease (e.g., ticks). In some cases, an insect bite may cause an allergic reaction, including anaphylaxis. Before treatment, it is important to attempt to identify the source of the bite by having the patient describe the insect. The CMA should ask the patient when the bite occurred and if they are experiencing symptoms such as fatigue, confusion, rash, or edema (swelling).

Insect bites are commonly managed by cleaning the site to prevent infection and managing symptoms. Patients with tick bites may need to be monitored for infections such as Lyme disease or Rocky Mountain spotted fever. The type of bite and the patient reaction will determine if a higher level of care is required.

When a patient presents with an **animal bite**, the CMA should first control any bleeding. Next, the wound site should be cleaned. Deep bites may need suturing, antibiotics, and a tetanus shot based on the patient's history. The CMA should apply a sterile dressing and triple antibiotic cream as the provider orders. If the bite is from a wild animal the patient may need anti-rabies treatment based on the provider's assessment.

REVIEW QUESTIONS

30. What infections can be caused by tick bites?

_____

31. What steps should a CMA take when caring for an animal bite?

_____

Insulin Shock

Insulin shock occurs when hypoglycemia (low blood sugar) is left untreated. This can occur when patients with diabetes miss a meal, take the incorrect amount of insulin, or do not increase their carbohydrate intake during vigorous exercise. Since hypoglycemia can rapidly progress to insulin shock, symptoms should be addressed immediately.

Symptoms of insulin shock include:

- dizziness
- tremors
- sweating
- mood change
- rapid pulse

- headache
- confusion
- fainting
- poor muscle coordination
- muscle tremors
- seizures
- coma

The CMA should obtain a baseline blood sugar and, if the patient is conscious, provide glucose followed by a complex carbohydrate. The patient's blood sugar should be rechecked after 20 minutes. If the patient is not responsive to treatment, the CMA should contact 911 and prepare for transport to a higher level of care. Unconscious patients are administered glucagon per the provider's orders and are prepared for transport to a higher level of care.

REVIEW QUESTIONS

32. What condition occurs if hypoglycemia is left untreated?

33. In a conscious patient with hypoglycemia, what should the CMA do?

Joint Dislocations, Sprains, and Strains

Sprains and strains are common musculoskeletal injuries that share similar signs and symptoms. **Sprains** involve the tearing or stretching of ligaments, whereas **strains** involve the tearing or stretching of muscle or tendons. Symptoms of sprains and strains include pain, swelling, and reduced range of motion.

A **dislocation** is when the bone shifts from its natural position. Patients with dislocations may present with swelling, skin redness, and pain. It is possible to see the misplaced joint with a joint dislocation.

Musculoskeletal injuries cannot be diagnosed with a visual exam, so the CMA should always assume a fracture is possible until it has been ruled out. To prevent further injury, the area should be immobilized with a splint. The provider will determine what type of **splint** is required. Ice should be applied to the affected area to prevent or decrease swelling.

REVIEW QUESTIONS

34. What type of injury is caused by overstretching of ligaments?

---

35. Why is ice applied to a musculoskeletal injury?

Poisoning

Poisoning—ingestion of a toxic substance—is considered a medical emergency. If possible, the CMA should determine what was ingested and then consult poison control regarding treatment. It is also important to obtain and document the time the incident occurred, presenting symptoms, age and weight of the patient, and a set of vital signs. The poison control center will advise on treatment, and the provider will instruct on provision. The CMA should not induce vomiting unless instructed by poison control and the provider. The patient may need to be transported to a higher level of care.

REVIEW QUESTION

36. What information is helpful to obtain before contacting poison control?

Seizures

A **seizure** is caused by abnormal electrical discharges in the cortical gray matter of the brain; the discharges interrupt normal brain function. **Epilepsy** is a condition characterized by recurrent seizures.

There are many types of seizures. **Convulsive seizures** include rapid, uncontrolled contraction and relaxation of muscles. In an **absence seizure**, the patient loses consciousness but does not have uncontrolled muscle contractions. **Status epilepticus** occurs when a seizure lasts longer than 5 minutes or when seizures occur repeatedly without a period of recovered consciousness between them.

Tonic-clonic seizures (a type of convulsive seizure) start with a tonic (contracted) state in which the patient stiffens and loses consciousness; this phase usually lasts less than 1 minute. The tonic phase is followed by the clonic phase, in which the patient's muscles rapidly contract and relax. The clonic phase can last up to several minutes.

New-onset seizures in patients with no prior seizure history are treated as an emergency, and 911 should be contacted so the patient can be transferred to a higher level of care.

During a seizure, the CMA should act to secure the safety of the patient:

- Remove any objects that might cause injury.
- Loosen tight clothing.
- Never restrain a seizing patient.

- Do not place anything in the patient's mouth.
- Monitor the patient's airway.
- If needed, place the patient in the recovery position (on their side).
- Post-seizure patients are usually lethargic; allow recovery time.
- Ensure that the physician is aware of the situation.
- Follow provider's decision on transfer to a higher level of care.

REVIEW QUESTIONS

37. What is the priority intervention for a patient having a tonic-clonic seizure?

_____

38. What position should patients be placed into during or immediately after a seizure?

_____

Shock

Shock occurs when the cardiovascular system is compromised.

Cardiogenic shock occurs when the heart can no longer pump effectively, reducing blood flow and available oxygen throughout the body. This type of shock is most commonly seen in individuals having a heart attack.

Hypovolemic shock (decrease in blood volume) occurs when rapid fluid loss decreases circulating blood volume and cardiac output, resulting in inadequate blood flow to tissues.

Septic shock is the result of a massive inflammatory response to systemic infection. It can lead to multi-organ failure and death.

Signs and symptoms of cardiogenic, hypovolemic, and septic shock are similar and may include:
- hypotension (low blood pressure)
- rapid heart rate
- difficulty breathing
- cool, clammy skin
- low urine output

Neurogenic shock is a form of shock caused by injury or trauma to the spinal cord. Neurogenic shock disrupts the functioning of the autonomic nervous system, producing massive vasodilation (widening of blood vessels). Signs and symptoms include:
- rapid onset of low blood pressure
- slow heart rate
- hypothermia

All types of shock are considered life-threatening conditions that require immediate care. In the medical office, the CMA should expect to help the provider address the patient's symptoms and prepare the patient for transfer to an emergency department.

REVIEW QUESTIONS

39. Which type of shock occurs in response to a severe systemic infection?

40. Which type of shock causes slow heart rate instead of a rapid heart rate?

Syncope

Syncope (fainting) is temporary partial or full loss of consciousness caused by decreased circulation of blood to the brain. Often syncope is in response to temperature changes, low blood pressure, fear or surprise, or low blood sugar. Symptoms that may precede an episode include flushing, dizziness, sweating, weakness, and paleness.

If the patient presents with syncopal symptoms, the CMA should make sure they are not in danger of falling by having them sit or lie down. The provider will conduct a full examination, document vital signs following the episode, and possibly order an ECG. The provider will determine if the patient should be transferred to a higher level of care.

DID YOU KNOW?

Vertigo is a sensation of spinning or dizziness. As with syncopal patients, vertigo patients should be helped so as to prevent injury. Medical assistants can provide reassurance and monitor the patient to prevent them from falling.

REVIEW QUESTIONS

41. When caring for syncope and vertigo patients, what risk should they be monitored for?

42. What symptoms might a patient demonstrate prior to a syncopal episode?

Wounds

Patients may present to the medical office with different types of wounds, which are categorized based on the type and severity of the injury.

- **abrasion:** scrape on the skin surface
- **laceration:** deep cut or skin tear
- **puncture:** hole, usually caused by a sharp, slim object
- **avulsion:** partial or complete tearing of the skin that may look flap-like

The goal of wound management is to facilitate healing and prevent infection. Minor wounds can usually be easily treated. Wounds should be cleaned and irrigated as necessary. The CMA should check the patient's medical record; a tetanus shot may be needed if they are not up to date. For deep or heavily bleeding wounds, the CMA should prepare to assist with suturing.

REVIEW QUESTIONS

43. What is the goal of wound management?

44. Describe the difference between a skin avulsion and a puncture wound.

ANSWER KEY

1. In a triage system, patients with emergent symptoms who need immediate care are color-coded as red.

2. Emergent symptoms that require immediate care include airway compromise, agonal breathing, chest pain, uncontrolled bleeding, signs of shock, unresponsive or responsive only to painful stimuli.

3. The CMA's initial assessment should be brief and focused on airway, breathing, and circulation.

4. During anaphylactic shock, the blood vessels widen and the airways in the lungs constrict.

5. Anaphylactic shock is treated with an epinephrine injection, which can come in the form of an EpiPen carried by the patient.

6. A bronchodilator like albuterol or ipratropium is used to widen lung airways during an asthma attack. A corticosteroid is sometimes used as well.

7. Status asthmaticus is characterized by unmanageable asthma exacerbations with limited or no pauses between the exacerbations.

8. Arterial blood is bright red and spurts or pulses from the pressure of the heart pumping.

9. The treatment for all types of bleeding wounds is to apply direct pressure to the site.

10. A spiral fracture is a twisting break around the circumference of the bone. This type of fracture is common in sports injuries.

11. The CMA should immobilize and elevate the suspected fracture. For an open fracture, the CMA should control bleeding and monitor for symptoms of shock. The patient should be prepared for further diagnostic evaluation or transfer.

12. Partial-thickness burns (second-degree burns) are characterized by damage to the dermis and epidermis accompanied by severe pain.

13. The CMA should take care not to break burn blisters, remove loose tissue on the burn, or remove material adhering to the burn. These actions can lead to infection and further damage.

14. During CPR, chest compressions should be 2 inches in depth.

15. During rescue breathing, the CMA should provide 10 – 12 breaths per minute.

16. For single-rescuer CPR, chest compressions should be performed at a rate of 30 compressions to two breaths, with a goal of 100 compressions a minute.

17. Common symptoms of stroke are face drooping, arm weakness, speech difficulty, confusion, vision changes, severe headache, dizziness, mobility issues, or breathing difficulties.

18. A hemorrhagic stroke occurs when a vessel ruptures in the brain.

19. Frostbite most commonly affects fingers and toes.

20. Medical assistants should always ensure that any cold-exposed tissue is clean and use only clean sterile dressings to bandage blistered or broken skin.

21. Common concussion symptoms include headache, nausea, vomiting, tinnitus, dizziness, speech changes, fatigue, and brain fog.

22. Athletes may resume playing sports when all symptoms are resolved and the provider has cleared them.

23. DKA is most common in people with type 1 diabetes. It can also be caused by uncontrolled blood sugar from missed medication or from illness.

24. Symptoms of DKA include elevated blood glucose, fruity breath, rapid breathing, extreme thirst and fatigue, and frequent urination.

25. The CMA should never perform a blind sweep, as this might lodge the object farther in the airway.

26. The CMA should alternate between five back slaps and five abdominal thrusts to clear the obstruction.

27. The medical assistant should apply cool compresses to the neck, armpits, and groin.

28. Heat exposure causes the heart rate to increase.

29. The CMA should reassure the patient with techniques for slowing their breathing, including pursed lip breathing, breathing from their belly, breathing through their hands, intermittently holding their breath for 10 – 15 seconds.

30. Patients with tick bites may need to be monitored for infections such as Lyme disease or Rocky Mountain spotted fever.

31. When caring for an animal bite, the CMA should first control any bleeding, then clean and irrigate the wound site. The CMA should apply a sterile dressing as the provider orders.

32. Insulin shock occurs when hypoglycemia is left untreated.

33. The CMA should provide glucose immediately, followed by a complex carbohydrate.

34. A sprain is a musculoskeletal injury that involves the stretching or tearing of ligaments.

35. Ice is applied to a sprain or strain to prevent or decrease swelling.

36. Before contacting poison control, the CMA should find out what was ingested and when, as well as presenting symptoms, age and weight of the patient, and a set of vital signs.

37. The CMA should first provide a safe environment by removing nearby objects. Other interventions include monitoring the patient's airway and loosening tight clothing.

38. During or following a seizure, patients should be placed in the recovery position (on their side).

39. Septic shock is the result of a massive inflammatory response to systemic infection. It can lead to multi-organ failure and death.

40. One of the symptoms of neurogenic shock is slow heart rate.

41. Syncope and vertigo patients are a fall risk and should try to remain seated or lying down to prevent injury.

42. A syncopal patient might present with flushing, dizziness, sweating, weakness, and paleness before an episode.

43. The goal of wound management is to promote healing and prevent infection.

44. An avulsion is tearing of the skin, and a puncture wound is a hole in the skin usually caused by a slim object.

8 LEGAL AND ETHICAL ISSUES

Medical assistants encounter scenarios that involve potential legal and ethical issues on a daily basis. The American Association of Medical Assistants (AAMA) Code of Ethics establishes the guiding principles for the ethical standards of medical assisting, which are similar to those of any medical profession. CMAs are expected to maintain current knowledge of the profession, demonstrate respect for all patients and providers, and participate in activities that will improve the overall health of their communities. Although a medical assistant is an agent of the physician, their primary responsibility is protecting the dignity, confidentiality, and safety of the patient.

Medical Assistant Scope of Practice

There is no nationally accepted **scope of practice** for medical assistants, although there are many commonalities among the states. All medical assistants must work under the supervision of a licensed health care professional who maintains ultimate responsibility for the actions of the medical assistant. Most states allow medical assistants to perform a wide variety of clinical tasks in the medical office as long as they have been properly trained and the tasks are not prohibited by state nursing or medical laws. However, because they are not licensed health care professionals, medical assistants cannot:

- triage, assess, evaluate, diagnose, or treat patients (although they can often provide education after the provider has diagnosed the patient)
- interpret test results

- administer IV medications or anesthetics intended to render the patient unconscious
- prescribe or refill medications without an order from the licensed practitioner
- perform physical therapy (other than assisting)
- perform any other procedure, technique, or treatment that would be deemed practicing medicine

It is important for medical assistants to know the scope of practice laws, because if they do anything for which they are not qualified (whether the task was delegated by a licensed practitioner or not), they are liable and open to litigation. The AAMA's website contains links to state laws (http://www.aama-ntl.org/employers/state-scope-of-practicelaws) affecting the medical assistant's scope of practice and provides a resource for direct inquiries about state scope of practice.

REVIEW QUESTIONS

1. A CMA has finished attaching ECG leads to a patient, and the patient asks if the waveform on the monitor means she is sick. How should the CMA respond?

_____

2. What is required for a CMA to request a prescription refill for a patient?

_____

3. Why should medical assistants know the scope of practice laws?

_____

Health Insurance Portability and Accountability Act (HIPAA)

In 1996, the US federal government enacted the **Health Insurance Portability and Accountability Act (HIPAA)**. One of HIPAA's primary purposes is to guarantee health insurance access, portability, and renewal. It limits the exclusion of some preexisting conditions and prohibits discrimination based on a person's health status. Under HIPAA guidelines, a preexisting condition is one for which the patient has received medical advice, a diagnosis, or treatment within 6 months of the enrollment date. Pregnancy or treatment of a newborn is not considered a preexisting condition. HIPAA normally guarantees that a person's current coverage can be renewed regardless of health conditions.

HIPAA also regulates the security and protection of protected health information, electronic medical records (EMR), and electronic health records (EHR).

HIPAA defines **protected health information (PHI)** as any information that allows a patient to be identified, including:

- patient and family names
- geographic areas
- dates of birth, death, admission, and discharge
- telephone and fax numbers
- home and email addresses
- social security numbers
- health plan beneficiary members
- vehicle, device, and equipment numbers
- medical records and account numbers
- photographs
- biometric identifiers
- any unique identifying number, code, or characteristic

In most cases, an authorization form signed by the patient is required prior to the release of any PHI. Authorization forms vary by facility but usually include the name of the patient, the covered entity releasing the information, the effective dates of the authorization (if not open-ended), the extent of the authorization (the patient has the right to withhold records relating to mental health, communicable diseases, HIV or AIDS, and treatment of alcohol or drug abuse), and the patient's signature.

HIPAA allows for the disclosure of PHI without a signed authorization form when that information will be used for treatment, payment, or health care operations (e.g., case planning, customer service, medical review, or training purposes). This provision allows providers to consult each other regarding a patient's care, to provide referrals, and to coordinate care with third parties (e.g., long-term care facilities, medical equipment providers). HIPAA regulations can be very complex, so it is best to seek the advice of the office's HIPAA compliance or privacy officer with any questions.

REVIEW QUESTIONS

4. According to HIPAA, what is a preexisting condition?

_____

5. When can PHI be disclosed without patient consent?

_____

6. What is protected health information (PHI)?

_____

Patients' Right to Access Medical Records

Electronic health records (EHR) provide patients with an increased ability to track and monitor their health, help them more effectively follow their treatment plans, allow them to find any errors in their health records, and give them the freedom to provide their information directly to researchers. The ability to access health records in real time empowers patients to actively participate in their health care decisions, leading to a more patient-centered health care system. The HIPAA Privacy Rule requires that covered entities (providers and health plans) allow patients to review and/or receive copies of their medical records upon request.

There are a few cases in which providers are not required to provide the patient with access to their records, most notably in the case of psychotherapy notes or records related to legal proceedings. The notice of privacy practices provided by each covered entity gives the patient information on how to request the records, whom to contact with questions, and how to file complaints. The request for medical records must be made in writing, and the provider generally has 30 days after receiving the request to provide the records. Most providers do charge a fee for making the copies.

Patients have the right to restrict certain items within their medical records to prevent them from being disclosed. For example, if a patient was embarrassed by having a previous sexually transmitted infection, she may request that part of her medical record not be shared with future providers. In most cases, the covered entity is not required to honor the patient's request, as it could affect future health care decisions. If the covered entity does agree to grant the patient's request, it must comply with the request at all times unless the patient needs emergency treatment and the disclosure of the information is necessary to provide treatment. The covered entity must then also request that the information not be disclosed in the future.

If patients discover errors in their medical records, they can file written requests detailing the proposed corrections. The covered entity must issue a response within 60 days (although an additional 30 days is acceptable if the patient is given an explanation of the delay and a new completion date in writing). If the request for correction is denied, the covered entity must explain the reason for the denial and how the patient can make a complaint about the decision.

REVIEW QUESTIONS

7. In what type of cases are providers NOT required to provide the patient with access to their records?

8. If a patient discovers an error in their medical record, what can they do?

9. What does the HIPAA Privacy Rule require?

Security of Electronic Transmission of Information

Electronic health records (EHR) contain information on the patient's demographics, medical history, immunization dates, allergies, diagnoses, medications, imaging, treatment plans, and laboratory and test results. The office's patient database can be used to search for patients by name, diagnosis, and CPT codes; reports can be printed based on these criteria.

The use of EHR is governed by **meaningful use regulations**, which set standards for exchanging patient health information between all providers and insurers involved in the patient's care. The program is run by the Centers for Medicare and Medicaid Services (CMS), and health care providers that adhere to these regulations are eligible for incentive payments. According to meaningful use, information from EHR can be shared when it:

- is meaningful (i.e., it serves a purpose for the patient).
- contributes to improvements in quality of care.
- is being sent to the Department of Health and Human Services as part of the incentive program.

Security is a central concern when using electronic applications. Medical assistants have access to patients' protected health information (PHI), which should be safeguarded at all times. Below are guidelines for maintaining a secure environment when using electronic applications.

- Use a secure password or ID card to log in to any office computer.
- Log off the computer any time it is not being used.
- Use encryption software when appropriate to send PHI.
- Equip all computers with up-to-date firewalls and antivirus software.
- Never leave medical documents unattended on printers, copiers, or fax machines.
- Double-check the name, address, and/or fax number when sending documents containing PHI.

Patients may be able to access parts of their EHR through a **patient portal**. These websites allow patients to schedule appointments, see test results, and send messages to health care providers. As with other electronic applications, the patient portal process should be carefully monitored to ensure patient privacy. CMAs may need to provide patients with passwords or access codes, and they should always ensure that this information is given only to the patient.

REVIEW QUESTIONS

10. Can information from EHR be shared with the Department of Health and Human Services?

_____

11. While using an electronic application with access to PHI, what steps should the CMA take to protect patient privacy?

_____

12. When speaking on the phone, can a CMA provide a patient with an access code or password for an electronic patient portal?

_____

Confidentiality

All medical assistants are responsible for keeping patient records secure and confidential. The decision to disclose patient information is the patient's choice. The physician cannot refuse to release records if the patient requests disclosure to another party. However, each party to whom a physician discloses information requires new authorization. The patient has the right to rescind an authorization of record release, which is best done with a written and dated request. Physicians need permission to disclose records unless:

- they are issued a court subpoena.
- they are being sued by a patient.
- they believe disclosure of the information will protect the welfare of the patient or a third party.

Because most medical assistants perform multiple duties in the office, the use of **electronic protected health information (ePHI)** allows or even requires them to access many areas of a patient's record, not just the minimum information. However, availability of this information does not authorize them to access any areas of the medical record other than those necessary for patient care.

Health care organizations must have security policies in place to hold staff accountable for the information they access. Security audits should be conducted periodically to ensure compliance with the facility's ePHI security policies or may be conducted on demand in response to a suspected or reported incident. Use of audit logs and audit trails can identify transactions such as what was accessed or modified. Audits can be useful for many purposes, including:

- detecting unauthorized access or intrusion attempts to a patient's ePHI
- tracking ePHI disclosures
- reducing the risk of unauthorized employee access and creating accountability
- responding to patient concerns about unauthorized access of their ePHI
- addressing legal and/or accreditation compliance requirements

REVIEW QUESTIONS

13. How frequent is patient authorization needed for a physician to disclose patient records?

14. When is patient permission NOT needed for disclosure of their records?

15. What type of information is the CMA allowed to access in a patient's medical record?

Patient's Bill of Rights and the Patient Care Partnership

The **American Hospital Association (AHA)** formulated the **Patient's Bill of Rights in 1973**. This document outlines a patient's right to:

- receive respectful, considerate, and appropriate care.
- expect privacy and confidentiality.
- consult the physician of his or her choice.
- make decisions regarding health care.
- receive all information regarding diagnosis, treatment, and prognosis.
- refuse treatment.
- make informed decisions related to health care.
- obtain copies of his or her medical record.
- participate or refuse to participate in research.
- receive continuity of care.

In 2003, the AHA replaced the Patient's Bill of Rights with *The Patient Care Partnership*. This brochure explains to patients what to expect during their hospital stay and outlines the hospital's responsibilities. The *Patient Care Partnership* describes six key rights for all patients:

- high-quality hospital care
- clean and safe environment
- involvement in care
- protection of privacy
- help when leaving the hospital
- help with billing claims

REVIEW QUESTIONS

16. According to the Patient's Bill of Rights, what are the patient's rights regarding research participation?

_____

17. What is *The Patient Care Partnership?*

_____

Consent to Treat

Consent for various medical services and health care involves verbal or written permission from the patient. Consent is a contract that can either be expressed in writing or verbally or implied by circumstances or actions. **Implied consent** is usually made in life-threatening circumstances and medical emergencies based on the assumption that the patient would consent to lifesaving care.

Expressed consent must be **informed**, which requires a trained health care worker explaining the necessary information to the patient so he or she can make an educated decision. Components of the consent involve the reason for and explanation of the test or procedure; the possible side effects, risks, and complications; alternative therapies and their side effects, risks, and complications; the prognosis with or without the test or procedure; and any additional information that assists in the decision-making process.

Only certain people can give consent for medical services and care:

- patient
- competent legal adult in charge of patient's care
- emancipated minor
- minors in the armed forces
- minors seeking services for sexually transmitted infections (STIs)
- minor parent with custody of his or her minor child

REVIEW QUESTIONS

18. What type of consent is used when the patient is unconscious and having a life-threatening emergency?

_____

19. Which of these patients CANNOT give consent?

a 17-year-old in the military with an ankle injury

b 16-year-old asking about an STI

c 15-year-old who is pregnant and vomiting

d 17-year-old college student with a broken ulna

20. What is informed consent?

Torts

Civil law regulates behavior between individuals or individual entities. Cases are filed by or on behalf of the injured individual, and the trial outcome is usually decided by a judge. In civil cases, the plaintiff (who filed the suit) has the burden of proof, meaning they must prove that harm has been done to them by the defendant. Civil law includes contracts and torts.

A **tort** is a wrongful civil act. Tort laws involve the accidental or intentional harm to a person or property that results from the wrongdoing of a person or persons. **Negligence** is a type of tort, defined as failure to offer an acceptable standard of care that is comparable to what a competent medical assistant, nurse, or other health care worker would provide in a similar situation. There are four types of negligence:

- Nonfeasance: a willful failure to act when required
- Misfeasance: the incorrect or improper performance of a lawful action
- Malfeasance: a willful and intentional action that causes harm
- Malpractice: a professional's failure to properly execute their duties

Malpractice is the most serious form of negligence. To prove malpractice, four legal points must be shown: the patient-physician relationship was established (duty), the professional neglected to act or acted improperly (dereliction), a negative outcome occurred from an action or lack of an action (direct cause), and the patient sustained harm (damages).

Invasion of privacy is the violation of tort law that involves the intrusion into the personal life of another without just cause.

Intentional torts are committed when a person purposefully causes harm to another. Some examples are listed below:

- battery: harmful or offensive contact with another person
- assault: an attempted battery in which there was threat of injury, but no injury occurred
- slander: saying something false about someone that causes damage to their reputation
- libel: writing something false about someone that causes damage to their reputation

REVIEW QUESTIONS

21. Which of the four types of negligence involves a willful and intentional action that causes harm?

_____

22. What are the four legal points that must be shown to prove malpractice?

_____

23. What are the similarities and differences between slander and libel?

_____

Medical Assistant Liability

Although medical assistants work under the supervision of a licensed health care provider, they are not protected from **liability**, or legal responsibility. A medical assistant who makes a mistake while caring for a patient (e.g., hits a nerve while administering an injection) or oversteps the scope of practice boundaries (e.g., administers an intravenous medication) is potentially exposed to being sued. The result could be a civil fine of up to several thousand dollars, criminal charges, or other penalties in addition to legal fees.

The **standard of care** varies from state to state or region to region but is often considered "minimum safe professional conduct." The test for standard of care is determining if someone with equal training and experience would have acted the same under the same or similar circumstances. Failure to meet this standard of care is known as **negligence**, in which case the health care provider, the medical practice, and the medical assistant can all be sued.

Every employer should have a **code of conduct** detailing the professional behaviors expected from employees. This will provide guidance to all parties and will help to ensure that the practice is run in a lawful and ethical manner. While some situations will involve only a legal issue or only an ethical issue, most situations will involve both. The code of conduct should include such topics as how to deal with conflict of interest (e.g., caring for a family member);

responsible marketing practices; how to handle potential cases of fraud or abuse; accounting policies and procedures; and, of course, confidentiality.

Malpractice or **professional liability insurance** gives the employee peace of mind knowing that if there is a claim or lawsuit, the risk will be transferred to the insurance company. Even if the facility has liability insurance that covers the employees, it is best for the medical assistant to have an individual policy as well. If a medical assistant is found liable for negligence, they would be responsible for all or part of the settlement with the patient and may also be responsible for reimbursing the employer's insurance company. The premiums for these policies are relatively inexpensive compared to the risk associated with not carrying insurance.

REVIEW QUESTIONS

24. What are the MOST common causes for lawsuits against a medical assistant?

_____

25. What is negligence in the health care setting?

_____

26. Why should an employer have a code of conduct?

_____

Physician-Patient Contracts

Contract laws involve the rights and obligations of contracts, which are promises of obligation. A contract is an obligatory agreement between two or more parties. For a contract to be legal and binding, five things must occur: (1) an offer was made, (2) the offer was accepted, (3) there was an exchange of something of value (consideration), (4) all parties were legally capable to accept the terms (capacity), and (5) the intent was legal. Once a physician establishes the physician-patient relationship, there are certain legal obligations that must be met throughout that relationship.

- The physician has a responsibility to communicate with patients in a timely manner regarding their diagnoses, medications, procedures, and potential side effects or dangers.

- Physicians must provide competent care to all patients without discrimination based on race, gender, sexual orientation, or religion.

- The physician is obligated to continue treating the patient until the patient no longer needs the physician's services, the patient fires the physician, or there is a mutual agreement to terminate the relationship.

Despite the physician's best efforts, some patients are **noncompliant** and will not follow their treatment plans or take prescribed medications. Noncompliance is a risk not only for the patient but also for the physician. A patient's lack of improvement or worsening health might be blamed on the physician not meeting the standard of care, even though the patient is noncompliant. If a patient continually refuses to comply with the treatment plan or fails to keep appointments, the physician may consider terminating the relationship.

If the physician decides to terminate the physician-patient relationship, the patient must be given sufficient time to find a new physician. The decision to terminate medical care could be based on several factors including patient noncompliance, failure to pay for services, or a disagreement with a patient that cannot be resolved. When terminating care, the physician should:

- notify the patient in writing of the decision to terminate care.
- provide documentation supporting the decision (if appropriate).
- specify the date on which the physician-patient relationship will end.
- advise the patient of the need for further care.
- offer to provide records to the new physician.

REVIEW QUESTIONS

27. What does it mean for a patient to be noncompliant?

_____

28. Before terminating care of a patient, what types of clinical records should be documented to avoid accusations of abandonment?

_____

29. When terminating a physician-patient relationship, how should the physician notify the patient?

_____

Pharmaceutical Laws

Drug Schedules

The **Controlled Substances Act (CSA)** is the federal drug policy under which certain stimulants, anabolic steroids, opioids, depressants, hallucinogens, and other chemicals are regulated. There are five schedules (I – V) used to classify drugs according to their potential for abuse, likelihood of causing dependence, accepted medical application, and safety. Medical assistants can only administer controlled substances under a physician's direct order and supervision (unless there is a state law prohibiting medical assistants from administering controlled substances).

PRESCRIPTIONS AND ELECTRONIC PRESCRIPTIONS

Medical assistants are not allowed to **prescribe** medications. This authority is limited to physicians, dentists, physician assistants, and nurse practitioners (although this may vary by state). Medical assistants are also not authorized to **dispense** medications, meaning they cannot prepare, package, compound, or label drugs for patients. Medical assistants may **distribute** packaged drugs to patients per the prescriber's order. However, they cannot distribute controlled substances.

Medical assistants may be asked to submit prescriptions to pharmacies, although the regulations will vary by state. In most states, the medical assistant is authorized to call or place an electronic prescription for refills but not for new or modified prescriptions. Calling in refills must be done under the supervision of the prescriber, and the refill must be recorded in the patient's medical record.

E-prescribing refers to the provider's ability to electronically send an accurate, legible prescription directly to the pharmacy. Health care providers can view a patient's medication history, create and refill prescriptions, connect to a pharmacy, and integrate the prescription with the patient's electronic medical record. An e-prescribing system will also inform the provider about generic alternatives as well as provide warnings for potential allergic reactions or medication interactions.

REVIEW QUESTIONS

30. According to the Controlled Substance Act, alprazolam (Xanax) is included in which schedule?

_____

31. Can a medical assistant dispense alprazolam (Xanax) to a patient?

_____

32. In most states, what type of prescription is the medical assistant allowed to call in to the pharmacy?

_____

MANDATORY REPORTING AND PUBLIC HEALTH

Public health activities focus on the health of a population group or entire population and are carried out primarily by governmental agencies at the local, state, and national levels. The goals of public health activities are to prevent the onset and spread of disease, diminish the likelihood of injury, offer outreach and health education, and provide culturally sensitive care and translation services. HIPAA recognizes the role that public health plays in the health and safety of the whole population and, consequently, allows certain PHI to be released without patient authorization. Covered entities can disclose information to public health agencies legally authorized to receive reports of certain incidents described below.

- **Communicable diseases**: Information regarding those at risk of contracting or spreading a communicable disease may be released, and those who have potentially been exposed may be contacted to prevent or control further transmission of the disease. Currently, over 200 infectious diseases are listed in the American Public Health Association's Control of Communicable Diseases Manual. Some diseases are required to be reported by telephone within an hour of diagnosis, while others have up to 7 calendar days.

- **Vital statistics**: Information regarding births, deaths, marriages, divorces, and changes in civil status are collected to assess population trends and needs.

- **Abuse, neglect, or exploitation of a child or elder**: There are laws to protect vulnerable populations unable to protect themselves or adequately meet their own essential needs. Covered entities are required to report known or suspected cases of child (under 18) or elder (over 60) abuse or neglect to social services or another agency designated to receive this report. Most states also have laws protecting individuals between 18 and 59 with known disabilities that prevent them from caring for or protecting themselves. The offenses that must be reported include physical, emotional, psychological, financial, and sexual abuse or exploitation; neglect; and abandonment.

- **Domestic abuse**: The requirements for reporting domestic abuse vary from state to state. While it is mandatory for health care providers to report suspected cases of domestic abuse to the police, some states require that only providers of medical services for physical injuries report the abuse while excluding mental health professionals from the mandatory reporting requirements. Similarly, some states require only physical violence to be reported, while other states include emotional, psychological, or financial abuse. It is important to be aware of state laws regarding mandatory reporting of suspected domestic abuse.

- **Wounds of violence**: The requirements for reporting "wounds of violence" vary from state to state, so it is important to be aware of what injuries are reportable according to state law. Some of the most commonly reportable injuries include:
  - bullet wounds, powder burns, or other apparent firearm-related injuries

◦ injuries suspected to be caused by knife, axe, or other sharp instrument that appear to have been caused by a criminal act

◦ injuries, illnesses (e.g., poisoning), or burns that appear to have been caused by a criminal act (e.g., fight, robbery, rape)

REVIEW QUESTIONS

33. What medical conditions or injuries have mandatory reporting requirements?

34. What types of abuse are considered reportable?

35. Which specialty may be exempt from reporting domestic abuse?

Medical Ethics

Ethics are moral principles, values, and duties. Whereas laws are enforceable regulations set by the government, ethics are moral guidelines set and formally or informally enforced by peers, the community, and professional organizations. Ethics include norms and duties. A **norm** is short for "normal," a behavior or conduct that is valued and usually expected. **Duties** are commitments or obligations to act in an ethical and moral manner.

The code of ethics is a statement of the expected behaviors of its members. This code also sets standards and disciplinary actions for violations, including suspension, censure, fines, or expulsion. The **American Medical Association (AMA)** code of ethics was written in 1847 and has been continually revised since then. The AMA specifies the physician's ethical duty to the patient.

The **American Association of Medical Assistants (AAMA)** sets forth principles of moral and ethical conduct for the practice of medical assisting. Medical assistants pledge to:

- uphold the honor and principles of the profession.
- accept the profession's disciplines.
- render service with full respect for human dignity.
- respect confidential information.
- participate in additional service activities for the improvement of community health.

REVIEW QUESTIONS

36. What is the difference between laws and ethics?

Advance Directives

Advance directives state the patient's wishes for medical decisions and are used if the patient becomes incapable of making decisions. These documents must be signed by the patient, witnessed by state policy, and notarized by a legal notary. Advance directives may limit or permit a range of medical care.

- **Do not resuscitate (DNR)** typically indicates that no resuscitation measures (e.g., CPR, defibrillation) should be taken.

- **Do not intubate (DNI)** indicates that the patient does not wish to be intubated if the need presents.

- **Allow natural death (AND)** indicates the patient does not want any intervention that may sustain life or prevent a natural progression to death.

Living wills allow an individual to state which treatments they would like in the event they are unable to express their wishes during an illness. A **durable power of attorney** is a document that authorizes a person acting on the patient's behalf (the **health care proxy**) to make medical decisions if the patient is incapacitated.

The federal **Patient Self-Determination Act of 1990 (PSDA)** requires that patients with Medicare and/or Medicaid be provided with information about their rights to make health care decisions. This legislation is intended to improve the use of advance directives and increase the appropriateness of care while ensuring the patient has the right to make various decisions. This act encourages patients to decide about the extent of medical care they want early in the care process.

Under the PSDA, the patient chooses which treatments and care activities they wish to accept or refuse. The act requires that all health care organizations recognize the advance directive(s) and explain the patient's rights under state law, including the right to make medical care decisions such as refusing or accepting treatment options. Additionally, the patient is entitled to information about their right to create an advance directive.

REVIEW QUESTIONS

38. When is an advance directive used?

39. Should the medical staff perform CPR on a patient with a DNR advance directive in their chart?

Other Medical Laws and Regulations

Medical care is governed by a complex set of laws and regulatory agency guidelines, many of which are relevant to medical assistants, including laws that cover patient rights, confidential information, and workplace safety. The most important of these laws and regulations are discussed below.

AMERICANS WITH DISABILITIES ACT AMENDMENTS ACT (ADAAA)

The **Americans with Disabilities Act Amendments Act (ADAAA)** was originally passed in 1990 as the **Americans with Disabilities Act (ADA)**. It prohibits employers with more than 15 employees from discriminating against individuals with disabilities. This act provides protection through the job application process, hiring, training, promotion, compensation, and termination. It requires employers to make reasonable accommodations for employees with disabilities. For example, an employee with diabetes should be allowed to take additional breaks to eat or monitor their blood sugar levels.

The ADA also provides protection for those seeking medical services. Patients with disabilities must be given the same opportunities to receive the same level of care as those without disabilities. This could mean providing accessible exam rooms or equipment (e.g., exam tables, lifts), providing staff members to read forms to patients who are blind or have low vision, or providing access to a telephone relay system or a telecommunications device for the deaf (TDD). The ADAAA, which went into effect January 1, 2009, made substantial changes to and broadened the scope of the ADA's definition of a disability. These changes made it easier for individuals to demonstrate qualifying disabilities under the ADA guidelines.

CLINICAL LABORATORY IMPROVEMENT AMENDMENTS (CLIA '88)

The **Clinical Laboratory Improvement Amendments (CLIA)** statute was passed by Congress in 1988 and was developed to improve the quality of laboratory testing. Under this legislation, all laboratories must follow certain quality control and assurance standards, including employee training, written policies, documented maintenance of instruments, equipment, and procedures, and proficiency testing. Quality assurance does not apply to CLIA waived tests, but it does apply to moderate-complexity, high-complexity, and performed microscopy tests.

Quality control measures allow for testing accuracy through careful monitoring of various procedures. The laboratory must follow these procedures, which include control samples, calibration, reagent control, maintenance, and documentation. **Calibration** involves testing procedures in which the equipment generates a result set by a known value. **Control samples** are specimens with known values, used to check for testing accuracy. Reagents are chemicals that react in specific ways when exposed to known substances. A **reagent control log** documents the quality of reagents. **Documentation** of all quality control measures depends on facility policy, as well as CLIA standards and requirements.

CLIA Waived Tests

- urinalysis, dipstick
- urinalysis, tablet reagent
- fecal occult blood (guaiac)
- urine pregnancy test
- blood glucose
- erythrocyte sedimentation rate (ESR)
- hemoglobin (Hgb)
- hematocrit (Hct)
- strep A test
- ovulation testing

Moderate-Complexity Tests

- blood chemistry performed with automated analyzer
- hematology performed with automated analyzer
- pinworm preparation
- gram staining
- microscopic analysis of urine sediment

High-Complexity Tests

- cytology testing
- blood cross matching
- blood typing
- Pap smears

Genetic Information Nondiscrimination Act of 2008 (GINA)

The **Genetic Information Nondiscrimination Act of 2008 (GINA)** is a federal law prohibiting health insurers and employers from discriminating against a person based on genetic information. Genetic information includes family health history, the use of genetic services or counseling, or the results of genetic tests. This act allows patients to discuss family health history or genetic information with their health care providers with the assurance that the information cannot be used to discriminate against them. GINA prohibits health insurers from requiring or using genetic information to determine eligibility for insurance, establish preexisting conditions, or determine premiums.

Health Information Technology for Economic and Clinical Health (HITECH) Act

The **Health Information Technology for Economic and Clinical Health (HITECH) Act** was enacted under a section of the American Recovery and Reinvestment Act of 2009. The HITECH Act promotes the adoption of health information technology and electronic medical records (EMR) and electronic health records (EHR). The federal government created an incentive program to encourage medical practices to use EMR technology. Areas affected include medical billing, patient records, and employee communication. The goal is to make better use of technology for patient care and affordability.

Uniform Anatomical Gift Act

In 1968, the US government passed the **Uniform Anatomical Gift Act**, which specified that any person of sound mind and legal age could donate any part(s) of their body after death, whether to research or for transplantation purposes. Most states allow residents to sign the back of their driver's license to notify medical personnel of their donor status. No money can be exchanged for organs, and organs cannot be sold for profit.

REVIEW QUESTIONS

41. Which government act requires that patients with disabilities be given equal opportunities to receive the same level of care as those without disabilities?

42. What is the purpose of the Health Information Technology for Economic and Clinical Health Act (HITECH)?

43. Why can insurers NOT use a patient's family medical history to determine premiums?

44. Does CLIA quality assurance apply to urine pregnancy testing?

_____

45. What is the goal of calibration?

_____

Medical Regulatory Agencies

CENTERS FOR DISEASE CONTROL AND PREVENTION (CDC)

The **Centers for Disease Control and Prevention (CDC)** is an agency of the federal government within the Department of Health and Human Services. The main goals of the CDC are to protect and improve public health and safety by controlling and preventing disease, injury, and disability, as well as to research and provide information on noninfectious diseases (e.g., obesity, diabetes). The CDC collaborates with other agencies to provide expertise on health-related matters and to develop disease control and prevention policies.

The CDC focuses its attention on several key areas of public health:

- infectious disease
- foodborne pathogens
- environmental health
- occupational health and safety
- health promotion
- injury prevention
- preparedness for new health threats
- educational activities

The CDC publishes several resources to assist health care providers with assessing and reducing exposure to infectious disease in the workplace. These resources include but are not limited to the following publications:

- _Hand Hygiene in Health Care Settings_
- _Guide to Infection Prevention for Outpatient Settings: Minimum Expectations for Safe Care_
- _Guideline for Disinfection and Sterilization in Health Care Facilities_
- _Guideline for Isolation Precautions: Preventing Transmission of Infectious Agents in Health Care Settings_
- _Management of Multidrug-Resistant Organisms in Health Care Settings_
- _Guidelines for Environmental Infection Control in Health Care Facilities_
- _Guideline for Infection Control in Health Care Personnel_

Drug Enforcement Agency (DEA)

The **Drug Enforcement Agency (DEA)** is responsible for enforcing the controlled substances laws as well as recommending and supporting programs to reduce the availability of illegal controlled substances. The DEA maintains the list of who is authorized to manufacture (drug companies), order, handle, prescribe (physicians, physician assistants, nurse practitioners, and some pharmacists), dispense (pharmacy), or store controlled substances. These individuals are responsible for maintaining logs that accurately reflect their inventory at any given time (usually at the end of a shift or end of the day).

Food and Drug Administration (FDA)

The **Food and Drug Administration (FDA)** is an agency within the Department of Health and Human Services. One of the core functions of the FDA is to oversee medical products and tobacco, including drugs, biologics, medical devices, tobacco products, and special medical programs. Within the organization, there are several other centers of responsibility:

- Center for Biologics Evaluation and Research: regulates biological products for human use
- Center for Devices and Radiological Health: ensures safety, effectiveness, and quality of medical devices and safe radiation-emitting products
- Center for Drug Evaluation and Research: ensures the safety and effectiveness of prescription and over-the-counter drugs as well as products that fall into the "drug" classification, such as sunscreen, fluoride toothpaste, antiperspirants, and dandruff shampoos
- Center for Tobacco Products: ensures safety and effectiveness of new and modified-risk tobacco products, warning labels, and advertising restrictions; oversees Family Smoking Prevention and Tobacco Control Act
- Oncology Center of Excellence: helps expedite the development of oncology and hematology medical products; evaluates drugs, biologics, and devices for cancer treatment

Occupational Safety and Health Administration (OSHA)

The **Occupational Safety and Health Administration (OSHA)** is part of the US Department of Labor and was created to set and enforce workplace standards, provide training and outreach, ensure compliance, prevent on-the-job injuries, and protect the well-being of American workers. OSHA guidelines for the medical office focus on minimizing incidents that could expose employees to communicable diseases or other hazards found specifically in medical offices. OSHA has five primary standards for the medical office:

1. Bloodborne Pathogens: all occupational exposure to blood or other potentially infectious materials

2. Hazard Communications: classification of chemicals and provision of hazard information on labels and safety data sheets

3. Ionizing Radiation: protection against occupational radiation exposure by radioactive materials or X-rays

4. Emergency Exit Routes: exit route identification, safety features, design, and construction requirements

5. Electrical: electrical hazards, grounding requirements, electrical requirements for equipment

A complete description of each standard can be found on the OSHA website.

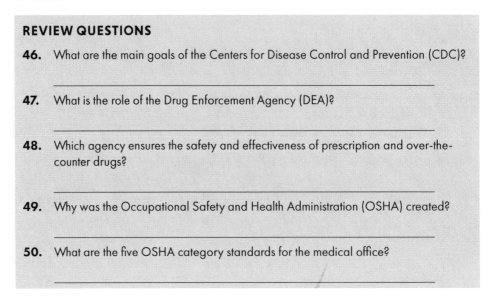

REVIEW QUESTIONS

46. What are the main goals of the Centers for Disease Control and Prevention (CDC)?

47. What is the role of the Drug Enforcement Agency (DEA)?

48. Which agency ensures the safety and effectiveness of prescription and over-the-counter drugs?

49. Why was the Occupational Safety and Health Administration (OSHA) created?

50. What are the five OSHA category standards for the medical office?

ANSWER KEY

1. CMAs cannot interpret test results or diagnose patients; the CMA should inform the patient that the provider will be able to answer her questions.

2. To prescribe or refill medications, CMAs must have an order from the licensed practitioner.

3. If medical assistants do anything they are not qualified to do, they are liable and open to litigation (even if the task was delegated by a licensed practitioner).

4. Under HIPAA guidelines, a preexisting condition is a health condition for which the patient has received medical advice, a diagnosis, or treatment within 6 months of the enrollment date.

5. HIPAA allows for the disclosure of PHI without a signed authorization form when that information will be used for treatment, payment, or health care operations.

6. HIPAA defines PHI as any information that allows a patient to be identified, like patient and family names, birth date, and telephone number.

7. Providers are not required to provide patients with psychotherapy notes or records related to legal proceedings.

8. Patients who discover such errors can submit a written request with proposed corrections.

9. The HIPAA Privacy Rule requires that covered entities allow patients to review and/or receive copies of their medical records upon request.

10. According to meaningful use regulations, EHR information can be shared with the Department of Health and Human Services as part of the incentive program.

11. While using an electronic application with access to PHI, the CMA should use a secure password or ID card to log in to any office computer, and log off the computer any time it is not being used.

12. When speaking on the phone, the CMA can provide an access code or password for an electronic patient portal as long as it is only given directly to the patient.

13. The physician must obtain patient authorization each time information is disclosed to a new party.

14. Physicians do not require patient permission to disclose their records if (1) they are issued a court subpoena, (2) they are being sued by a patient, or (3) they believe disclosure of the information will protect the welfare of the patient or a third party.

15. The CMA is only authorized to access areas of the medical record that are necessary for their role in patient care.

16. Patients have the right to participate or refuse to participate in research trials.

17. *The Patient Care Partnership* is a brochure published by the AHA explaining to patients what to expect during their hospital stay and outlining the hospital's responsibility.

18. Implied consent is usually made in a life-threatening situation based on the assumption that the patient would consent to lifesaving care.

19. Of these minors, only the 17-year-old college student cannot give consent. Minors in the military, minors with a child, and minors seeking information on STIs can give consent.

20. Informed consent is given after a trained health care worker has explained the procedure's purpose, benefit, risks, and alternatives.

21. Malfeasance involves a willing and intentional action that causes harm.

22. To prove malpractice, it must be shown that (1) the patient-physician relationship was established (duty), (2) the professional neglected to act or acted improperly (dereliction), (3) a negative outcome occurred from an action or lack of an action (direct cause), and (4) the patient sustained harm (damages).

23. Both slander and libel cause damage to someone's reputation by spreading false information about them. Slander is saying the false information, and libel is writing it.

24. The most common reasons for lawsuits against medical assistants are medication errors, lack of monitoring, and office administration errors.

25. Negligence is failure to meet standard of care.

26. All employers should have a code of conduct outlining professional behaviors expected from employees to ensure that the practice is run in a lawful and ethical manner.

27. A noncompliant patient refuses to follow the treatment plan or fails to keep appointments.

28. To avoid accusations of abandonment, the physician (and the CMA) should keep a record of missed appointments, refusal of care, noncompliance, or failure to pay for services.

29. The physician should notify the patient in writing of the decision to terminate the relationship.

30. Alprazolam (Xanax) is considered a Schedule IV drug by the Controlled Substances Act.

31. Medical assistants can only dispense controlled substances under a physician's direct order and supervision.

32. Medical assistants may call in an electronic prescription for refills but not for new or modified prescriptions. This must be done under the supervision of the prescriber, and the refill must be recorded in the patient's medical record.

33. Although requirements vary from state to state, most covered entities are required to report certain communicable diseases, known or suspected cases of child or elder abuse or neglect, domestic abuse, and wounds of violence.

34. Reportable abuses include physical, emotional, psychological, financial, sexual abuse or exploitation; neglect; and abandonment.

35. Some states exclude mental health professionals from mandatory reporting requirements.

36. Laws are set and enforced by the government. Ethics are moral guidelines set and enforced by peers, the community, and professional organizations.

37. The American Association of Medical Assistants (AAMA) sets forth principles of moral and ethical conduct for the practice of medical assisting.

38. Advance directives are used when the patient becomes incapable of making decisions.

39. No. A Do Not Resuscitate (DNR) order indicates that no resuscitative measures including CPR, intubation, or defibrillation should be done.

40. A health care proxy is a person, authorized by a durable power of attorney, to make medical decisions for a patient if the patient is incapacitated.

41. The Americans with Disabilities Act (ADA) prohibits employers with more than 15 employees from discriminating against individuals with disabilities and requires employers to make reasonable accommodations for employees with disabilities.

42. The HITECH Act encourages medical offices to adopt electronic medical record (EMR) and electronic health record (EHR) technology.

43. The Genetic Information Nondiscrimination Act (GINA) assures a patient that they can discuss family medical history or genetic information with their health care provider and that information cannot be used to determine insurance eligibility, establish pre-existing conditions, or determine premiums.

44. Urine pregnancy testing is a CLIA-waived test, and quality assurance does not apply to these tests. It does apply to moderate-complexity, high-complexity, and performed microscopy tests.

45. The goal of calibration is to verify that equipment is producing accurate, reliable results consistent with other similar equipment.

46. The main goals of the CDC are to protect and improve public health and safety by controlling and preventing disease, injury, and disability, as well as to research and provide information on noninfectious diseases.

47. The DEA is responsible for enforcing the controlled substances laws and supporting programs to reduce the availability of illegal controlled substances.

48. The Food and Drug Administration (FDA) is responsible for ensuring the safety and effectiveness of prescription and over-the-counter drugs.

49. OSHA was created to set and enforce workplace standards, provide training and outreach, ensure compliance, prevent on-the-job injuries, and protect the well-being of American workers.

50. OSHA has five primary standards for the medical office, including blood borne pathogens, hazard communications, ionizing radiation, emergency exit routes, and electrical.

9 COMMUNICATION

Communication is an essential part of a medical assistant's day-to-day work. Medical assistants will interact with patients and their families, other members of the health care team, and insurance companies. In order to communicate effectively with each of these groups, a medical assistant should know how to obtain and share information efficiently and accurately.

The Communication Cycle

The communication cycle starts with the **sender**, who sends a verbal or nonverbal **message**. The message is sent through a **channel**, such as a phone call, email message, or in face-to-face conversation. The **receiver** receives the message and interprets it using their own context and knowledge. Finally, the receiver offers feedback to the sender, which allows the sender to decide if their message was interpreted correctly.

The receiver can help ensure they are interpreting the message correctly by being an active listener. **Active listening** simply means fully concentrating on the sender and the message. Nonverbal signals of active listening include making direct eye contact, smiling, and leaning toward the sender. The receiver can also provide verbal clues that they are listening closely to the message. These include:

- reflection: repeating words or phrases back to the sender
- restatement: paraphrasing the message back to the sender
- clarification: asking questions to better understand the sender
- feedback: responding to the content of the message

REVIEW QUESTIONS

1. In the communication cycle, how is a message sent to a receiver?

2. What are examples of nonverbal signals of active listening?

3. How is reflection used to signal active listening?

Types of Communication

Communication can be verbal or nonverbal. **Verbal communication** refers to words that are spoken or written. Verbal communication style should be appropriate for the situation. For example, words should be kept simple when working with patients and families. The medical assistant should avoid using abbreviated names, technical jargon, or medical terminology that is unfamiliar to the patient or family. On the other hand, accurate technical language is necessary when working with physicians or insurance companies.

Nonverbal communication includes all the physical aspects of communication, including posture, facial expression, and eye contact. These behaviors are an essential part of communication and have a significant impact on how the listener will interpret the message. Medical assistants should strive to keep their nonverbal communication professional and appropriate by:

- maintaining good posture (e.g., not slouching on a desk)
- keeping a polite facial expression when dealing with patients and the health care team
- respecting other people's personal boundaries (e.g., not hugging coworkers or touching patients without their consent)
- maintaining eye contact when speaking with patients and the health care team
- not using rude or inappropriate hand gestures

Some general guidelines for effective verbal and nonverbal communication are given in the table on the next page.

REVIEW QUESTIONS

4. What is the difference between verbal and nonverbal communication?

5. When is it NOT appropriate to use medical jargon?

6. Why is professional nonverbal communication important?

TABLE 9.1. Dos and Don'ts of Patient Communication

Do	Don't
Introduce yourself and use the patient's name.	Use medical jargon.
Speak directly to the patient when possible.	Threaten or intimidate the patient.
Speak slowly and clearly.	Lie or provide false hope.
Show empathy for the patient.	Interrupt the patient.
Be silent when appropriate to allow patients time to think and process emotions.	Show frustration or anger.
	Make judgmental statements.

Communication Barriers

The communication cycle can be disrupted by internal and environmental factors. These **barriers to communication** can prevent effective communication between the medical assistant and patient. For example, the discomfort caused by pain, hunger, extreme temperatures, and loud noises can interfere with the sender's ability to compose a message and with the receiver's ability to interpret the message. Strong emotions such as anger and sadness can also lead to miscommunication. Medical assistants should take care to notice if any of these barriers are preventing clear communication with either patients or other members of the health care team.

Medical assistants will often encounter members of diverse populations who may require specialized communication techniques. These groups are summarized in Table 9.2.

DID YOU KNOW?

Time constraints are common in all care settings and can be the result of understaffing, high-acuity patient loads, or unanticipated emergencies. When speaking with patients and their families under time constraints, the medical assistant should share this issue with the patient. Being clear with patients will prevent misunderstandings.

TABLE 9.2. Communicating with Diverse Populations

Population	Communication Techniques
Blind or low vision	Announce when you enter or leave the room. Address the patient by name. Describe the layout of the room. Narrate your actions.
Deaf or hard of hearing	Speak slowly and clearly. Allow the patient to see your face while you speak. Provide written materials. Use a sign language interpreter when needed.

continued on next page

TABLE 9.2. Communicating with Diverse Populations *(continued)*

Population	Communication Techniques
Geriatric	Adjust language for confused or cognitively impaired patients. Rely on family members or caregivers as needed.
Pediatric	Move to patient's eye level. Use simple language. Explain exam procedures before you start. Allow patient to hold blunt, safe instruments.
Seriously or terminally ill	Respond promptly and allow patients any needed extra time. Be direct but kind. Do not offer false hope or make unfulfillable promises.
Intellectually disabled	Match the patient's level of vocabulary and sentence complexity. Speak directly to the patient.
Illiterate	Notice when patients do not read materials. Read or explain important documents.
Non-English speaking	Have materials available in multiple languages. Use an interpreter when needed.
Anxious, angry, or distraught	Stay calm and speak clearly. Wait for the patient to calm down before relaying complex information.
Socially, culturally, or ethnically diverse	Understand that many aspects of communication, including volume and eye contact, have a cultural component. Be respectful of the cultural needs of patients.

REVIEW QUESTIONS

7. How can discomforts like pain, hunger, anger, or sadness affect communication?

8. When communicating with a patient who does not speak English, what steps should be taken?

9. While caring for a blind or low-vision patient, what can the CMA do to improve communication with the patient?

De-Escalation Techniques

Patients and their families often face stress and uncertainty during medical care. These heightened emotions may lead to angry or aggressive behaviors directed toward medical staff. **De-escalation techniques** can be used to prevent these behaviors from disrupting care or threatening the safety of health care providers. When using de-escalation techniques, the key is to remain calm and not react strongly. Specific de-escalation techniques include:

- be non-judgmental
- express empathy (e.g., "This must be a very difficult time for you.")
- maintain neutral body language and a non-threatening tone
- allow the person to express their feelings
- ask the person to move to a quiet, non-stimulating environment
- set clear limits with the person (e.g., "If you continue to shout, you will be asked to leave.")

If de-escalation techniques are ineffective and the person continues to be disruptive or threatening, the medical assistant should notify their supervisor and security.

REVIEW QUESTIONS

10. What is key when using any de-escalation technique?

_____

11. If a patient or family member continues to threaten staff despite attempts at de-escalation, what should be done next?

_____

Meeting Patients' Emotional Needs

CRISIS AND PATIENT COPING MECHANISMS

For many patients, a serious illness and resulting hospitalization constitute a crisis. A **crisis** is the overwhelming event or series of events that create a situation perceived as threatening or unbearable. Crises often lead to disruption of normal psychological functioning.

A **situational crisis** occurs when an unexpected event causes stress to a person or family. Examples of situational crises include an unwanted pregnancy, a new baby, a divorce, the death of a loved one, onset or change in a disease process, loss of job or career, and being a victim of a violent act. Community situational crises are events that affect an entire community. These include terrorist attacks, floods, hurricanes, earthquakes, and tornadoes.

The successful handling of a crisis includes four phases:

- Phase 1. External precipitating event: A situation occurs, such as a death or a divorce.

- Phase 2. Threat: A perceived or actual threat causes increased anxiety wherein the patient copes or fails to cope.

- Phase 3. Failed coping: The patient fails to cope, which produces physical symptoms, relationship problems, and increased disorganization.

- Phase 4. Resolution: There is mobilization of internal and external resources, and the patient returns to the precrisis level of function.

Many patients respond to crises using various coping skills they have learned over time. **Coping mechanisms** are learned external behaviors and internal thought processes used to decrease discomfort and pain. Coping behaviors can be emotion-focused or problem-focused. With **emotion-focused behaviors**, the patient alters a response to stress by thinking, saying, or doing something that makes him or her feel happier or normal. These behaviors include crying, screaming, and talking with others. **Problem-focused behaviors** are done to alter the stressor in some way, such as investigating the facts of a problem or devising a plan to overcome the situation.

Defense Mechanisms

A **defense mechanism** is an unconscious psychological process designed to protect a person from stress or emotional pain. Recognizing these defenses can help medical assistants work with distressed patients. Common defense mechanisms include:

- denial: avoidance of a problem by refusing to recognize it or by outright ignoring it

- displacement: transfer of feelings for a threatening person, place, or thing to a neutral person, place, or thing

- intellectualization: expressive thinking and logic adoption to avoid uncomfortable thoughts and feelings

- projection: assignment of personal feelings or motivation to another person, place, or thing

- rationalization: giving logical and acceptable explanations to hide a feeling, concern, or motive that is not socially acceptable

- regression: the demonstration of behavior characteristics from an earlier age

DEATH AND DYING STAGES

Loss is the absence of something wanted, available, and loved. With actual loss, others can identify the situation or event, whereas with perceived loss, the patient experiences something others cannot comprehend or verify. Anticipatory loss is when the patient expects and experiences the loss before it occurs.

Grief is a normal response to loss, and **mourning** is the public expression of grief. The three types of grief are acute (short-term), chronic (long-term), and anticipatory (grief before an impending loss). **Bereavement** is the time period of mourning after a loved one has died.

TABLE 9.3. Stages of Grief and Loss Response	
Stage 1: Shock and Disbelief	The survivor feels numb, has emotional outbursts, denies the situation or event, and isolates self.
Stage 2: Experiencing the Loss	The survivor feels angry regarding the loss/death, bargains regarding this event, and suffers from depression.
Stage 3: Reintegration	The survivor starts to reorganize his or her life, adapts to the situation/event, and accepts reality.

The medical assistant's role when handling patients' grief and loss is to provide a safe, emotionally supportive environment. When working with grieving patients and families, it is important to consider their religion, culture, and family dynamics. Medical assistants may also process patient referrals to mental health professionals.

REVIEW QUESTIONS

12. Which of the four phases of handling a crisis involves the patient's inability to cope, which produces physical symptoms, relationship problems, and increased disorganization?

_____

13. What is rationalization?

_____

14. What is a common response during the first stages of loss or grief?

_____

15. If an adult patient begins to act childlike in response to a traumatic event, what type of defense mechanism might the patient be using?

_____

16. What social factors can impact how a patient or family grieves?

_____

Cultural Diversity

All patients and their families deserve to be treated with compassion and respect. Medical assistants should strive to treat everyone they encounter in the office equally, without regard to race, religion, age, gender identity, sexual orientation, socioeconomic status, physical challenges, special needs, or lifestyle choices. To do this, medical assistants should be aware of their own stereotypes and biases. **Stereotypes** are widely held but oversimplified or incorrect assumptions about a group of people. **Bias** is a prejudice for or against a group of people. If stereotypes and biases are not examined and corrected, both can lead medical assistants to treat patients unfairly.

REVIEW QUESTION

17. What term describes a widely held, oversimplified, incorrect assumption about a group of people?

Health Care Team Roles

In addition to physicians, the medical assistant will work with a variety of health care team members, each of whom performs a specific set of duties. Medical assistants should be familiar with the roles and skills of other health care team members.

- Admissions Clerk: An admissions clerk in a medical office has general administrative office skills. They obtain basic medical history and information from patients when they come into the facility.

- Laboratory Technician: Often called a medical technologist, a laboratory technician works under the supervision of a pathologist or physician. These health care workers perform chemical, microscopic, and/or bacteriologic testing on blood and body tissues.

- Phlebotomist: Also called an accessioning technician, a phlebotomist is trained in drawing blood.

- Radiologic Technologist (RT): Also called an X-ray technician, an RT is trained to operate radiologic equipment under the supervision of a physician.

- Emergency Medical Technician (EMT): An EMT is trained in the administration of emergency care and transportation of patients to the medical facility.

- Certified Nursing Assistant (CNA): A CNA provides basic nursing skills and patient care to people in adult day care centers, nursing homes, office settings, and hospitals. CNAs are registered and/or licensed.

- Licensed Practical Nurse (LPN): An LPN is a one-year nurse trained in patient care and licensed by the state.

- Registered Nurse (RN): An RN is a two- or four-year nurse trained in patient care and licensed by the state.

- Nurse Practitioner (NP): An NP is an RN with advanced training to diagnose and treat patients.

- Physician Assistant (PA): A PA practices medicine under the supervision of a physician and is authorized to assess, diagnose, and treat patients. The position requires a master's degree in a specialized PA program.

Physician: A physician has a doctor of medicine (MD) degree and is trained in diagnosing and treating illnesses and providing preventive care.

All the members of the health care team work together to ensure patients receive the care they need. To accomplish this goal, medical assistants should build good professional relationships with other health care team members by:

- being responsive to the needs of other team members.

- communicating information promptly and clearly.

- successfully completing their job responsibilities.

Advocates represent or plead the cause of those who cannot speak for themselves. CMAs are often considered patient advocates because they serve in this role for patients.

One of the most important ways that CMAs can assist patients is to help them navigate their health care experience. CMAs can provide information on available community resources and help them access those resources by providing necessary contact information.

CMAs also help patients with **referrals**. When the physician refers a patient to a specialty practice, the CMA usually initiates the process. The physician may request a particular practice, or the patient may specify a preference. Patients with HMO or PPO insurance plans must be referred to physicians associated with that plan. A referral form must be completed and sent to the insurance agency per protocol, with one copy for the specialist and one for the patient's record.

DID YOU KNOW?

NPs, PAs, physicians, psychiatrists, and dentists are the only health care providers authorized to write prescriptions in all 50 states.

REVIEW QUESTIONS

18. Who on the health care team is licensed to prescribe medications?

Telephone Etiquette and Techniques

The telephone is the most-used technology for patient interaction within the medical office. For telephone communication to be effective, medical assistants should adhere to the guidelines in Table 9.4.

TABLE 9.4. Telephone Guidelines	
Speaking voice	Enunciation: Speak clearly.
	Pronunciation: Speak words correctly.
	Speed: Speak at a normal rate.
	Volume: Use a normal voice.
	Inflection: Use correct pitch and tone.
	Courtesy: Speak politely.
	Attention: Focus on the caller.
Answering calls	Answer before the fourth ring.
	Greet the caller with "Good morning" or "Good afternoon."
	Provide the name of the facility, as well as your name.
	Use a standard closing phrase, such as "Thank you for calling."
	Allow the caller to hang up first.
Directing multiple incoming calls	Ask the first caller if they mind being placed on hold. Be sure to explain that you have another call.
	Ask the second caller to wait and allow time for a response before placing them on hold.
	Attempt to respond within 30 seconds but provide options if the hold will be longer.
	Thank callers for waiting.
Screening calls	Manage physicians' time by referring only necessary calls and taking messages for other calls.
	Refer patients to the appropriate source for assistance.

Routing calls	Tell the caller whom you are forwarding the call to.
	Provide the forwarding number in case of disconnection.
	Inform the caller that if the party does not respond, the caller may leave a voicemail.
Dealing with emergencies	Notify the physician of the emergency immediately.
	Activate the emergency medical system (EMS).
	Instruct the caller to hang up and call 911.
	Provide EMS with necessary information, including advance directives.
Managing difficult callers	Keep voice at a normal tone and remain calm when speaking with angry callers.
	Notify the appropriate staff member after determining the problem.
	Follow up with the patient to be sure the problem was addressed.
	Notify the office manager, administrator, or physician of irate callers or callers with unresolved issues.
	Obtain the identity of threatening callers and notify the appropriate supervisor.
Telephone confidentiality The following guidelines from the Health Insurance Portability and Accountability Act (HIPAA) should be observed when using the phone:	Verify that the caller is indeed the patient.
	Give information only to the patient.
	Be sure the conversation is not heard by other patients.
	Avoid discussing telephone conversations around patients.
	Do not leave information on a patient's voicemail.

REVIEW QUESTIONS

21. Why is it important to verify that the caller is actually the patient before discussing health information with them?

_____

22. Who should be notified about irate or difficult callers?

_____

ANSWER KEY

1. The sender sends a verbal or nonverbal message through a channel (e.g., a phone call, in-person conversation, or email).

2. A receiver can demonstrate active listening with nonverbal signals like leaning in toward the sender, making eye contact, and nodding or smiling.

3. The receiver can signal active listening by using reflection, which involves repeating words or phrases back to the sender.

4. Verbal communication involves speaking; nonverbal communication refers to physical actions (e.g., eye contact, posture, and facial expression).

5. CMAs should not use medical jargon when speaking with patients or their family.

6. Medical assistants should strive to keep their nonverbal communication professional because it will affect how the listener will interpret the message.

7. Any of these discomforts can lead to miscommunication by interfering with the sender's ability to convey a message and with the receiver's ability to interpret the message.

8. The CMA should use an interpreter and have paperwork available in the patient's language when possible.

9. The CMA can improve communication with blind or low-vision patients by announcing when they are entering or leaving the room, addressing the patient by name, explaining what they are doing, and describing the room layout.

10. It is important that the CMA use de-escalation techniques to maintain care and ensure the safety of health care providers. The key to doing this is to remain calm and not react strongly.

11. The medical assistant should notify a supervisor and security if de-escalation efforts are unsuccessful.

12. A patient's inability to cope with resultant physical symptoms, relationship problems, and increased disorganization is indicative of phase 3: failed coping.

13. Rationalization is giving logical and acceptable explanations to hide a feeling, concern, or motive that is not socially acceptable.

14. In the first stages of loss or grief, the survivor feels shock and disbelief, including feelings of numbness, emotional outbursts, denial, and isolation.

15. A patient demonstrating childlike behavior in response to trauma is using regression as a defense mechanism.

16. Religion, culture, and family dynamics can all affect how a patient or family grieves.

17. A widely held, oversimplified, incorrect assumption about a group of people is a stereotype.

18. Physicians, nurse practitioners, and physician assistants (as well as dentists and psychiatrists) are the only health care team members licensed to prescribe medications in all 50 states.

19. A laboratory technician, or medical technologist, works under the supervision of a physician or pathologist and performs chemical, microscopic, and/or bacteriologic testing on blood and body tissues.

20. CMAs advocate for patients by helping them navigate their health care experience, providing information on available community resources, assisting them to access resources, and initiating referrals.

21. Discussing health information with someone other than the patient or approved guardian violates the Health Insurance Portability and Accountability Act (HIPAA).

22. The CMA should notify a supervisor, administrator, or physician of irate or difficult callers.

10 BILLING, CODING, AND INSURANCE

Medical assistants may be responsible for tasks related to patient billing, including filing insurance claims, billing patients, and collecting payments. In order to do this work effectively, the medical assistant must understand the foundations of coding and insurance coverage.

Coding Applications

A universal set of codes is used to simplify health care communication, particularly for reimbursement. These medical codes define diagnoses, procedures, equipment, and services for health care professionals, insurance companies, and government health programs.

INTERNATIONAL CLASSIFICATION OF DISEASES

The **International Classification of Diseases (ICD)** is a coding system used to classify diseases. It was created by the International Statistical Institute and entrusted to the World Health Organization (WHO) in 1948. The most current version is the ICD-10. Each ICD code corresponds to a different medical diagnosis. The codes are used to help identify and group diseases for billing, disease monitoring, and other research or public health purposes. There are multiple coding reference books with the complete list of ICD-10 codes available for purchase, but the ICD-10 reference book can be ordered or accessed for free through a search application on the WHO website.

The ICD-10 codes are alphanumeric. The first character is always a letter, and the second character is always a number. The rest of the code could contain between one and five more characters, which could be letters or numbers, and there is always a decimal after the first three characters. For example, the ICD-10 code for "fatty changes of the liver" is K76.0, and "nonalcoholic fatty liver inflammation" is K75.81.

WHO released the ICD-11 in June 2018, but it will not go into effect until January 1, 2022.

CURRENT PROCEDURAL TERMINOLOGY

Current Procedural Terminology (CPT) uses a set of standardized five-digit codes to identify medical, surgical, or diagnostic services. CPT codes refer only to medical procedures and are used with ICD codes (which give the diagnosis for the underlying medical condition). The CPT coding system was developed by the American Medical Association (AMA), which releases updated codes every October.

Medical assistants who handle billing and patients' records need to be familiar with CPT/ICD codes and know how to read bills and reports containing these codes. For example, the CMA may be asked to use codes to create patient bills or submit claims to insurance companies.

CPT is divided into three categories of codes:

- Category I is for common medical procedures that are widely used. This category includes evaluation and management, medicine, surgery, anesthesiology, radiology, pathology, and laboratory codes.

- Category II codes are optional and are used for tracking and performance monitoring. For example, they document an assessment of tobacco use or blood pressure measurement.

- Category III codes are temporary codes for new procedures or technology that is involved in research.

Sometimes a simple CPT code is not enough, and a **CPT code modifier (CM)** is needed to give extra information to the insurance company. For example, a modifier may describe why a procedure was necessary, where on the body a procedure was performed, if multiple procedures were performed, or if multiple physicians were present.

CPT modifiers are always two characters; they may be numeric or alphanumeric. The modifier is added to the end of a CPT code with a hyphen. If more than one modifier is needed, the functional modifier is coded first and the informational modifier second.

Sometimes the unexpected happens during an office visit or procedure, and more time or more resources are needed to care for a patient. For example, an office visit that was supposed to take 30 minutes turns into 60 minutes based on information obtained during a physical assessment, or an in-office procedure needs to happen on the same day.

CPT codes must be adjusted to account for the additional time or procedure, and proper documentation must be made in the patient's chart to explain the reason for the code change. The physician may need to provide a new ICD-10-CM if a new medical condition is diagnosed as a result of an assessment or test findings. This documented explanation for code changes is extremely important so the physician and/or practice will not be accused of upcoding. **Upcoding** is the act of using a CPT code in a claim to insurance companies that indicates a higher level of service or a more complex diagnosis not supported by medical necessity, medical facts, or the medical provider's documentation.

Healthcare Common Procedure Coding System

The Centers for Medicare and Medicaid Services (CMS) uses the **Healthcare Common Procedure Coding System (HCPCS)** for billing and reimbursement. HCPCS Level I codes are the same as the CPT codes and are used for medical, surgical, or diagnostic services. HCPCS Level II codes are unique to CMS and are used for products, supplies, and services not included in CPT codes. Level II codes consist of a letter followed by four digits. The letter indicates the category of service.

DID YOU KNOW?

Upcoding, whether intentional or an oversight, is a serious compliance risk and is considered health care fraud with grave legal ramifications for all involved.

TABLE 10.1. HCPCS Code Categories

Code Category	Services
A	Transportation; Medical/Surgical Supplies; Administrative, Miscellaneous, and Investigational
B	Enteral and Parenteral Therapy
C	Outpatient Prospective Payment System
E	Durable Medical Equipment (DME)
G	Procedures and Professional Services
H	Alcohol and Drug Abuse Treatment
J	Chemotherapy and Other Drugs Administered other than Oral Method
K	DME Medical Administrative Contractors
L	Orthotic and Prosthetic Procedures
M	Medical Services and Screening Procedures
P	Pathology and Laboratory Services
Q	Temporary Codes
R	Diagnostic Radiology Services
S	Temporary National Codes (Non-Medicare)
T	State Medicaid Agency Codes
V	Vision and Hearing Services

LINKING PRCEDURE AND DIAGNOSIS CODES

Every CPT code must be linked to a corresponding ICD-10-CM code to support medical necessity for the service or procedure performed. For example, "chest pain" (R07.9) would be linked to a corresponding 93000 or 93010 CPT code to establish the medical necessity of the electrocardiogram. For patients with more than one diagnostic code the physician must identify the relevant diagnosis related to the service or procedure and list it in Column E of the CMS-1500 form after the CPT code, thereby linking the diagnosis to the procedure. (CMS stands for "Centers for Medicare and Medicaid Services"; these services are discussed later in the chapter.)

TABLE 10.2. Summary of Medical Coding Systems

System	Used For	Examples
ICD-10	medical diagnoses	K35.2 (Acute appendicitis with generalized peritonitis)
		S72.3 (Fracture of shaft of femur)
CPT	CPT codes: medical, surgical, or diagnostic services CPT code modifier: additional information about procedures	CPT codes: 44960 (Appendectomy; for ruptured appendix with abscess or generalized peritonitis) 45378 (colonoscopy) CPT code modifiers: 22 (Increased Procedural Services) 32 (Mandated Services)
HCPCS Level II	products, supplies, and services not included in CPT codes (Medicare and Medicaid)	K0003 (Lightweight wheelchair) H0005 (Alcohol and/or drug services; group counseling by a clinician)

DIAGNOSIS-RELATED GROUP

To simplify reimbursement and reduce costs, Medicare pays a predetermined amount for a given diagnosis while a patient is hospitalized, a system called the **Inpatient Prospective Payment System (IPPS)**. The **Diagnosis-Related Group (DRG)** is a classification system used to determine payments in the IPPS.

Medicare uses **Medicare Severity Diagnosis Related Groups (MS-DRGs)** to classify patients. The DRG is assigned to the patient based on:

- the primary diagnosis
- any secondary diagnoses
- surgical procedures performed during the hospital stay

- complications and comorbidities (CC) or major complications and comorbidities (MCC)

Each DRG is a three-digit number describing a specific diagnosis (e.g., 176: "pulmonary embolism without MCC"). Medicare then determines the cost of the average resources used to treat patients in that DRG and pays the hospital a flat rate for each patient assigned that DRG. This process ensures that the hospital is paid the same amount for every patient hospitalized with the same DRG. Medicare's use of DRGs is designed to incentivize hospitals to provide only necessary care.

Other organizations have developed more complex DRG systems that incorporate factors such as the severity of the illness, the age and sex of the patient, and the patient's status at discharge. Some hospitals use these for billing outside the Medicare program. These systems include:

- All Patient DRGs (AP-DRGs)
- All Patient Refined DRGs (APR-DRGs)
- International Refined DRGs (IR-DRGs)

DIAGNOSTIC AND STATISTICAL MANUAL OF MENTAL DISORDERS

The Diagnostic and Statistical Manual of Mental Disorders (DSM) is published by the American Psychiatric Association. It lists the symptoms of psychiatric disorders and their related states and provides guidelines regarding differential diagnosis of mental disorders and how to determine the severity of a diagnosis (e.g., length of time symptoms have been present, number of symptoms present). The DSM-5, published in 2013, is the most recent version. Clinicians and researchers use the DSM as a diagnostic tool. Like medical diagnoses, the diagnoses in the DSM have corresponding ICD-10 codes, so clinicians can use them to bill for services.

REVIEW QUESTIONS

1. What do International Classification of Diseases codes represent?

_____

2. What do CPT codes represent?

_____

3. What is upcoding?

_____

4. Why is a CPT code modifier used?

_____

5. What system does Medicare use to classify patients for billing?

_____

Managed Care Organizations

Health insurance companies act as the financial "middleman" between patients and medical providers. The consumer pays the insurance company a **premium**—a regular, predetermined amount of money. In return, the insurer covers some amount of the financial costs of the consumer's medical care. The types of services covered and the amount the insurance company will pay are determined by each person's individual health insurance plan.

Most health care in the United States is provided through **managed care organizations (MCOs)**, which seek to control quality and costs by managing patients' use of medical services. MCOs use a variety of techniques to meet these goals. They contract with providers so their members can access their services at a discounted rate, and they may require patients to use only specific providers. MCOs may also require referrals or preapproval for specialized medical care while easing access to lower-cost preventive care. They may also limit the amount paid for specific services or deny payment for services they feel are not medically necessary.

MCOs also minimize the money they pay out for a patient's medical care by sharing the cost of care with the patient. In addition to the cost of their premium, patients also share the cost of their medical expenses through payments referred to as co-pays, deductibles, and coinsurance. **Co-pays** are set payments that patients pay every time they seek medical care. For example, their insurance requires them to pay a $15 co-pay every time they see their medical provider.

A **deductible** is a set amount that patients must pay before the insurance company will cover any of their medical care. Typically, a deductible is much higher than a co-pay, but the patient only has to pay it once a year. A patient could also have both a co-pay and a deductible. In that instance, if a patient has a deductible of $1,000 a year and a $250 co-pay for emergency room care, she will have to pay $1,000 of her emergency room care even if it only costs $1,001. If she needs additional emergency room care at any time during the remainder of the covered year, she would only have to pay the $250 co-pay no matter the total cost of the additional emergency room care.

Another way insurance companies share the cost of medical care with the patient is through coinsurance. **Coinsurance** is the total percentage an insurance company will pay for a patient's medical care. If a patient has an insurance policy with an 80 percent coinsurance, that means the insurance company will only pay 80 percent of the cost of the care regardless of the total amount. This is not a set amount; the amount the patient ends up paying depends on the total cost of care.

It is possible for a patient to have a coinsurance, a deductible, and a co-pay in one insurance policy. Fortunately, insurance policies usually come with a maximum out-of-pocket limit. For example, a patient might have a maximum out-of-pocket limit of $5,000 per year, an 80/20 coinsurance, and a deductible of $1,500 for hospital care. If the patient experiences a costly medical problem and is admitted to the hospital, they will have to pay the $1,500 deductible and 20 percent of the cost of his care until they have paid an additional $3,500. If their care costs more than that or they end up back in the hospital, the insurance company is responsible for paying the remaining cost.

There are four main types of MCOs available to patients:

- preferred provider organization (PPO)
- exclusive provider organization (EPO)
- health maintenance organization (HMO)
- point-of-service (POS) plans

These plans exist on a spectrum that balances flexibility and cost. PPO health care plans offer the most flexibility but are also the most expensive. HMO plans offer the least flexibility but generally will be cheaper for the consumer.

Preferred Provider Organizations

In a **preferred provider organization (PPO)**, providers contract with the insurance company to create a network. If the plan member sees medical professionals included in this network, the member receives the PPO's negotiated rate, which is usually substantially lower than the provider's cash rate. The insurer will then cover some portion of the cost (depending on the plan), and the member pays the specified coinsurance.

In a PPO, pre-authorization for medically necessary services may be required. In addition, the insurance company might not pay for a service a physician requests if the service is not deemed medically necessary. For example, a PPO plan might not authorize payment for an expensive brand-name prescription if a cheaper generic version is available.

PPO plans allow members to go directly to a specialist without a referral from a primary care physician. However, prior authorization from the insurance company may be needed to ensure coverage.

Members in a PPO may use the services of health care providers outside the network but will have to pay higher rates and will have a higher coinsurance and maximum out-of-pocket amount (which may not be limited for out-of-network services).

DID YOU KNOW?

In a PPO, providers are usually compensated using a fee-for-service arrangement whereby they bill the insurance company for each separate service provided.

PPO plans typically have higher premiums than other health plans. Once members have met their annual deductible, the insurance company will pay a larger portion of the cost. If members meet their out-of-pocket maximum, the insurer will cover all approved health care costs. Deductibles and max out-of-pocket costs are usually lower for in-network care and much higher for out-of-network care.

EXCLUSIVE PROVIDER ORGANIZATIONS

An **exclusive provider organization (EPO)** also contracts with providers to form a network. The EPO will cover in-network health care services in the same manner as a PPO. However, out-of-network services are not covered except in cases of medical emergencies (once the patient is stable, the insurance plan may request to transfer to an alternative hospital within the network). Because the plan member is responsible for all out-of-network costs, the premiums for an EPO plan are usually lower than those for a PPO.

A referral to a primary care physician (PCP) is not needed for specialist services, but the patient is responsible for ensuring that all providers are in-network. Pre-authorization is usually required to have services approved for reimbursement.

HEALTH MAINTENANCE ORGANIZATIONS

A **health maintenance organization (HMO)** requires the member to have a primary care physician who coordinates all care. Members may choose their own PCP from a list of in-network providers. If a PCP is not chosen, the insurance company will assign one.

Referrals from the PCP are needed for any type of medical service, including specialist visits, diagnostic tests, and medical equipment. The primary care provider in an HMO contract is often referred to as a **gatekeeper.** They oversee all primary and preventive care. The gatekeeper authorizes referrals, lab studies, diagnostic testing, and hospitalization.

All medical providers must be in-network for the insurance company to pay for their services. If the gatekeeper refers the patient to a specialist, and the patient attempts to see a different specialist, services will not be covered. Because HMOs can control costs by excluding out-of-network providers, their premiums are lower than those for a PPO or an EPO.

Providers are reimbursed by the HMO through an arrangement called **capitation**, in which providers are paid a fixed amount per member, per month. If a patient sees his HMO primary care physician several times in 1 month, the primary care physician is only paid the amount provided in the contract.

HMOs may have some services, called **carve-outs**, that are excluded from the capitation rate and are usually handled by a designated provider. Common carve-outs include mental health and addiction services, cancer treatments, and ambulance services. The insurance company's payment and pre-authorization policies may be different for carve-outs than for other covered specialist services.

POINT-OF-SERVICE PLANS

Point-of-service (POS) health plans combine characteristics of HMO and PPO plans. As in an HMO plan, the member must designate a PCP to act as gatekeeper for medical services. The insurer will cover authorized, in-network services much like an HMO. However, the patient may choose to go out of network and pay higher out-of-pocket expenses. Typically, a POS plan will have a high deductible and coinsurance to encourage members to use in-network services. This type of health plan is designed for individuals who want the lower premiums and PCP-centered care of an HMO but also want some coverage for out-of-network costs.

REVIEW QUESTIONS

7. What is a co-pay?

8. What is a deductible?

9. What restrictions are placed on patients with HMO insurance plans?

10. Which insurance plan typically has higher premiums, HMOs or PPOs?

11. Does a PPO plan require a referral for a specialist in order to cover the cost of care?

12. How much of the cost of care must the patient provide after they have paid the maximum out-of-pocket cost for their insurance plan?

Private Benefit Programs

Consumers can purchase insurance plans through their employer as part of a group plan or through the health insurance marketplace established under the Affordable Care Act (ACA).

EMPLOYER-SPONSORED HEALTH COVERAGE

Companies may choose to offer health coverage through **employer-sponsored health coverage**. These plans are also called **group plans** because the same insurance coverage is offered to all members of the group (in this case, the employees). The employer picks the insurance policy and pays for part of the premiums. All employees and their dependents are offered the insurance.

Employer-sponsored plans tend to have more comprehensive coverage and cost less than individually purchased plans. As a group, businesses can negotiate better rates for their members, and businesses will often offer high-quality benefit plans to recruit and retain employees.

The **Consolidated Omnibus Budget Reconciliation Act of 1985 (COBRA)** requires employers with twenty or more employees to offer employees and their dependents continued coverage if they have a qualifying event. These events include:

- employee is laid off
- divorce that ends spouse's eligibility for benefits
- death of the employee
- dependent child reaches the age at which benefits end

COBRA coverage is offered for up to 18 months. During this time, the insured person must pay the entire premium as well as an administration fee (usually 2%). This added expense can make COBRA coverage unaffordable for many people. Some states have passed legislation that extends COBRA coverage by applying regulations to smaller businesses or adding qualifying events.

INDIVIDUALLY PURCHASED INSURANCE

Consumers can purchase individual health care plans through the **Health Insurance Marketplace** (also called the **Exchange**). The **Patient Protection and Affordable Care Act (PPACA)**, colloquially referred to as "Obamacare," regulates the type of insurance available through the marketplace. All plans available to consumers must meet the following requirements:

- Plans must cover **essential health benefits**: ambulatory care, emergency services, hospitalization, maternity and newborn care, mental health and substance abuse services, prescription drugs, rehabilitative and habilitative services, laboratory services, preventive and wellness services, and pediatric services.
- Plans cannot include an annual spending cap on essential health benefits spending.
- No insurer may exclude patients or vary rates based on a patient's preexisting conditions.

Individually purchased plans are managed care plans with the same structure as employer-based plans. They can be PPOs, HMOs, EPOs, or POS plans and can carry highly variable premiums, deductibles, coinsurance, and max out-of-pocket amounts. Plans are categorized as bronze, silver, gold, or platinum based on the level of insurance provided.

The Exchange has an **open enrollment period** (typically from November 1 to December 15) during which individuals can purchase insurance. Consumers can also purchase insurance from the Exchange if they have a qualifying event (e.g., losing employer coverage).

INDEMNITY INSURANCE

Indemnity insurance does not use a network and instead allows members to use the services of any medical provider, including specialists. Indemnity plans provide a flat fee for services based on the **usual, customary, and reasonable rate (UCR)** for a specific location (and thus are sometimes called fee-for-service plans). For example, if an indemnity plan includes $5,000 in coverage for hospitalization costs, the plan will pay up to $5,000 for hospitalization at any location. However, the patient will be responsible for any additional costs. The patient may also be asked to pay medical costs up front and then be reimbursed by the insurer. In addition, most indemnity plans will include a deductible.

Indemnity plans used to be the main type of health insurance available, but today they are very rarely used as primary insurance. Instead, they are used as a supplemental policy to help cover co-pays, deductibles, and coinsurance fees accumulated from a primary managed care insurance plan. Some plans will cover only hospital-surgical costs, and others may cover other medical services.

REVIEW QUESTIONS

13. What are considered qualifying events under COBRA?

_____

14. What is indemnity insurance?

_____

15. How long is COBRA coverage offered for?

_____

16. Can a patient be excluded from insurance coverage due to preexisting conditions?

_____

17. What are the essential health benefits that every insurance plan must cover?

_____

Public Benefit Programs

Federal health insurance programs are available to some individuals, including people with disabilities or low incomes, veterans, and people over 65. These programs do not require a premium, or require only a small premium, and are largely funded through taxes. The services covered under these programs are defined by federal and state laws and regulations.

MEDICARE

The US federal government provides insurance for certain individuals through the **Medicare** program, which is administered through the Centers for Medicare and Medicaid Services (CMS). People eligible for Medicare include those who:

- are 65 or older and have paid payroll taxes
- are younger than 65 and have a disability
- have end-stage renal failure
- have amyotrophic lateral sclerosis (ALS)

Medicare includes four parts. **Medicare Part A (hospital/hospice)** covers inpatient services, including hospitalization, rehabilitation or nursing services at a skilled nursing facility, and hospice care. Hospitalization is covered for up to 90 days, with coinsurance required after 60 days. Stays at a skilled nursing facility are covered for 100 days with co-pays required after 20 days. Patients will only be covered after hospitalization and must receive medically necessary care or therapy; inpatient services solely for activities of daily living are not covered. Hospice services will be covered for patients with less than 6 months to live.

Medicare Part B (medical) covers outpatient services, including preventive services, diagnostic tests, outpatient procedures, emergency care treatment, home nursing and therapy visits, and some ambulance services. Part B also covers **durable medical equipment (DME)**, which is equipment that provides medical benefits to patients in their day-to-day life. DME must:

- have a primarily medical purpose
- be prescribed by a physician
- be used at home
- be for repeated use (durable)

Medicare Part C (Medicare Advantage plans) is administered through a private insurer that contracts with the government. These plans must include coverage for all services covered in both Medicare Part A and Part B. They are usually HMO-style plans with a network and a PCP who acts as a gatekeeper; however, a small number are PPOs.

Medicare Part D (prescription drug plans) is administered by private insurers or pharmacy benefits managers who provide prescription drug coverage. The insurer may choose which drugs to cover, but the CMS requires that insurers cover drugs from specific classes. In addition, the CMS also provides a list of drugs that it does not allow Part D plans to cover. Part D plans can be stand-alone prescription drug plans (PDPs) or can be bundled with Medicare Advantage (Part C) plans.

Medicare has a system of premiums, deductibles, and coinsurance that is similar to private insurance plans. These costs vary by part.

- Medicare Part A has no premiums if the person or their spouse has paid Medicare taxes for 10 years (40 quarters). People over 65 who do not meet the tax requirement may buy into Medicare by paying premiums. There is also a standard deductible and coinsurance amount set by the CMS.

- Medicare Part B requires a monthly premium that is based on income. It also has a standard deductible set by the CMS. After meeting the deductible, patients will usually pay 20% of the cost of treatment (as set by Medicare).

- The premiums, deductibles, and coinsurance for Medicare Parts C and D are set by the individual insurance plan purchased.

- Neither Medicare Part A nor Part B has an annual maximum out-of-pocket amount. Purchased plans for Parts C and D may set a maximum out-of-pocket amount.

HELPFUL HINT:

Medicaid also provides nursing home coverage that is not covered by Medicare.

MEDICAID

Medicaid is a joint federal-state program that provides health coverage for individuals with low incomes. Because Medicaid is partially funded and regulated by states, eligibility and coverage vary widely. Generally, Medicaid will cover individuals with low incomes and has special provisions for coverage of pregnant people, children, the elderly, and people with disabilities.

The ACA expanded Medicaid coverage in 2014 to cover all individuals whose household income is below 133% of the federal poverty line. However, the Supreme Court ruled that states could refuse to participate in the expansion, creating a division in Medicaid coverage between states that chose to expand and those that did not. In addition, some states have implemented cost-sharing measures such as premiums, coinsurance, and deductibles (these costs cannot be imposed for pregnancy-related services, emergency care, or preventive care for children).

Depending on state requirements, some people may qualify for both Medicare and Medicaid. For those with **dual eligibility**, Medicare must be billed first, with Medicaid billed second for services Medicare does not cover.

SOCIAL SECURITY DISABILITY INSURANCE

Social Security Disability Insurance (SSDI) is a benefit program for people who are blind or disabled and cannot work. It is paid for out of the federal disability trust fund. To be eligible, recipients must have been employed for at least 10 years or be the dependent of someone who has been employed for at least 10 years. Recipients must also be blind or fit the Social Security Administration's definition of permanently disabled. The amount of SSDI recipients receive depends solely on what they earned during their working years. If they are a dependent, the amount is based on their provider's earnings. After 2 years of being on SSDI, a patient is also eligible to receive federal health insurance through Medicare.

Supplemental Security Income

Unlike SSDI, **Supplemental Security Income (SSI)** is a cash benefit for those who are disabled and have a limited income. It is paid for through tax revenues. Eligibility does not have any requirements regarding former employment. A recipient must meet the federal government's definition of disabled or blind, or they must be older than 65 and have a limited income. Typically, because of their limited income, SSI beneficiaries are also immediately eligible for their state's Medicaid health insurance program.

TRICARE

TRICARE is a health care program for military personnel, including active-duty US armed forces, those in the National Guard or military reserve, and military family members. Dependents and surviving spouses are also covered if the veteran was killed in active duty. The Defense Health Agency manages the program, but health benefits are provided by a civilian provider network.

TRICARE offers many different options. Costs vary and are based on the plan selected, whether the service member enlisted before or after January 1, 2018, and whether the member is currently on active duty, retired, or medically retired. Survivors are also eligible to enroll and pay the same rates as medically retired members. Premiums for TRICARE are referred to as enrollment fees and can be a one-time fee or a monthly fee, depending on the plan. Active-duty members typically do not pay an enrollment fee. Active-duty TRICARE Prime members pay nothing for deductibles, premiums, and max out-of-pocket rates, but TRICARE For Life medically retired members pay a $300 premium, a $3,500 deductible, and a coinsurance of 20 percent for all in-network care and 25 percent for all out-of-network care with no cap.

- **TRICARE Prime** is a managed care plan and the least expensive plan available. It is for active-duty members who live within Prime service areas in the United States. Eligible enrollees include active-duty military and their families, retired military and their families, National Guard reserve members who have been on active duty for more than 31 consecutive days, nonactivated Guard/reserve members and their families who qualify for Transitional Assistance benefits, retired Guard/reserve members age 60 and older and their families, surviving family members, Medal of Honor awardees and their families, and qualified ex-spouses of non-active military members and their families who live and receive their medical care within the United States.

- **TRICARE Prime Remote**, **TRICARE Prime Overseas**, and **TRICARE Prime Remote Overseas** are all managed care policies for active-duty service members, including National Guard/reserve members who are ordered to active-duty service for 31 or more consecutive days and family members who live with enrolled service members. Plan eligibility depends on where the member lives in relation to a military health care facility. **TRICARE Select** is a fee-for-service plan. The same members who are eligible for a Prime plan and receive their medical care within the United States are eligible for the Select plan.

- **TRICARE Select Overseas** is a fee-for-service plan that has more options but is more expensive than the Prime Overseas plans. Membership eligibility is the same as above.

- **TRICARE For Life** is accepted worldwide, but a beneficiary must have Medicare A and B to be eligible. It is the secondary insurance for those on Medicare but acts as the primary insurance when Medicare is not accepted. It has no annual premium. There is a deductible of $150 for an individual and no more than $300 for a family whose members are medically retired or for a surviving family member.

- **TRICARE Reserve Select** is a managed care plan for reserve members that may be used with any TRICARE authorized provider, but services may require pre-authorization.

- **TRICARE Retired Reserve** is a PPO plan for qualified retired reserve members and surviving family members.

- **TRICARE Young Adult** plans are open to eligible adult children of service members between the ages of 21 and 26. Prime, Prime Overseas, and Prime Remote managed care options are available for the young adult policies as well as a Select PPO option similar to the general TRICARE policies with the same names.

- **US Family Health Plan (USFHP)** and **TRICARE Young Adult** are managed care plans that require the service member to choose a provider for care, but the member cannot receive care from providers who are eligible for reimbursement through TRICARE or Medicare, or from a military medical provider.

TRICARE also offers other benefits, such as pharmacy and dental programs.

CHAMPVA

CHAMPVA (Civilian Health and Medical Program of the Department of Veterans Affairs) is another military health coverage benefit. CHAMPVA provides comprehensive health coverage for a spouse or dependent of a veteran who is permanently disabled due to military service, or a spouse or dependent of a veteran who was totally and permanently disabled due to a service-related injury at the time of death. The family members are also eligible for CHAMPVA if the military member died in the line of duty and the death was not caused by misconduct. Typically, those beneficiaries are eligible for TRICARE rather than CHAMPVA.

REVIEW QUESTIONS

18. Who is eligible for Medicare?

_____

19. What does Medicare Part A cover?

_____

20. What is Supplemental Security Income (SSI)?

_____

21. What do active-duty TRICARE Prime members pay for deductibles, premiums, and max out-of-pocket rates?

_____

22. How is the monthly premium for Medicare B determined?

_____

Pharmacy Benefits Management

A **pharmacy benefits manager (PBM)** is a third-party administrator who handles prescription medication claims for insurance companies and federal benefits programs. The goal of pharmacy benefits management is to reduce the amount patients and insurers spend on prescription medications. PBMs accomplish this goal through a variety of techniques:

- processing prescription claims
- maintaining a network of participating pharmacies
- negotiating drug costs
- managing patients' access to specialty medications
- obtaining rebates from drug manufacturers
- operating mail-order pharmacies

Another major PBM duty is maintaining the **formulary**, a list of medications that are approved for reimbursement. Most formularies use a tiered system designed to encourage physicians and patients to choose lower-cost drugs. **Tier 1 drugs** are usually generic and available to the patients at little to no cost. Higher-tier drugs are specialty or brand-name medications; the patient usually pays an escalating co-pay or coinsurance for drugs in each tier. Medications not on the formulary are not covered by the insurance or benefits providers, meaning the patient must pay the full price out of pocket.

REVIEW QUESTIONS

23. What is the goal of pharmacy benefits management?

_____

24. What are Tier 1 drugs?

_____

Workers' Compensation

Workers' compensation (sometimes known as workman's compensation) is an insurance benefit that most employers are required to carry in the United States (the only exception is the state of Texas). States determine which businesses must carry workers' compensation and the type of insurance carrier that can carry it. Workers' compensation provides medical benefits and a replacement income while an employee recovers from a work-related injury. If the injury results in a permanent disability, workers' compensation benefits would provide the employee with an income for a predetermined length of time or a lump sum compensation payment, medical benefits, and job retraining. If an employee is killed on the job, some states require a predetermined minimum benefit to be paid to the employee's dependents.

The Occupational Safety and Health Administration (OSHA) has defined a "work-related" injury as an injury occurring while the employee was performing a work-related task. When an employee is injured on the job, the employer is required to mail or give the employee a claim form and directions on how to file a workers' compensation claim within 1 business day of the injury being reported. Once the employee files the claim, the insurance company will then instruct the employee to see a physician who will evaluate the injury. This physician then reports back to the insurance company on the severity of the injury and confirms if it is work related. If it is determined that the employee's injury qualifies for workers' compensation, the employee can choose to claim these benefits. However, by claiming workers' compensation benefits, employees give up their right to sue their employer for any negligence regarding their injury.

REVIEW QUESTIONS

25. What is the purpose of workers' compensation?

_____

26. What right does an employee give up by claiming workers' compensation benefits?

_____

Reimbursement and Payment Methodologies

With a **fee-for-service reimbursement**, each item involved in patient care is billed separately. If an insurance policy is not a managed care policy, it is typically a fee-for-service policy. Even a policy that uses a PPO can be a fee-for-service policy. If, for example, a patient is to have a hip replacement, medical supplies, hospital room, fees for surgeons and all other medical professionals involved, and anesthesia would be individually charged. By contrast, **bundled payments** are reimbursed as one fee for all medical care provided. In the example of the hip replacement, all items would be reimbursed in one lump sum.

Bundled payments for health care were created to encourage quality medical care and reduce health care costs. Many Medicaid insurance companies use bundled payments. The expected costs for all provider services are predetermined prior to the services being rendered. In order to make money, or at least to not lose money, providers need to minimize complications and provide effective and efficient services to their patients. **Case rates** are a type of bundled payment. They are a flat fee typically paid by the day for a specific diagnosis, such as myocardial infarction. Bundled payments can also take the form of capitated payments. The payment made to the provider is based on a specific length of time and a specific number of patients. For example, an Accountable Care Organization (ACO) may pay a primary care organization $3,500 per patient per month to manage all care for their patients.

Medicare is a type of **prospective payment system**. The payments for patient services are determined according to the average cost of the services provided and the severity of the patient's diagnoses prior to treatment. The facility uses these predetermined rates to cover all services needed for a specific patient. The payment amounts for the same services will differ among patients depending on their diagnoses. If the care is inefficient or the patient has a preventable complication, like a hospital-acquired infection, or if the patient is readmitted to the hospital within a certain time frame, it will negatively impact the hospital's reimbursement for that patient. Hospitals that have multiple readmissions will be subject to decreased payments for all Medicare patients.

HELPFUL HINT:

Medicare payments are based on **relative value units (RVUs)**, a cost formula that includes the physician and practice expense of a procedure multiplied by a geographic practice cost index that accounts for differences among regions.

REVIEW QUESTIONS

27. How are payments for prospective payment systems calculated?

_____

28. What type of payments are reimbursed as one fee for all medical care provided?

_____

29. How are services billed in a fee-for-service reimbursement plan?

_____

Coverage for Patient Services

For most medical services, the patient's insurance eligibility must be **verified** before the patient is seen. (This is not required for emergency care or for patients paying for care out of pocket.) To verify insurance eligibility, the medical assistant should collect the patient's insurance information, including:

- insurance name and phone number
- policy/ID number and group number
- name of the insured and relationship to patient

In many medical offices, eligibility verification is built into billing software or is handled by a third-party contractor who manages billing. Verification may also be done through the insurer's website or by calling the insurer.

Some hospital admissions, procedures, and medications require **precertification** (also called **prior authorization**) from insurance companies. During the precertification process, the medical provider submits a request for a specific procedure or service along with the relevant parts of the patient's electronic health record (EHR). The insurance company then decides whether they consider the procedure or service medically necessary and how much of the cost they will cover. As with eligibility verification, this process can be handled through billing software or by contacting the insurance company.

After treatment, the medical provider **submits** a claim to the patient's insurance detailing the services provided. The insurer then decides how much of the claim they will pay. They base this decision on many factors, including the patient's insurance plan benefits, negotiated rates for services, and previous patient payments (e.g., payments toward the deductible).

The patient is notified of their insurance coverage through an **explanation of benefits (EOB)**, which explains how much the insurance company has paid the medical provider and gives an estimate of the remaining balance. Patients should be reminded that the EOB is not a bill from the provider. The provider will receive a **remittance advice** from the insurer that explains how much they will be paid.

HELPFUL HINT:

An insurance **group number** is assigned to each group plan purchased through an employer. Plans purchased individually may not have a group number.

DID YOU KNOW?

Precertification does NOT guarantee that the insurer will cover the full cost of care.

DID YOU KNOW?

An **Advance Beneficiary Notice (ABN)** is a notice from Medicare that a certain procedure or service is not covered. It is given to patients before care is provided so that the patient is aware that they may be responsible for the full cost of the procedure or service.

An insurance company **denies** a claim if they refuse to cover the cost of a procedure or service. If an insurance claim is denied, the patient has the right to **appeal** the decision. An **internal appeal** is done by the insurance provider, and an **external appeal** is done by a third-party reviewer. The provider may need to assist in the appeal process, particularly if the denial is caused by clerical errors. Common reasons for denial include:

- coding errors or incomplete forms
- service was deemed not medically necessary
- use of out-of-network services

Insurance claims are **rejected** if the required forms are not completed correctly. These claims are not processed by the insurance provider. Rejected claims do not need to be appealed; instead, the forms should be corrected and resubmitted.

REVIEW QUESTIONS

30. What information should the CMA gather from the patient to verify insurance eligibility?

_____

31. What will happen if an insurance claim form is not completed correctly?

_____

32. How is an explanation of benefits different from a bill?

_____

Financial Procedures

BILLING PROCEDURES

Itemized statements are monthly bills summarizing invoices and are a request for payment. These statements should reflect the service rendered on each date, the date the claim was submitted to the insurance company, the date of payment from the insurance company, and how much the insurance company covered, as well as the balance due from the patient. Time limits for payment and payment due must also be stated along with the balance due. Typically, patients are expected to pay bills within a 30-day period, called a **billing cycle**.

Offices should establish a regular system of mailing statements, and larger physician practices or facilities may spread out the monthly billing of patients over the 30-day period. For example, invoices can be sent to patients whose last names begin with A – E on one day, and then to those whose names begin with F – G on another day, and so on, to minimize the time spent each day on this process.

COLLECTION PROCEDURES

Accounts with overdue payments fall into the **delinquent account** category. Payment on overdue accounts is the most difficult to collect from patients who are going through hardship or who have moved and may not have received an invoice. However, physicians must be paid in order to pay company expenses and to continue to treat patients.

Aging of accounts is the process of classifying and reviewing delinquent accounts by age from the first date of billing. Credits are usually classified as 1 to 30 days past due, 31 to 60 days past due, and so on. Most accounting software has an age analysis tool to help identify and classify delinquent accounts. Delinquent accounts should list all patient account balances, when these charges were incurred, the most recent payment date, and any notes regarding attempts to contact patients for payment or conversations with patients regarding payment due.

Collection techniques may include telephone calls and letters or statements. Letters including statements should be sent when the account is 30 days past due, again at 60 days, 90 days, and 120 days. Calls to the patient should be made in private and during business hours. Being respectful and willing to help the patient meet their financial obligation assists in collecting past-due debts on delinquent accounts.

Preplanned payment options, or a payment plan agreement, may be another option offered by the practice. It is based on an estimate of cost for a procedure provided by the patient's insurance carrier and physician, not a guarantee of what will be owed, and includes what the patient is expected to owe after any co-payments, coinsurance, or deductibles have been billed and paid. This option allows for a predetermined monthly payment to be billed to the patient's bank card or credit card on a certain date so that payment can be secured on a monthly basis and the patient can spread out the cost over a predetermined amount of time.

If a patient is not able to make the full payment at the time services are rendered, the practice may make a **credit arrangement** or extension of credit so that a procedure can be performed without the cost paid up front. This option carries more risk to the physician and also requires the establishment of a payment schedule to satisfy the amount due.

Collection agencies are used when internal follow-up has been exhausted on an outstanding account and payment has not been received. If a patient has failed to respond to the final letter sent when the account is 120 days past due, or has failed to fulfill a promise on payment, the account should be sent to a collection agency. Once an account has been handed over to a collection agency, the patient can no longer make payments to the physician's office but must be referred to the collection agency to resolve the account.

DID YOU KNOW?

It is illegal to harass a creditor by making threatening calls or calls late at night (after 9:00 p.m.). It is also illegal to threaten legal action that is not intended to be taken.

HANDLING PAYMENTS

Processing patient payments will depend on the forms of payment accepted by the practice (e.g., credit cards, checks, or cash). Co-pay amounts depend on the patient's insurance plan and are determined by the insurance company. Co-pays for services are generally due in full at the time of the office visit.

For extenuating circumstances, such as procedures and services involving large fees, patients may be able to set up a payment plan or extensions of credit if the practice has provisions in place. Patients setting up payment plans should be informed of what the charges will be, what services these charges will cover, credit policies of the practice, when payment is due, circumstances that require payment at the time of services, insurance benefits that may be accepted, and whether the office staff or the patient will be responsible for completing insurance forms for submission. In addition, collection procedures, including circumstances in which accounts will be sent to a collection agency, should be discussed.

After payments are collected, a receipt is printed and given to the patient stating payment in full. A record of the money received should be included in the general journal (book of original entry), often called the day sheet, where all transactions are first recorded.

FINANCIAL CALCULATIONS

Some of the medical assistant's daily financial duties include handling co-payments, which involves making change for patients paying with cash, data entry, daily balancing of petty cash (if included in job responsibilities), and reconciliation of bank statements for the practice.

The CMA may also have to make financial calculations to determine the best deal when ordering office or medical supplies in order to save the practice money without sacrificing quality. On large orders suppliers will often discount the price for items commonly used, such as gloves. The medical assistant must be able to balance the demand for supply against the discount offered.

For example, a case of 20 packs of gloves costs $50, but if four cases or more of gloves are ordered at a time, the price is reduced to $40 per case. The practice generally uses 80 packs of gloves per month, so ordering four cases of gloves reduces the unit cost from $2.50 to $2 per box. The practice will use approximately 80 gloves per month, so ordering enough gloves to get the discount will work in the practice's favor.

FINANCIAL TERMINOLOGY

Accounts payable is the money due to utilities or for lease payments for office space. Also included on the medical office's balance sheet are the amounts due for the goods purchased by the medical office from suppliers, such as medical and office supplies needed for daily operations. Accounts payable is considered a liability because it is money owed to creditors. When suppliers are paid for goods purchased, the accounts payable is reduced, which in turn reduces the company's **liability.**

Accounts receivable is the money that companies are owed for services provided to a customer. In the medical field, these services may include the nursing and/or physician's assessment, any medications administered during the office visit, and the amount of billable time of the office visit (e.g., 30 versus 60 minutes). Accounts receivable is considered an **asset** because when payments are received for services rendered, they are converted into cash.

HELPFUL HINT:

Accounts Receivable = Debits = Money in

Accounts Payable = Credits = Money out

REVIEW QUESTIONS

33. What is the aging of account process?

_____

34. Can a patient make a payment to the medical provider after a bill has been handed to a collection agency?

_____

35. What is the difference between accounts receivable and accounts payable?

_____

36. Why are preplanned payment options usually offered to patients?

_____

37. When should an outstanding payment be sent to a collection agency?

_____

ANSWER KEY

1. International Classification of Diseases codes represent medical conditions.

2. CPT codes represent medical, surgical, or diagnostic services.

3. Upcoding is the act of using a CPT code in an insurance claim that indicates a higher level of service or a more complex diagnosis than is supported by medical facts.

4. A CPT code modifier may be needed to give extra information to an insurance company.

5. Medicare uses Medicare Severity Diagnosis Related Groups (MS-DRGs) to classify patients for billing.

6. The HCPCS Level II code category for this area of billing and reimbursement is H001–H999.

7. Co-pays are set payments made by patients every time they seek medical care.

8. A deductible is a set amount that patients must pay before the insurance company will cover any of their medical care.

9. The patient must see in-network providers in order for HMO insurance to cover the cost, and they must get referrals from their primary care provider to see a specialist.

10. A PPO typically has higher premiums than other health care plans, including HMOs.

11. No. A PPO allows patients to go directly to a specialist without a referral from a primary care physician.

12. Nothing—the insurance company covers the cost of care past the max out-of-pocket cost specified in the patient's plan.

13. COBRA qualifying events include the employee being laid off, a divorce that ends the spouse's eligibility for benefits, death of the employee, or a dependent child reaching the age at which benefits end.

14. Indemnity insurance does not use a network and instead allows members to use the services of any medical provider, including specialists. Indemnity plans provide a flat fee for a service.

15. COBRA coverage is offered for up to 18 months.

16. Under the Patient Protection and Affordable Care Act (PPACA), no insurer may exclude patients or vary rates based on a patient's preexisting conditions.

17. All plans must cover ambulatory care, emergency services, hospitalization, maternity and newborn care, mental health and substance abuse services, prescription drugs, rehabilitative and habilitative services, laboratory services, preventive and wellness services, and pediatric services.

18. People who are 65 or older and have paid payroll taxes, are younger than 65 and have a disability, have end-stage renal failure, or have ALS are eligible for Medicare.

19. Medicare Part A covers inpatient services, including hospitalization, rehabilitation or nursing services at a skilled nursing facility, and hospice care.

20. Supplemental Security Income (SSI) is a cash benefit for those who are disabled and have a limited income.

21. Active-duty TRICARE Prime members pay nothing for deductibles, premiums, and max out-of-pocket rates.

22. Medicare Part B requires a monthly premium that is based on income.

23. The goal of pharmacy benefits management is to reduce the amount patients and insurers spend on prescription medications.

24. Tier 1 drugs are usually generic and available to patients at little to no cost.

25. Workers' compensation is an insurance benefit that provides medical benefits and a replacement income while an employee recovers from a work-related injury.

26. An employee claiming workers' compensation benefits gives up their right to sue their employer for any negligence regarding their injury.

27. These payments are determined according to the average cost of the services provided and the severity of the patient's diagnoses prior to treatment.

28. Bundled payments are reimbursed as one fee for all medical care provided.

29. For fee-for-service reimbursements, each item involved in patient care is billed separately.

30. The CMA should obtain the patient's insurance name and phone number, policy/ID number and group number, and the name of the insured and relationship to the patient.

31. The claim will be rejected and must be corrected and refiled before payment can be processed.

32. An explanation of benefits is sent by the insurance company to explain how much they will pay for specific services; a bill comes from the medical provider and may include some or all of the remaining cost to the patient.

33. The aging of account process classifies and reviews delinquent accounts by age from the first date of billing.

34. Once a bill has been handed to a collection agency, the patient can no longer make payments to the medical provider but must be referred to the collection agency to resolve the account.

35. Accounts receivable is the amount of money owed to a business for providing a good or service. Accounts payable is the amount the business owes for goods and services.

36. Preplanned payment options allow the patient to spread the cost of care out over a predetermined amount of time.

37. If a patient has failed to respond to the final letter sent when the account is 120 days past due, or has failed to fulfill a promise on payment, the account should be sent to a collection agency.

11 SCHEDULING APPOINTMENTS AND HEALTH INFORMATION MANAGEMENT

Reception is about more than letting patients into the waiting room: It is a patient's first impression of the physician and the practice. The CMA plays a key role in making it a positive impression and serves as the interface between the patient and the practice. The CMA's attitude and demeanor set the tone for the patient's experience and can mean the difference between calm, cooperative patients and anxious, fearful patients who are resistant to health care interactions.

Medical Reception

Preparing the patient's chart is one of the CMA's first administrative responsibilities. Most offices keep digital records, so the CMA may need to access and print relevant sections per office protocols. Organization of medical record hard copies is up to the physician.

As part of establishing the patient-physician relationship, the patient must receive a practice information packet. This packet should be prepared before the patient arrives and will include the following important policies and notifications as well as forms for the patient to complete:

- patient demographic information
- patient consent for evaluation and treatment
- practice policies for patients
- insurance assignment/information
- notice and written acknowledgment of receipt of patient privacy practice
- Medicare Part B signature authorization
- advance directives

- patient history
- family history
- medication list

If the medical office uses a sign-in sheet, the CMA should keep a blank sheet accessible to patients with clear directions for how to use the sign-in sheet. Throughout the day, the CMA should update the sign-in sheet by crossing off the names of patients who have been seen and adding blank sheets as needed.

When current patients check in, the CMA should perform a **demographic data review** to ensure that the patient's information is up to date. The patient should be asked to verify demographic information (in person or on a form), and the CMA should make any necessary updates to the patient record. Patient demographics are the starting line of the patient health record and include:

- name
- date of birth
- gender
- marital status
- address, phone number, and email address
- physician referral information
- insurance information and responsible party
- emergency contact information

Depending on office procedures, the CMA may also ask the patient to provide a specific piece of demographic data to verify their identity. Identity theft prevention is a priority in all medical practices. Diverted medical records are in demand because stolen records are used to obtain prescription medication, commit insurance fraud, and obtain health care via Medicare and Medicaid.

For new patients, the CMA should ask for identification and insurance information, and will need to scan both for the patient's file. **Insurance eligibility verification** should occur before services are provided. This information is usually collected when the appointment is made and is verified before the patient's arrival. If no insurance information is on file, the CMA should follow office procedures to verify the insurance before the patient is seen by the medical provider.

REVIEW QUESTIONS

1. What is white coat syndrome?

   _____

2. What is the purpose of demographic data review?

   _____

Electronic Health Records

TYPES OF RECORDS

Medical records contain all the information relevant to a patient's health care, including demographic information, medical history, diagnoses, diagnostic tests, treatment plans, and outcomes. While some offices may keep hard copies of these records, most medical providers store medical records digitally. Digital medical records come in two forms: electronic medical records and electronic health records.

Electronic medical records (EMRs) are digital copies of a patient's chart for a single medical practice. They contain information about the patient's medical history with only that provider. They are easily accessible within the practice but usually cannot be accessed by anyone outside the practice.

Electronic health records (EHRs) include the patient's medical history with multiple providers, including primary care physicians, specialists, and diagnostic facilities. Ideally, when a patient interacts with a medical provider of any kind, their information is included in the EHR, making it available to all medical providers treating them. In practice, however, the IT infrastructure to support EHRs is still being developed, and EHRs are often incomplete or duplicated.

Both hard copy and digital medical records are categorized as active, inactive, or closed based on the last date the patient was seen in the office. These guidelines are set by individual practices, but general guidelines are below:

- **Active**: Patient has been seen within the past 3 – 5 years.
- **Inactive**: Patient has not been seen within the past 3 – 5 years.
- **Closed**: Patient is deceased, has moved, or has reached legal age limit (pediatrics).

OWNERSHIP AND STORAGE OF MEDICAL RECORDS

Ownership of medical records is viewed differently from state to state, but as a general rule patients own the information in their medical record. However, whether paper or electronic, the record itself belongs to the physician or facility. Patients can get copies of their medical records, but the facility is required by law to maintain the original record. The facility is responsible for protecting the medical record from loss, alteration, or unauthorized use. The original medical record is a legal document that cannot be removed from the facility without a court order.

Retention (how long records are kept) and **destruction** of closed medical records are covered by state law. For hard copy medical record retention, the typical guidelines are 7 – 10 years after the last date of treatment. When that time period has passed, the files should be destroyed, usually by shredding. This process is often handled by an outside contractor.

Retention and destruction of EMRs are less clearly regulated, but most states follow a similar policy as with hard copy records. Destruction of EMRs can be complicated, as the goal is not only to delete the digital file but also to ensure that no PHI can later be retrieved. This goal is usually accomplished by deleting and writing over the file. This process can be especially important when disposing of office equipment (such as computers or printers) that may contain PHI.

MEDICAL RECORD TASKS

CMAs are responsible for a variety of tasks related to medical records. The process for each task will depend on medical office systems and policies. Described generally, these tasks include:

- Assembling: Constructing files in the correct order.
- Filing: Keeping medical records in a secure storage area.
- Maintaining: Adding and updating all medical record documentation.
- Retrieving: Recovering medical records from storage when needed.
- Transferring: Sending medical records to another physician's office.
- Protecting: Keeping medical records secure at all times.
- Retaining: Keeping medical records for a specified length of time.
- Purging: Removing medical records kept past the statute of limitations.
- Destroying: Shredding medical records.

READING MEDICAL RECORDS

Recognizing and understanding the data in medical records is a crucial aspect of CMA responsibility that helps assist the physician and promotes safe patient care. This data is outlined below:

- The **history** and **physical** give concise, up-to-date information about the patient's medical history and the findings of their physical exam.

- The **discharge summary** summarizes the following efforts and outcomes of patient treatment:
  - reason for the visit
  - significant findings
  - treatment and procedures provided
  - patient's condition at the end of the visit
  - patient and family instructions, if any
- **Operative notes** discuss the details of operations the patient has undergone, as well as procedures the patient may have in the future.
- **Diagnostic tests** and **lab reports** show the results of tests such as CT scans.
- **Clinic progress notes** are made by health care practitioners to sequentially describe the patient's condition and the interventions provided or planned.
- **Consultation reports** are provided by practitioners other than the patient's primary care physician.
- **Correspondence** includes any patient-specific data received from or sent to the practitioner, health organization, or patient.
- **Charts**, **graphs**, and **tables** are the visual documents and summaries of patient data.
- The **flow sheet** is a graphic or checklist record of ongoing data collection such as vital signs or medications.

REVIEW QUESTIONS

5. What type of information is included in an EHR?

_____

6. How long should hard copy medical records be kept?

_____

7. What information is included in a flow sheet?

_____

8. How should hard copies of medical records be destroyed?

_____

9. What information is found in the patient's discharge summary?

_____

10. What information does the patient's history and physical contain?

_____

11. How does the CMA assist with maintaining medical records?

_____

Scheduling Appointments

Types of Schedules

The flow of patients can be managed using several scheduling styles. Most primary care physician offices use **stream scheduling**, in which patients are scheduled at regular intervals throughout the day. Typically, appointments are scheduled at 10-, 15-, 20-, or 30-minute intervals, although this will depend on the provider and the purpose of the visit. New patient appointments take longer than those for established patients, so extra time should be built into the schedule. The schedule should be flexible to accommodate established patient requests for urgent or emergency appointments.

Some offices may use a **wave schedule**, in which several patients are booked at the same time at regular intervals throughout the day (e.g., three patients at 9:00 a.m., three patients at 10:00 a.m., and so on). Patients are usually seen on a first-come, first-serve basis, although more urgent patients may be seen first. This system is often used when there are enough rooms and personnel to quickly move people out of the waiting room. A wave schedule is also useful for practices that often have no-shows.

Specialists often use **cluster scheduling** to group similar appointments together during the day or week. For example, pediatricians may schedule all well-baby checks between 9:00 and 11:00 a.m., or a cardiac clinic may book appointments for patients with a specific dysrhythmia only on Tuesdays and Thursdays. This practice can help streamline care by requiring less time setting up specialized equipment. Cluster schedules may be necessary when specialized staff or equipment have limited availability.

Urgent care clinics and emergency rooms use **open hours scheduling**, whereby patients are seen on a first-come, first-serve basis. Patients may also be triaged by a medical professional when they arrive so that the most urgent patients can be seen first. Community clinics and other medical offices that see underserved populations may also use this system.

Scheduling Guidelines

When scheduling appointments, it is important to provide the patient's full name, use correct spelling, list the patient's date of birth, and obtain both home and work telephone numbers. Depending on office policy, the purpose of the visit should be recorded as well.

Appointments are usually scheduled on a computer with scheduling software. An **appointment matrix** is any kind of scheduling software or desktop chart that shows the date and time of physician availability, usually in color-coded grids or sections. Patient name and the appointment date and time are entered into the matrix.

Scheduling of two or more patients for the same appointment slot is called **double-booking** and is often done to accommodate patients with specific needs who cannot wait for another day. **Advanced scheduling** involves scheduling patients weeks or months in advance. **Under-booking** occurs when there are too many gaps between appointments and can be costly to the practice.

Patient flow refers to the round-turn traffic in and out of a physician's practice. The CMA must effectively balance patient needs (e.g., their work schedule) with the physician's schedule and preferences. The CMA is also responsible for coordinating patient activities that require limited equipment or other facilities, such as electrocardiogram (ECG) machines and ultrasonography rooms.

Making appointments for patients to obtain outside services such as X-rays, outpatient procedures, and hospital admissions requires the CMA to work with both sides, since outside facilities usually have their own schedules and limited equipment.

The medical office should have systems in place to help patients remember their appointment times. Reminders/recall systems may include appointment cards, telephone calls, and mailed reminders. **Appointment cards** are given to the patient at the end of their visit when they schedule new appointments. Phone calls can be made in person or through automated messaging systems. A **tickler file** is a manual or automated system that alerts office staff to send out reminders for patient appointments in chronological order.

APPOINTMENT PROTOCOLS

When scheduling appointments, the CMA may be asked to **screen calls** to evaluate the urgency of the appointment. When screening calls, the CMA must work within their scope of practice: CMAs cannot triage, treat, or diagnose patients, nor can they interpret test results or give medical advice to patients. However, the CMA should be able to question the patient about their complaint and place them accordingly in the schedule. In offices where urgent calls are frequent, such as a pediatrician's office, screening calls may be handled by a nurse.

Physician referrals should be prioritized. When making appointments for referrals, the CMA will usually call the patient using the information provided by the referring physician's office. If a patient calls about a referral that has not yet been received, the CMA should let the patient know that the office will call them as soon as their referral information is available.

If the patient cancels their appointment, the missed appointment must be removed from the schedule before another one is made. If the cancellation

DID YOU KNOW?

Tracking arrival time, wait time, and departure time for each patient can help the medical office set realistic guidelines for scheduling patients.

DID YOU KNOW?

The phrases **screening calls** and **phone triage** are often used interchangeably in the practice office. Regardless of the term, CMAs can follow strict clinical protocols when screening calls, but they may not make triage decisions independently.

is made by the physician, the patient must be notified of the reason for the cancellation and offered an alternative appointment. The cancellation then needs to be documented in the chart.

For **no-show** patients, the patient should be contacted to determine why the appointment was missed and to schedule another appointment. A note must be made in the patient's chart documenting the no-show and any attempts to contact the patient.

Physician delay is often unavoidable. If the physician is late getting to the office, the CMA should call scheduled patients to notify them and ask if they can come in later or reschedule. If the physician is delayed seeing patients who have already arrived at the office, the patients should be notified and given a reason for the delay. The delay needs to be charted in the patient's medical record.

HELPFUL HINT:

A patient appointment with the physician is a kind of contract. The reason for delay and cancellation must always be entered in the chart to prevent the liability of patient abandonment.

REVIEW QUESTIONS

13. What type of scheduling groups similar appointments together through the day or week?

_____

14. How are patients booked for wave scheduling?

_____

15. What is a tickler file?

_____

16. What is the role of the medical assistant when screening calls?

_____

17. A physician is still in surgery and will be late for the scheduled office appointments. What should the CMA do to notify patients?

_____

18. Why is under-booking a problem?

_____

19. A patient does not show up for an appointment. What step should be taken next?

_____

20. A patient is an hour late to an appointment and must be rescheduled. What should the CMA do?

_____

ANSWER KEY

1. White coat syndrome is the term used to describe the anxiety some patients experience in medical environments, usually evidenced by an atypically high blood pressure reading.

2. The CMA performs a demographic data review to ensure that the patient's information is up to date.

3. Throughout the day, the CMA should update the sign-in sheet by crossing off the names of patients who have been seen and adding blank sheets as needed.

4. The CMA should ask new patients for identification and insurance information before services are provided.

5. Electronic health records (EHRs) include the patient's medical history with multiple providers, including primary care physicians, specialists, and diagnostic facilities.

6. Hard copy medical records should be kept 7 – 10 years after the last date of treatment, after which the files should be destroyed.

7. A flow chart is a graphic or checklist record of ongoing data collection like vital signs or medications.

8. After the time period for keeping hard copies has passed, the files should be shredded to prevent the information from being accessed or stolen.

9. The discharge summary contains the reason for the visit, significant findings, treatment and procedures provided, patient's condition at the end of the visit, and patient and family instructions, if any.

10. The history and physical give concise, up-to-date information about the patient's medical history and the findings of their physical exam.

11. The CMA should add and update all medical record documentation, correctly file records, and retrieve and destroy records as needed.

12. Clinic progress notes are made by health care practitioners to sequentially describe the patient's condition and the interventions provided or planned.

13. In cluster scheduling, similar appointments are grouped together during the day or week.

14. In wave scheduling, several patients are scheduled at the same time at regular intervals throughout the day.

15. A tickler file is a manual or automated system that alerts office staff to send out reminders for patient appointments in chronological order.

16. The medical assistant should question the patient about their complaint and place them accordingly in the schedule, and alert the supervisor when triage is necessary.

17. If the physician is late, the CMA should notify scheduled patients, give them the reason for the delay, ask if they can come in later or reschedule, and chart the delay in the patients' medical record.

18. Under-booking occurs when there are too many gaps between appointments and can be costly to the practice.

19. The patient should be contacted to determine why the appointment was missed and to schedule another appointment. A note must be made in the patient's chart documenting the no-show and any attempts to contact the patient.

20. The CMA should document the reason for delay and cancellation in the chart to prevent the liability of patient abandonment.

12 PRACTICE TEST

Read the question and then choose the most correct answer.

1. To ensure that an accurate blood pressure measurement is taken, the medical assistant SHOULD:

   A) ask the patient to cross their legs at the knee.

   B) take 2 measurements 30 minutes apart.

   C) have the patient remove tight-fitting clothing.

   D) use the appropriate size blood pressure cuff.

   E) place the patient in a supine position

2. Which of the following findings for an adult patient should the medical assistant IMMEDIATELY report to the nurse?

   A) An axillary temperature of 104.2°F (40.1°C)

   B) An oxygen saturation of 96%

   C) A heart rate of 72 beats per minute

   D) A weight of 309 pounds

   E) A respiratory rate of 16 breaths per minute

3. Which of the following describes patient cycle time?

   A) the length of time the average patient spends in the medical office

   B) the average length of time the physician spends with each patient

   C) the average length of time each patient waits to be seen

   D) an estimated amount of time the patient will need for their visit

   E) the average length of time the physician has between patients

4. Which of the following terms describes the position of the palm relative to the elbow?

   A) distal

   B) posterior

   C) superior

   D) medial

   E) dorsal

5. A patient is scheduled for a colposcopy. The medical assistant should assist the patient into which position?

   A) Sims' position

   B) supine position, with the head of the bed elevated 15 degrees

   C) left-side-lying position, knees to chest

   D) lithotomy position

   E) Fowler's position

6. When measuring a patient for crutches, the top of the crutches should be how far below a standing patient's armpits?

   A) 0 inches

   B) 1 – 2 inches

   C) 2 – 5 inches

   D) 5 – 10 inches

   E) > 10 inches

7. The medical assistant is speaking with a patient who has been ordered to wear a Holter monitor. Which statement by the patient indicates a need for further patient education?

   A) "I can wear the monitor while I shower."

   B) "I should keep the monitor on when I sleep."

   C) "I should avoid metal detectors and electric razors while wearing the monitor."

   D) "I should keep a log of any chest pain, shortness of breath, or skipped beats while wearing the monitor."

   E) "I will return the Holter monitor to my physician's office when the forty-eight-hour monitoring period ends."

8. The dipstick portion of a urinalysis tests for all of the following EXCEPT:

   A) pH.

   B) RBC.

   C) parasites.

   D) glucose.

   E) ketones.

9. A patient is having a tonic-clonic seizure. What should the medical assistant do first?

   A) call 911

   B) restrain the patient

   C) turn the patient on their side

   D) take the patient's vital signs

   E) provide a safe environment

10. Which of the following statements is NOT true of eating disorders?

    A) Patients with anorexia nervosa may compensate for binges by using laxatives or diuretics.

    B) Patients with bulimia may have erosion of the tooth enamel.

    C) Bingeing and purging can occur in both anorexia nervosa and bulimia.

    D) Extreme exercising and calorie restriction are common with anorexia nervosa.

    E) Patients may develop eating disorders because of issues of power and control.

11. Which of the following is a disease or dysfunction of one or more peripheral nerves, typically causing numbness and weakness?

    A) sarcoma

    B) neuropathy

    C) meningitis

    D) pertussis

    E) tuberculosis

12. Which body part is affected by a right tibia fracture?

    A) upper arm

    B) lower arm

    C) upper leg

    D) lower leg

    E) head

13. To prevent birth defects of the brain and spine, pregnant women should take a prenatal vitamin containing:

    A) folic acid.

    B) vitamin K.

    C) hemoglobin.

    D) calcium.

    E) vitamin D.

14. Which of the following medications is used to prevent seizures?

    A) oxycodone hydrochloride (OxyContin)

    B) levothyroxine sodium (Synthroid)

    C) prednisone (Sterapred)

    D) pregabalin (Lyrica)

    E) aripiprazole (Abilify)

15. A patient shows signs of anaphylaxis after being administered ciprofloxacin. What should the medical assistant do first?

    A) induce vomiting

    B) obtain the patient's vital signs

    C) complete an incident report

    D) notify the health care provider

    E) begin rescue breathing and chest compressions

16. Leukocytosis means which of the following?

    A) abnormally shaped platelets

    B) abnormally shaped white blood cells

    C) decreased red blood cells

    D) elevated white blood cells

    E) abnormal change in plasma volume

17. When removing sutures, where should the suture be cut?

    A) on the opposite side of the knot

    B) immediately under the knot

    C) on the knot

    D) inside the wound

    E) the medical assistant should decide for each patient

18. Which of the following is a standardized coding system that is used primarily to identify products, supplies, and services not included in the CPT code list, such as ambulance charges and prosthetic devices?

    A) ICD-10-CM codes

    B) CPT modifier codes

    C) HCPCS modifier codes

    D) HCPCS level II codes

    E) supplemental service codes

19. Which of the following precautions would the medical assistant expect to be in place for a patient with influenza?

    A) contact precautions

    B) droplet precautions

    C) airborne precautions

    D) contact and airborne precautions

    E) protective environment

20. Which of the following signs are seen in a patient with cardiogenic shock?

    A) hypertension; slow, labored breathing

    B) decreased urine output; warm, pink skin

    C) increased urine output; cool, clammy skin

    D) hypotension; weak pulse; cool, clammy skin

    E) hyperventilation; warm, pink skin

21. The medical assistant is submitting prescription refill requests to a pharmacy. One of the medication orders is illegible. Which of the following actions should the medical assistant take?

    A) ask another medical assistant to verify the order

    B) ask the prescribing physician for clarification

    C) scan the order to the pharmacy and let the pharmacy staff decipher it

    D) figure it out based on the patient's diagnosis and home medications

    E) call the patient to confirm the prescription details

22. Which of the following is the very brief, preferably quoted statement of the patient that is entered into the medical record giving the purpose of the office visit or hospitalization?

    A) summary of origin

    B) main objective

C) chief complaint

D) personal statement

E) reason summary

23. When changing a patient's dressing, a medical assistant should do which of the following?

    A) put on clean gloves before placing a new dressing

    B) place wet gauze at the base of all wounds

    C) scrub all wound bases vigorously

    D) express out any drainage from the wound

    E) place dry gauze at the base of all wounds

24. Which of the following BEST describes bias?

    A) speaking loudly to ensure that you are heard

    B) showing an unfair preference or dislike of a group of people

    C) being passive, withdrawn, and quiet when communicating

    D) being aggressive and outraged when communicating with an angry patient

    E) positive stereotyping

25. A urea breath test is done to test for which of the following infectious agents?

    A) presence of Helicobacter pylori

    B) strep throat

    C) Influenza A

    D) pneumonia

    E) Epstein–Barr virus

26. Which of the following patients should be seen immediately by the provider?

    A) a forty-five-year-old female on oral contraceptives with unusually heavy menstrual bleeding

    B) a twenty-four-year-old with a dog bite to the leg from the family dog who is current on rabies shots

    C) an irritable four-month-old with a petechial rash and temperature of 103.4°F

    D) a sixteen-year-old football player with a twisted ankle who has no deformity and a pedal pulse

    E) a forty-year-old male with a headache and no serious medical history

27. Which of the following conditions is characterized by a low number of platelets?

    A) glycolysis

    B) thrombocytopenia

    C) thrombocytosis

    D) leukocytosis

    E) anemia

28. The medical assistant has just administered an IM injection to a patient. How should the nurse dispose of the needle?

    A) re-cap the needle and discard it in the nearest puncture-resistant container

    B) break the needle and discard it in the nearest puncture-resistant container

    C) discard the needle in a puncture-resistant container in the central medication area

    D) discard the needle in a puncture-resistant container in the patient's room

    E) re-cap the needle and discard it in a trash can

29. The medical assistant should anticipate that the health care provider will order which of the following vaccinations for a six-month-old patient at a wellness check?

    A) DTaP and MMR

    B) Hib and varicella

    C) influenza and DTaP

    D) hepatitis A and MMR

    E) hepatitis B and DTaP

30. Which of the following shows where the V1 lead should be placed?

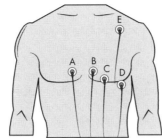

A) site A

B) site B

C) site C

D) site D

E) site E

31. In medical coding, what do ICD codes represent?

A) category codes

B) diagnosis codes

C) procedure codes

D) organizational codes

E) filing codes

32. According to the scale, an infant weighs 4.3 kg. What is the infant's weight in pounds?

A) 1.95 lbs.

B) 5.2 lbs.

C) 8.6 lbs.

D) 9.46 lbs.

E) 68.8 lbs.

33. The eating disorder anorexia nervosa is defined as:

A) binge eating at least twice a week for three months.

B) taking excessive actions to compensate for caloric intake, such as purging.

C) not consuming enough essential nutrients to maintain healthy body fat levels.

D) using laxatives to compensate for excessive calorie intake.

E) an uncontrollable urge to binge eat.

34. Which of the following statements about a choking patient is INCORRECT?

A) The Heimlich should be performed on conscious patients who are unable to speak.

B) A blind sweep of the airway should be done to clear the foreign body.

C) The Heimlich should be performed with five abdominal thrusts between the rib cage and navel.

D) Infants should receive an alternating five back slaps and five abdominal thrusts.

E) Unaddressed choking can lead to cardiac arrest.

35. Which of the following describes a lithotripsy?

A) surgical removal of the gallbladder

B) surgical removal of a kidney stone or gallstone

C) incision of the abdomen

D) procedure to crush a stone

E) procedure to examine the bladder

36. If a correction to the medical chart is necessary, what should the provider do?

A) cross out the incorrect information

B) create a completely new chart

C) erase the incorrect information

D) add an addendum with a time and date stamp to the bottom of the chart

E) leave the chart alone

37. Which of the following is a two-character suffix attached to a category I CPT code that provides supplemental information?

A) modifier

B) ICD-10-CM code

C) supplemental service code

D) HCPCS level II code

E) experimental service code

38. Which element allows hemoglobin to carry oxygen?

A) iron

B) calcium

C) magnesium

D) phosphorus

E) ascorbic acid

39. An autoclave sterilizes equipment using which of the following techniques?

A) using a dry heat for one hour at 320°F

B) soaking the equipment in closed containers of a strong disinfectant chemical

C) applying a steam heat under pressure at high temperatures between 250 – 254°F

D) rinsing equipment with hot soap and water for ten minutes

E) wrapping equipment in sterile cloth to prevent contamination

40. Which of the following would NOT elevate a patient's blood pressure?

A) smoking

B) salt intake

C) alcohol intake

D) diuretics

E) pseudoephedrine

41. How many hours after administration of a Mantoux tuberculin skin test should a patient return to the medical office to have the results determined?

A) two to four hours

B) twelve to twenty-four hours

C) twenty-four to forty-eight hours

D) forty-eight to seventy-two hours

E) seventy-two to eighty-four hours

42. Which of the following tests checks for abnormalities in the middle ear by placing a tube into the outer ear that changes the pressure?

A) tympanometry

B) speech recognition

C) pulmonary function test

D) pure tone audiometry

E) chemical stress test

43. A typical multidose vial should be discarded within how many days of opening?

A) five

B) ten

C) twenty

D) twenty-eight

E) thirty

44. Hypotension; a weak, rapid pulse; pale skin; and diaphoresis are signs of:

A) shock.

B) bladder infection.

C) strep throat.

D) cerebrovascular accident.

E) anxiety.

45. A conscious patient who is normally responsive does not answer any of the medical assistant's questions when they enter the room to collect vital signs. The medical assistant SHOULD:

A) report the change in the patient's status to the nurse.

B) gently shake the patient to see if they are awake.

C) tell the patient they will be punished if they do not respond to questions.

D) come back at a later time to collect vital signs.

E) see if the patient has recently taken medication.

46. Which type of file is labeled by date and organized in a way that the medical assistant knows what actions should be taken on future dates?

A) reminder file

B) tickler file

C) follow-up file

D) future-action file

E) to-do file

47. Which of the following insurance programs covers people sixty-five or older, younger people with disabilities, and people with end-stage renal disease?

A) managed care organization

B) preferred provider organization

C) commercial insurance

D) Medicaid

E) Medicare

48. Which of the following organs is NOT correctly matched with its main function?

A) large intestine: nutrient absorption and waste collection

B) small intestine: nutrient absorption

C) pancreas: produces digestive enzymes (lipase and amylase)

D) stomach: creates an acidic food bolus, known as chyme

E) liver: bile production to break down fat

49. Which of the following precautions must a health care worker take when checking the blood pressure of a patient who is HIV-positive?

A) wear gloves

B) wear a gown

C) wash hands

D) use contact precautions

E) use droplet precautions

50. In which of the following positions should an infant be placed to measure length?

A) standing

B) supine

C) sitting

D) prone

E) reclined in a car seat

51. A patient who has osteoporosis should take which of the following supplements?

A) calcium

B) iron

C) iodine

D) vitamin C

E) vitamin K

52. When recording visual acuity, the left eye is recorded as:

A) OU.

B) OD.

C) OS.

D) OL.

E) OR.

53. In the waiting room, the medical assistant notices a woman clutching her throat. The woman is unable to speak. The medical assistant asks the woman if she is choking, and the woman indicates yes. Which of the following should the medical assistant do first?

A) establish an airway by tilting the chin back

B) administer five quick chest compressions

C) administer two rescue breaths

D) perform the Heimlich maneuver

E) have someone call 911

54. A nephrologist is a specialist who treats the:

A) nervous system.

B) brain and spinal cord.

C) kidneys.

D) liver.

E) lymphatic system.

55. A BMI greater than 40 is categorized as which of the following?

A) very underweight

B) underweight

C) overweight

D) morbidly obese

E) normal weight

56. Which of the following procedures is a surgical opening of the skull?

A) arthrotomy

B) laparotomy

C) thoracotomy

D) osteotomy

E) craniotomy

57. A phlebotomist is a medical professional who is trained to perform which of the following tasks?

A) provide hospice care

B) draw blood

C) administer medications

D) perform moderate- and high-complexity laboratory testing

E) provide home health care

58. Which portion of a SOAP note includes information the health care provider has observed or measured?

A) measures and observations

B) examination notes

C) planning notes

D) subjective notes

E) objective notes

59. Which of the following is a specified amount of money that the insured must pay before the insurance will begin to pay claims?

A) co-payment

B) benefit

C) network

D) payer

E) deductible

60. Which of the following types of tissue is found in bones, ligaments, and cartilage?

A) nervous tissue

B) muscular tissue

C) epithelial tissue

D) connective tissue

E) membranous tissue

61. Which of the following is NOT a common parasitic infection?

A) flukes

B) lice

C) ticks

D) tapeworm

E) ringworm

62. Which dysrhythmia is shown in the following ECG readout?

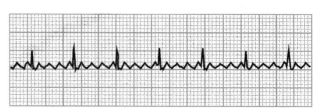

A) atrial flutter

B) atrial fibrillation

C) asystole

D) normal sinus rhythm

E) ventricular fibrillation

63. When using a sphygmomanometer to take a manual blood pressure, where is the stethoscope most commonly placed?

A) carotid pulse

B) femoral pulse

C) dorsalis pedis pulse

D) radial pulse

E) brachial pulse

64. Which hemoglobin A1C result would suggest that the patient's blood sugar levels and diabetes have been poorly controlled for the past several months?

A) 0

B) 1

C) 2.5

D) 5

E) 10

65. Which symptom is a possible adverse drug effect for a twelve-year-old patient who has begun taking amphetamine and dextroamphetamine for attention-deficit/hyperactivity disorder (ADHD)?

A) nausea

B) seizures

C) weight gain

D) constipation

E) bradycardia

66. Which of the following patients should be seen immediately by the provider?

A) a patient complaining of chest pain and nausea

B) a patient with a fracture of the radius from a fall on a staircase

C) a patient complaining of slight redness and itching at the site of a recent vaccine injection

D) a patient presenting with a sprained ankle from a tree branch falling on him

E) a patient complaining of a headache lasting twelve hours

67. Lingual means "near or next to" which of the following anatomical locations?

A) spine

B) tongue

C) head

D) gluteal muscle

E) pelvis

68. If a patient becomes hypotensive during their exam, they should be placed in which of the following positions?

A) Trendelenburg

B) supine

C) prone

D) Fowler's

E) Sims'

69. Which of the following vessels contains deoxygenated blood?

A) pulmonary artery

B) pulmonary vein

C) aorta

D) carotid artery

E) renal artery

70. A patient expresses sadness and loneliness about having to be on continuous tube feeds. The medical assistant SHOULD respond:

A) "I will check with the nurse to see if you are ready to start eating solid food."

B) "We have other patients with feeding tubes. I will see if they want to talk to you."

C) "If you get better soon then the tubes can come out."

D) "Complaining will only make you feel worse."

E) "I'm sorry you are having a difficult time with the feedings."

71. Which of the following locations provides the most accurate measurement of temperature in newborns?

A) Tympanic

B) Oral

C) Rectal

D) Axillary

E) Temporal

72. A stool sample that is black and tarry is called:

A) hematuria.

B) melena.

C) hematemesis.

D) hematochezia.

E) epistaxis.

73. Which type of health insurance requires patients to get a referral from their primary care physician before seeing a specialist?

   A) HMO

   B) PPO

   C) indemnity insurance

   D) Medicare

   E) EPO

74. A patient begins having a seizure at the primary care clinic. The health care provider should:

   A) restrain the patient.

   B) place a tongue blade in the patient's mouth.

   C) remove any objects that can cause injury.

   D) begin CPR.

   E) keep the patient supine during and after seizure.

75. Which of the following blood components is responsible for fighting infection?

   A) red blood cells

   B) platelets

   C) white blood cells

   D) hemoglobin

   E) plasma

76. Which of the following colors indicates a CONTACT HAZARD on a safety data sheet?

   A) red

   B) blue

   C) yellow

   D) white

   E) green

77. A patient checks into the emergency room with severe abdominal pain. She has diabetes, has recently quit smoking, and has no prior surgeries. Her mother has a history of hypertension. What is the chief complaint?

   A) diabetes

   B) no surgical history

   C) severe abdominal pain

   D) hypertension

   E) recent smoker

78. Which of the following should be done prior to eye irrigation?

   A) apply topical anesthetic drops

   B) test visual acuity

   C) record vital signs

   D) give the patient education handouts

   E) apply eye patch

79. Which color is incorrectly matched with its evacuated tube additive?

   A) light blue: sodium citrate

   B) light green: lithium heparin

   C) gray: clot activator

   D) lavender: ETA

   E) yellow: ACD solution

80. How long after a scratch test or intradermal skin test should the skin be checked for an allergic reaction?

   A) one minute

   B) five minutes

   C) fifteen minutes

   D) twelve hours

   E) twenty-four hours

81. If a nine-month-old child has received the first and second dose of the hepatitis B vaccine, what course of action will the provider recommend?

   A) no action; a third dose of the vaccine is not recommended

   B) immediately inoculate the child given the high risk of not having a third vaccine

   C) wait until the child is twelve months old to give the vaccine

D) schedule the child for the third vaccine at the earliest convenience

E) recommend the child receives a third dose as an adult

82. Which of the following vaccines should be stored in the freezer?

A) MMR

B) HPV

C) meningococcal

D) influenza

E) Hib

83. Sudden onset of weakness on one side of the body and face can be a sign of:

A) cardiac arrest.

B) seizure.

C) choking.

D) cerebrovascular accident.

E) deep vein thrombosis.

84. A patient is hyperventilating during a panic attack. How should the medical assistant attempt to help them?

A) have the patient recount a positive childhood memory

B) provide the patient with a glass of water

C) tell the patient to take deep breaths

D) ask the patient to identify the source of his anxiety

E) suggest the patient leave the office until they have calmed down

85. Which of the following is a partial flap-like tearing of the skin?

A) laceration

B) puncture

C) avulsion

D) abrasion

E) burn

86. When a patient rolls up their sleeve and presents their arm for a blood draw, this is an example of which type of consent?

A) informed consent

B) expressed consent

C) implied consent

D) indirect consent

E) direct consent

87. Which of the following refers to something of value owned by a company?

A) accounts receivable

B) accounts payable

C) assets

D) liabilities

E) credits

88. Health care–related surfaces and equipment should be cleaned with which disinfectant?

A) sodium hypochlorite

B) sodium hydroxide

C) diluted Lysol

D) 2:1 vinegar and distilled water solution

E) 10:1 vinegar and distilled water solution

89. Which of the following sets the rhythm for the heart?

A) Purkinje fibers

B) bundle of His

C) aortic valve

D) atrioventricular node

E) sinoatrial node

90. Which dietary change is suggested for patients with hypertension who are trying to decrease their blood pressure?

A) eating red meat daily

B) increasing potassium and calcium intake

C) increasing fluid intake

D) decreasing consumption of foods high in fat

E) decreasing sodium intake

91. Which patient position is the most common for a gynecological or pelvic exam?

A) Sims'

B) prone

C) Fowler's

D) Semi-Fowler's

E) lithotomy

92. Which of the following is the location for the V5 lead for a 12-lead ECG?

A) in the left midaxillary line

B) in the fifth intercostal right mid-clavicular line

C) in the fourth intercostal space to the left of the sternum

D) in the fourth intercostal space to the right of the sternum

E) on the right ankle

93. A patient collecting a stool sample should be told to collect samples on how many days?

A) one

B) two

C) three

D) four

E) five

94. Which of the following describes double-booking?

A) Patients arrive without appointments and are usually seen in the order of their arrival.

B) Each patient is given a specific time slot.

C) Patients are scheduled for the same time slot.

D) Patients are told to come in at the beginning of the hour and then seen in the order of their arrival.

E) Patients with similar procedures and examinations are scheduled in a specific block of time, sometimes only on specified days.

95. Which of the following medications can cause bradycardia?

A) beta blockers

B) insulin

C) levothyroxine

D) aspirin

E) albuterol

96. Which of the following describes the proper technique for performing infant CPR?

A) The femoral artery is checked for a pulse following each cycle of CPR.

B) Chest compression depth should be approximately 1.5 inches, or 4 cm.

C) A single rescuer should use three fingers on the dominant hand to do compressions.

D) The infant should be placed facedown on the forearm with the hand supporting the head and jaw.

E) CPR should be started as soon as the emergency response system has been activated.

97. Cholecystitis is which of the following?

A) infection in the urinary bladder

B) inflammation of the urinary bladder

C) inflammation of the lymph nodes

D) infection of the lymph nodes

E) inflammation of the gallbladder

98. The physician assistant has ordered acetaminophen 650 mg for a fifteen-year-old patient with a fever. How many 325-mg acetaminophen tablets should be given to the patient?

A) one

B) one and a half

C) two

D) two and a half

E) three

99. When communicating with a patient in a wheelchair, the medical assistant SHOULD:

   A) sit or squat to be at eye level with the patient.

   B) pat the patient on the head or shoulder to provide reassurance.

   C) speak loudly and clearly to the patient.

   D) lock the wheels on the wheelchair.

   E) ask the patient if they are comfortable.

100. Which of the following patients may NOT give informed consent?

   A) a twelve-year-old patient with a closed fracture of the ulna

   B) a seventeen-year-old patient seeking treatment for a sexually transmitted infection

   C) a pregnant minor

   D) an emancipated minor

   E) a married minor

101. Which of the following used items should be disposed of in a biohazard container?

   A) Used gloves

   B) Packaging

   C) Normal saline bag and connected IV tubing

   D) Suction containers with fluid inside the container

   E) Medical exam table paper

102. Which of the following laboratory tests is done to monitor patients taking warfarin?

   A) CBC

   B) PT/INR

   C) BMP

   D) BNP

   E) UA

103. Which of the following is NOT true of glucose monitoring?

   A) The center of a finger should be used for skin punctures in adults.

   B) The heel should be used for skin puncture in infants.

   C) A glucose level of 34 mg/dL should be reported immediately to the nurse.

   D) Lancets should be placed in the sharps container after use.

   E) Glucose monitors should be calibrated regularly.

104. Which of the following is the designated amount of money that some medical insurance plans require patients to pay at the time of service?

   A) deductibles

   B) co-payments

   C) balances

   D) partial payments

   E) coinsurance

105. The medical assistant has given a patient an injection and then notes that the sharps container is full. Which is the correct action by the medical assistant?

   A) exchange the full container for a new one

   B) place the syringe on top of the container so it will not roll off

   C) force the syringe into the top of the container as well as it will fit

   D) put the syringe into her pocket and dispose of it in another room

   E) place the syringe in an available trash can

106. The medical assistant answers a call to the medical office and receives a bomb threat. Which of the following is NOT an appropriate action from the medical assistant?

   A) assume the caller is making a real threat

B) follow facility protocol to ensure patient and staff safety

C) try to find out where the bomb is and when it will go off

D) alert the charge nurse, security, and the police department

E) evacuate patients, starting with those who are most mobile

107. Which of the following foods should a patient diagnosed with gastroesophageal reflux disease (GERD) avoid?

A) bananas

B) tomatoes

C) white bread

D) grilled salmon

E) steel-cut oatmeal

108. Which process involves externally tapping onto body structures and listening for the correlating sound to assess their density?

A) observation

B) palpation

C) percussion

D) auscultation

E) mensuration

109. An electrocardiogram (ECG) can be used to diagnose which of the following conditions?

A) diabetes

B) torn ligaments

C) cancer

D) tachycardia

E) influenza

110. Which of the following is a side effect of prednisone that should be immediately reported to the health care provider?

A) increased appetite

B) anxiety or confusion

C) strong, bounding pulses

D) weight gain of three pounds

E) nausea

111. Which of the following directional terms means "closest to the point of attachment"?

A) distal

B) proximal

C) lateral

D) medial

E) posterior

112. What is the first step for a patient to take when collecting a clean-catch urine sample?

A) Wash their hands

B) Void the first half of the urine into the toilet

C) Put on gloves

D) Clean the urinary meatus

E) Collect urine in urine specimen cup

113. Which of the following actions falls within the medical assistant's scope of practice?

A) obtaining a stool sample

B) prescribing medications

C) removing a patient from a ventilator

D) triaging patients in an emergency department

E) interpreting an ECG readout

114. Which part of PPE is kept on until after leaving the patient's room?

A) Gloves

B) Respirator

C) Gown

D) Face shield

E) Bouffant cap

115. An accurate equipment maintenance log is a legally required document:

A) for insurance purposes, and it may be subpoenaed if a patient was injured due to an equipment failure.

B) for warranty coverage to prove that regular maintenance occurred if the equipment should fail and need replacing.

C) for safety reasons in case an employee is injured while operating the equipment.

D) to prove that it has been maintained regularly for insurance replacement coverage in a case of loss.

E) for proof of office policy compliance.

116. Skeletal muscle is attached to bone by:

A) ligaments.

B) cartilage.

C) tendons.

D) nerves.

E) fascia.

117. An itemized form listing CPT and ICD-10-CM codes in which the physician will indicate the services rendered for submission to the payer is called a(n):

A) superbill.

B) provider form.

C) services form.

D) payer form.

E) insurance form.

118. A patient with slow blood clotting likely has low numbers of:

A) red blood cells.

B) plasma.

C) platelets.

D) hemoglobin.

E) white blood cells.

119. Which of the following patients is at the highest risk of developing pressure ulcers?

A) a twenty-seven-year-old patient who fractured her arm playing volleyball

B) a six-year-old patient on pelvic skin traction for muscle spasms

C) a forty-two-year-old obese patient with controlled atrial fibrillation who uses a wheelchair

D) a seventy-year-old patient with heart failure who uses a cane for ambulation in the room and hall

E) a thirty-five-year-old pregnant patient on bed rest

120. Which laboratory result will be elevated when a patient has renal failure?

A) hemoglobin

B) hematocrit

C) white blood cell

D) BUN and creatinine

E) blood glucose

121. A patient diagnosed with C. diff has soiled the bed, and the medical assistant is preparing to change it. Which of the following BEST describes how the soiled linens should be disposed of?

A) throw the linens in the trash can in the soiled utility room

B) leave the dirty linens in a bag in the patient's room until he is discharged

C) place the items in a red biohazard bag and place them in the soiled utility room

D) place the soiled linen in a regular dirty linen bag and place in the soiled utility room

E) rinse the soiled linens before placing them in a soiled linen bag

122. Which of the following is a common side effect of the drug levothyroxine taken for hypothyroidism?

A) weight loss

B) weight gain

C) light sensitivity

D) excessive sleepiness

E) dehydration

123. A seventy-year-old male is found unresponsive in the hallway. What should the medical assistant do first?

A) listen for breathing

B) feel for a pulse

C) assess his airway

D) check his blood pressure

E) check his temperature

124. The medical assistant is caring for a patient who adheres to a lacto-vegetarian diet. What is the BEST meal tray to deliver to this patient?

A) chicken sandwich, brown rice, yogurt, and milk

B) steamed vegetables with rice and apple slices

C) scrambled eggs, cottage cheese, dry toast, and milk

D) baked fish with roasted potatoes

E) baked zucchini, spinach salad with cheese, and yogurt

125. When dealing with an angry patient, the medical assistant should:

A) get angry and be aggressive.

B) speak loudly to ensure that he is heard.

C) remain calm and use a normal tone and volume of voice.

D) get defensive.

E) be passive, withdrawn, and quiet.

126. What is the appropriate FIRST action for a membrane exposure?

A) Alert the physician

B) Dispose of the sample

C) Call 911

D) File an incident report

E) Flush the area for 10 minutes using water or saline

127. A hospital patient has an NPO dietary order in place. The medical assistant sees him eating food brought in by his family. The medical assistant SHOULD:

A) bring a cup of water to the patient.

B) tell the patient's family that they must leave.

C) alert the nurse that the patient has been eating.

D) tell the patient that he can only eat food provided by the hospital.

E) take the food from the patient.

128. Drug samples left by a pharmaceutical representative should be placed

A) in the physician's office.

B) in the exam rooms.

C) in a locked cabinet or drawer.

D) in a cupboard in the reception area.

E) in a cupboard in the clinical area.

129. Which of the following is an accounts receivable report that lists unpaid customer debt in specific date ranges?

A) age analysis

B) diagnosis-related groups

C) relative value units

D) fee schedule

E) day sheet

130. Which term describes the position of the right ear relative to the right eye?

A) proximal

B) distal

C) medial

D) lateral

E) ventral

131. The common cold, influenza, and HIV are caused by which type of infectious agent?

A) bacteria

B) protozoan

C) virus

D) helminth

E) fungus

132. Which vitamin is important in blood clotting?

A) vitamin A

B) vitamin K

C) vitamin B

D) vitamin C

E) vitamin D

133. Clonazepam (Klonopin) is categorized as which type of medication?

A) proton pump inhibitor

B) blood thinner

C) antibiotic

D) antipyretic

E) benzodiazepine

134. A fifty-year-old construction worker presents to the ER with a forearm laceration. The blood spurts in a pulsatile rhythm from the wound when the dressing is removed. Which type of blood vessel injury is likely?

A) arterial

B) venous

C) capillary

D) aorta

E) jugular

135. A 2-year-old patient keeps trying to pull out his central line. What type of restraint is most likely to be used?

A) Chemical restraint

B) Belt restraint

C) Vest restraint

D) Enclosure bed

E) Elbow splints

136. According to Drug Enforcement Agency regulations, a medical assistant can only administer a controlled substance:

A) under a physician's direct order and supervision.

B) whenever there is a standing protocol.

C) if a patient requests a medication.

D) if a patient is out of their home medications.

E) if over-the-counter medication has not worked.

137. Which method of patient scheduling provides built-in flexibility to accommodate unforeseen situations and involves scheduling three or four patients at the top of each hour?

A) specified time scheduling

B) double-booking

C) grouping procedures

D) open office hours

E) wave scheduling

138. While verifying a patient's identity, the medical assistant notes that the date of birth on the patient's wristband is incorrect. The medical assistant SHOULD:

A) proceed after the patient verbally states their correct date of birth.

B) cross out the date with a permanent marker and initial the change.

C) tell the patient to ask for a new wristband.

D) alert a nurse so the discrepancy can be resolved.

E) take the patient's wristband and dispose of it.

139. Money owed to a business's creditors is called:

A) accounts receivable.

B) accounts payable.

C) debits.

D) credits.

E) liabilities.

140. What is the role of monocytes in wounds?

A) They increase blood clotting.

B) They release histamines.

C) They digest pathogens.

D) They prevent inflammation.

E) They store information about previously encountered pathogens.

141. Which of the following actions does NOT require the use of standard precautions?

A) contact with blood

B) contact with urine

C) contact with sweat

D) contact with vomit

E) contact with skin

142. Which of the following symptoms, identified by a female patient, is most consistent with a myocardial infarction (MI)?

A) palpitations

B) lower extremity swelling

C) uncomfortable feeling of pressure in the chest

D) nausea

E) difficulty breathing

143. Which diet should be followed by a fifty-five-year-old male diagnosed with gout?

A) soft diet

B) diabetic diet

C) clear liquid diet

D) low-purine diet

E) high-protein diet

144. Which of the following describes an adjustment?

A) posting charges for services rendered

B) posting third-party payments

C) posting payments made by the patient

D) any changes in the patient's financial account unrelated to charges or payments

E) any changes in the patient's financial account related to either charges or payments

145. Which of the following medications is prescribed to patients at high risk for deep vein thrombosis (DVT)?

A) sildenafil citrate (Viagra)

B) celecoxib (Celebrex)

C) zolpidem (Ambien)

D) topiramate (Topamax)

E) rivaroxaban (Xarelto)

146. Which of the following patients has a partial-thickness burn?

A) seventeen-year-old female with sunburn on her face with no blistering present

B) three-year-old male with painful blisters on his face from pulling a pot of hot water off the stove

C) twenty-five-year-old male with charred full-thickness burns to his hands sustained during a house fire

D) forty-five-year-old female with superficial, red, painful burns without blistering on her left hand

E) sixty-year-old female who reports a deep, painless burn from prolonged exposure to household drain cleaner

147. Which injury is INCORRECTLY described?

A) A joint dislocation occurs when the bone shifts from its natural position.

B) A sprain is damage to muscles and tendons.

C) A fracture is a break or injury to a bone.

D) A strain is damage to muscles and tendons.

E) A contusion is bruising to the tissues.

148. Examples of proper telephone etiquette include:

A) being polite and professional.

B) being friendly, casual, and conversational.

C) being angry and aggressive.

D) being passive, withdrawn, and quiet.

E) speaking loudly to ensure that you are heard.

149. Which of the following is an open-ended question the medical assistant could use to engage a patient?

A) "Are you hungry?"

B) "Do you watch TV?"

C) "How is your day so far?"

D) "Did you have a bowel movement today?"

E) "I would like to discuss your current symptoms."

150. The medical assistant should carefully document any patient cancellations or no-shows in the schedule and the patient's medical record to protect the physician from potential charges related to:

A) malpractice.

B) assault and battery.

C) abandonment.

D) invasion of privacy.

E) bias.

151. Which of the following is NOT contained within a ventral cavity?

A) digestive system

B) reproductive system

C) heart and lungs

D) kidneys

E) spinal cord

152. Which of the following is an example of transmission of an infectious agent through direct contact?

A) kissing an infected person

B) inhaling droplets from a sneezing infected person

C) an infected person coughing near a susceptible host

D) eating contaminated food

E) inhaling microorganisms in the air

153. Which of the following is NOT objective patient data?

A) pulse

B) temperature

C) chief complaint

D) blood pressure

E) respiratory rate

154. Which is NOT on the clear liquid diet?

A) broth

B) water

C) gelatin

D) popsicles

E) milk

155. Which location is a recommended blood draw site?

A) underside of wrist

B) antecubital fossa

C) ankles

D) same side of prior mastectomy

E) feet

156. A patient starting rosuvastatin calcium (Crestor) should be warned about all of the following side effects EXCEPT:

A) muscle pain.

B) headaches.

C) abdominal pain.

D) dizziness.

E) fever.

157. While assisting the surgeon with an emergency appendectomy in the operating room, the surgical assistant removed all jewelry before washing his hands and then applied a sterile gown and gloves. He carefully opened sterilized instruments and gauze onto the surgical tray. He then stepped away from the sterile field to sneeze. When the assistant turned back toward the table, he touched the sterile field with the back of his gown. Which of the following is a break in sterile technique?

A) removing jewelry prior to handwashing

B) donning sterile gown and gloves

C) inspecting instruments for sterile indicators

D) stepping away from the sterile field to sneeze

E) touching the sterile field with the back of his gown

158. Which of the following actions should the medical assistant perform to assess the airway in an unconscious patient?

A) head tilt and chin lift

B) jaw thrust

C) finger sweep

D) wait for paramedics to assess the airway

E) obtain a pulse oximetry reading

159. When questioning a patient through an interpreter, questions should be directed toward:

A) the interpreter.

B) the physician.

C) the patient's family.

D) other colleagues.

E) the patient.

160. Which of the following is an order to appear in court?

A) arbitration

B) deposition

C) tort

D) mediation

E) subpoena

161. Which of the following scheduling methods is used by urgent care facilities where patients are seen in the order of their arrival?

A) specified time

B) open office hours

C) wave scheduling

D) grouping

E) double-booking

162. In medical coding, what does a CPT code represent?

A) new patients

B) diagnoses

C) procedures

D) symptoms

E) abnormal laboratory results

163. Which of the following terms describes an excessive posterior curvature of the thoracic spine?

A) kyphosis

B) lordosis

C) scoliosis

D) acidosis

E) bad posture

164. Smoking and drinking habits are recorded in which portion of the patient's medical chart?

A) social history

B) chief complaint

C) history of present illness

D) past medical history

E) past surgical history

165. At what angle should the needle enter the skin during venipuncture?

A) 5 degrees

B) 10 degrees

C) 30 degrees

D) 60 degrees

E) 90 degrees

166. Which of the following is the class of drugs used to inhibit growth of or kill bacteria?

   A) antibiotics

   B) antihistamines

   C) calcium channel blockers

   D) antidepressants

   E) anticonvulsants

167. A forty-five-year-old male was playing baseball with his son. When he slid on the ground, he felt a "pop" and pain in the back of his right thigh. Since then, he has had tenderness to the posterior right thigh that is worse when walking. Which muscle did he likely injure?

   A) trapezius

   B) biceps

   C) pectoralis

   D) oblique

   E) hamstring

168. Which of the following is the ratio of chest compressions to breaths during single-provider CPR on an adult?

   A) 100:2

   B) 15:2

   C) 20:2

   D) 30:2

   E) 20:10

169. What is the most appropriate way for a medical assistant to handle conflict with coworkers in the medical office?

   A) take the issue directly to the physician in charge

   B) do not escalate the situation

   C) refuse to come to work until the situation is resolved

   D) take sides and defend his position

   E) ask for his coworkers' opinions to resolve the conflict based on what they witnessed

170. Salmeterol is used primarily to:

   A) prevent asthma attacks and bronchospasms.

   B) lower fevers and treat inflammation.

   C) treat autoimmune disorders.

   D) modulate estrogen levels.

   E) lower blood pressure.

171. Which of the following actions is upcoding?

   A) uploading diagnostic codes into a computerized billing software system

   B) uploading procedure codes into a computerized billing software system

   C) fraudulent billing by using a CPT code for a more expensive service than what was performed

   D) mistakenly using a billing code with a higher numeric value than the one intended

   E) submission of a billing code to a third-party payer

172. The carotid pulse can be palpated at which of the following locations on the body?

   A) the anterior wrist

   B) lateral to the trachea

   C) below the medial biceps tendon

   D) in the groin

   E) on the dorsum of the foot

173. After cleaning the intended venipuncture site with isopropyl alcohol, how long should the skin air-dry prior to venipuncture?

   A) ten seconds

   B) twenty seconds

   C) thirty seconds

D) one minute

E) five minutes

174. The withdrawal syndrome after stopping benzodiazepines is which type of adverse drug reaction?

A) augmented

B) bizarre

C) chronic

D) delayed

E) end of use

175. Which condition is NOT correctly paired with its recommended diet?

A) diabetes: diabetic diet

B) hyperlipidemia: low-cholesterol diet

C) hypertension: high-sodium diet

D) diarrhea: clear liquid diet

E) gallbladder disease: low-fat diet

176. Before having blood drawn for a fasting test, a patient informs the medical assistant that they drank water 2 hours ago. What should the medical assistant do?

A) alert the medical provider who ordered the draw

B) reschedule the testing for a different date

C) draw the labs but make a note in the patient's chart

D) have the patient wait an additional 6 hours

E) proceed with the ordered lab work

177. Which of the following statements about personal protective equipment (PPE) is NOT correct?

A) Hands do not need to be washed before putting on gloves.

B) A face shield is worn when there is likelihood of bodily fluid splashes.

C) Fluid-resistant gowns should be removed after leaving a patient's room.

D) PPE devices protect the mucous membranes.

E) PPE devices include gloves, gowns, eye shields, and masks.

178. Which procedure code set should be used when billing Medicaid or Medicare?

A) CPT

B) modifiers

C) add-ons

D) HCPCS

E) ICD

179. Gas exchange in the lungs occurs in which of the following structures?

A) bronchi

B) pulmonary artery

C) bronchioles

D) aorta

E) alveoli

180. Which type of waste is NOT matched with its correct disposal container?

A) capillary tubes: sharps container

B) feces: toilet

C) gauze with small amount of blood: regular garbage can

D) urine: poured down the drain

E) linen heavily soiled by blood: dirty linen receptacle

181. Which of the following describes tachypnea?

A) twelve to twenty breaths per minute

B) eighteen breaths per minute

C) fewer than twelve breaths per minute

D) more than twenty breaths per minute

E) fewer than twenty breaths per minute

182. Which of the following urine specimens is used specifically for diabetic screening?

A) random specimen

B) clean catch midstream specimen

C) two-hour postprandial urine

D) twenty-four-hour specimen

E) pediatric urine specimen

183. A 0.4 mg nitroglycerin sublingual tablet should be administered by which of the following methods?

A) placed on the skin via a patch

B) placed under the tongue and allowed to absorb

C) placed into the eye via drops

D) taken by mouth and swallowed

E) injected into the subcutaneous tissue

184. A fifteen-year-old thin female presents to the clinic with extreme fatigue, increased urination most noticeably at night, and extreme thirst. Which test might be ordered by the provider in triage?

A) hemoglobin A1C

B) fingerstick glucose

C) chest X-ray

D) visual acuity

E) abdominal ultrasound

185. Which type of white blood cells attack parasites?

A) neutrophils

B) eosinophils

C) B cells

D) T cells

E) macrophages

186. An elderly patient has a blood pressure of 140/90 when sitting. Her blood pressure when standing is 100/60. Which term describes her condition?

A) bradycardia

B) orthostatic hypotension

C) hypertension

D) syncope

E) tachycardia

187. Which of the following should a patient NOT do before a sputum culture?

A) use antibacterial mouthwash

B) use antibacterial hand soap

C) wear restrictive clothing

D) take an antihistamine

E) take acetaminophen

188. Which of the following angles and needle gauges is used to inject a medication into the dermal skin layer?

A) 45 – 90 degrees, 22 – 25 gauge

B) 90 degrees, 18 – 23 gauge

C) 15 degrees, 25 – 27 gauge

D) 30 degrees, 18 gauge

E) 45 degrees, 22 gauge

189. A large skin laceration over the site of a fractured bone can be a sign of which type of fracture?

A) closed fracture

B) compression fracture

C) oblique fracture

D) open fracture

E) stable fracture

190. Human immunodeficiency virus (HIV) attacks which of the following cells?

A) white blood cells

B) red blood cells

C) platelets

D) B cells

E) T cells

191. An asthmatic patient presents with cough, wheezing, and shortness of breath that has been worsening for the past few days. Which type of medication will the provider likely order?

A) warfarin

B) acetaminophen

C) albuterol

D) lorazepam

E) famotidine

192. Pulse oximetry can be measured on a patient at all of the following locations EXCEPT:

A) a finger.

B) the abdomen.

C) the great toe.

D) an earlobe.

E) an infant foot.

193. An RSV (respiratory syncytial virus) swab on a three-month-old is obtained using a:

A) throat swab.

B) nasopharyngeal swab.

C) genital swab.

D) wound culture swab.

E) breath test.

194. Which of the following should be used when drawing up medication from a single-use ampule?

A) filtered needle

B) butterfly needle

C) 21-gauge beveled needle

D) 27-gauge beveled needle

E) IV start kit

195. Which endocrine gland is NOT correctly matched to its function?

A) adrenal: fight-or-flight response, regulation of salt and blood volume

B) pituitary: growth, temperature regulation, reproductive function

C) parathyroid: metabolic use, hunger and thirst

D) ovaries: maturation of sex organs, pregnancy, lactations

E) thyroid: metabolism, energy use

196. A Pap smear collects cells from the:

A) heart.

B) skin.

C) cervix.

D) stomach lining.

E) lung.

197. A specimen is placed onto a microscopic slide, then a drop of water is applied and covered with a coverslip. This is an example of which type of specimen collection?

A) wet mount

B) wound culture

C) nasopharyngeal swab

D) blood culture

E) urinalysis

198. 5 cc is equivalent to how many milliliters?

A) 2.5

B) 5

C) 7.5

D) 10

E) 15

199. After a Pap smear, the specimen is placed into a liquid-base cytology container. All of the following information must be on the label EXCEPT:

A) vital signs.

B) the patient's name.

C) date of birth.

D) medical record number.

E) date of last menstrual cycle.

200. How is silence an effective therapeutic response when communicating with patients?

A) It is not therapeutic; it implies that the medical assistant is not listening.

B) It encourages the patient to keep her feelings to herself.

C) It allows the patient time to think and reflect and lead the conversation.

D) It allows the medical assistant to think about other tasks she needs to perform for the patient.

E) It helps the patient feel in control of the situation and her health.

Follow the link below to access your online study resources:

www.ascenciatestprep.com/medical-assistant-online-resources

ANSWER KEY

1. **D)** Using the wrong size blood pressure cuff can provide an inaccurate reading.

2. **A)** A severe fever (a temperature higher than 104°F, or 40 °C) should be immediately reported to the nurse.

3. **A)** Patient cycle time is the length of time that the average patient spends in the medical office, from when they enter to when they leave the office, including wait time.

4. **A)** The palm of the hand is distal (away from the trunk) relative to the elbow.

5. **D)** A colposcopy is a painless gynecological procedure, usually done after an abnormal Pap smear. Putting the patient in the lithotomy position, in which the patient is on their back with hips and knees flexed, allows the provider to access the cervix.

6. **B)** Crutches should hit 1 – 2 inches below a patient's armpits.

7. **A)** The Holter monitor should be kept dry and cannot be worn while swimming or bathing.

8. **C)** In the dipstick portion of a urinalysis, a dipstick placed into a urine sample tests for pH, RBC, glucose, and ketones. The microscopic portion of the urinalysis may be helpful in identifying bacteria, blood cells, parasites, and tumor cells.

9. **E)** Safety is the top priority during seizure activity, so the medical assistant should remove any objects in the immediate area that may cause the patient harm.

10. **A)** Following binges with the use of laxatives or diuretics is a diagnostic criterion for bulimia. The other statements are true.

11. **B)** Neuropathy is a disease or dysfunction of one or more peripheral nerves, typically causing numbness and weakness.

12. **D)** The tibia is a lower leg bone.

13. **A)** Taking folic acid before and during pregnancy aids in preventing brain and spine birth defects.

14. **D)** Pregabalin (Lyrica) is prescribed to patients with epilepsy to help prevent seizures.

15. **D)** The first action is to notify the health care provider for further orders.

16. **D)** Leukocytosis is elevated white blood cells.

17. **B)** Sutures should be cut immediately under the knot during removal. This allows the least amount of skin surface contamination to be dragged through the inside of the wound when the suture is pulled out.

18. **D)** The HCPCS (Health Care Common Procedure Coding System) level II is an alphanumeric code set that primarily includes non-physician-related services such as ambulance charges and prosthetic devices.

19. **B)** Influenza is spread primarily by droplets. Droplet precautions focus on diseases that are spread by large droplets (greater than 5 microns) expelled into the air and by being within 3 feet of a patient.

20. **D)** Classic signs of cardiogenic shock include a rapid pulse that weakens; cool, clammy skin; and decreased urine output. Hypotension is another classic sign.

21. **B)** The medical assistant should always get clarification from the prescribing physician.

22. **C)** A very brief, preferably quoted statement of the patient that is entered into the medical record giving the purpose of the office visit or hospitalization is called the chief complaint.

23. **A)** It is important to always change gloves after removing an old or dirty dressing. Before applying a new dressing, the medical assistant should change into a new set of gloves to prevent contamination.

24. **B)** Bias is showing an unfair preference or dislike of a specific group of people.

25. **A)** Helicobacter pylori (or H. pylori) is a stomach infection usually found in patients with gastric ulcers.

26. **C)** Petechial rash and fever are signs of meningitis, which is a medical emergency, especially in an infant.

27. **B)** Thrombocytopenia is a deficiency in the number of platelets.

28. **D)** Needles should be placed intact into the nearest puncture-resistant container.

29. **E)** This child is now due for the third round of the hepatitis B and DTaP vaccines.

30. **A)** The V1 lead should be placed at the fourth intercostal space to the right of the sternum.

31. **B)** ICD (International Classification of Diseases, 10th revision, Clinical Modification is the current version) codes are diagnosis codes used for billing purposes.

32. **D)** 1 kilogram is equal to 2.2 pounds: $4.3 \times 2.2 = 9.46$

33. **C)** People with anorexia generally avoid food to such an extreme degree that they are unable to maintain healthy body fat or necessary nutrient levels.

34. **B)** Never perform a blind sweep of the airway since this may cause the object to become further lodged into the airway.

35. **D)** Lithotripsy is a procedure to crush a stone (e.g., kidney stones).

36. **D)** Any corrections to the chart will need to be done with a timed and dated addendum.

37. **A)** A modifier is a two-character suffix attached to a category I CPT code with a hyphen. It provides supplemental information and is found in the appendix of the CPT code manual. The functionality modifier directly affects reimbursement and should be used first; the informational modifier is second.

38. **A)** Iron plays an important role in the ability of hemoglobin to carry oxygen. When a patient has iron deficiency anemia, their body cannot carry oxygen to the cells and tissues very well. This is why anemic patients often feel short of breath or chronically tired.

39. **C)** An autoclave uses a steam heat at high temperature and high pressure to sterilize equipment. The equipment is wrapped and closed with sterilized tape prior to sterilization.

40. **D)** Diuretic medication is used to lower a patient's blood pressure.

41. **D)** The Centers for Disease Control and Prevention recommends the skin test be read forty-eight to seventy-two hours after administration. Results read after seventy-two hours are not accurate, and another skin test should be conducted.

42. **A)** Tympanometry measures how the eardrum moves and responds to sounds under different pressures.

43. **D)** Typical multidose vials must be used or discarded within twenty-eight days of opening.

44. **A)** These are symptoms of shock. Shock can be cardiogenic (from the heart), an allergic reaction, hypovolemic (lots of vomiting or blood loss), septic (infection), or neurogenic (a brain injury).

45. **A)** Any changes in responsiveness or mental status should be reported to the nurse.

46. **B)** A date-labeled file organized so the medical assistant knows what actions should be taken on future dates is called a tickler file.

47. **E)** Medicare is the federal health insurance program that covers people sixty-five or older, younger people with disabilities, and people with end-stage renal disease.

48. **A)** The large intestine is responsible for most of the WATER absorption. The majority of nutrient absorption is performed in the small intestine.

49. **C)** Washing hands is sufficient, since taking a patient's blood pressure does not involve contact with blood or secretions.

50. **B)** To measure length, place the infant supine on the exam table.

51. **A)** Patients with osteoporosis need calcium supplements to promote bone health.

52. **C)** Eyesight is recorded as OU (both eyes), OD (right eye), OS (left eye). Remember: yOU look with BOTH eyes. The RIGHT meds will not OD. The only one LEFT is OS.

53. **E)** Based on directives from the American Red Cross, when confronted with a conscious, choking person who is unable to cough, speak, or breathe, the medical assistant should first send someone to call 911, then lean the person forward and give five back blows with the heel of their hand. If that is ineffective, the Heimlich maneuver should be performed to remove the obstruction.

54. **C)** A nephrologist specializes in the care and treatment of the kidneys.

55. **D)** A normal BMI is 18.5 – 24.9. A person with a BMI of < 15 is severely underweight, and > 40 is morbidly obese.

56. **E)** A surgical opening of the skull is called a craniotomy.

57. **B)** A phlebotomist is a medical professional trained to draw blood.

58. **E)** Objective notes are the portion of a SOAP note that includes information the health care provider has observed or measured.

59. **E)** A specified amount of money that the insured must pay before the insurance will begin to pay claims is called a deductible.

60. **D)** Connective tissue, such as bones, ligaments, and cartilage, supports, separates, and connects the body's organs and structures.

61. **E)** Ringworm is a fungal infection, not a parasitic infection.

62. **A)** In atrial flutter, there are no discernible P waves, and a distinct sawtooth wave pattern is present. The atrial rate is regular, and the PR interval is not measurable.

63. **E)** The stethoscope is placed over the brachial pulse (near the antecubital fossa) as the cuff is inflated and then slowly deflated.

64. **E)** A patient with A1C levels of > 6.5% is considered to have diabetes; patients who do not have diabetes should have an A1C of < 5.7%.

65. **B)** Seizures are a serious, adverse drug effect that may occur when taking dextroamphetamine. Nausea and constipation are common side effects but are not considered adverse drug effects.

66. **A)** Triage works on the principle that patients with the highest acuity have priority over patients with injuries or conditions that are not considered life-threatening. Chest pain and nausea indicate a possible myocardial infarction, which can be life-threatening and requires immediate intervention.

67. **B)** Lingual means "pertaining to, near, or next to the tongue."

68. **A)** In the Trendelenburg position, the patient is reclined with their feet higher than their head.

69. **A)** The pulmonary artery carries deoxygenated blood from the right ventricle into the lungs.

70. **E)** The medical assistant should listen to the patient's concerns and provide emotional support.

71. **C)** A rectal temperature is taken in infants and children under 3 years old to ensure an accurate measurement.

72. **B)** Melena is black or tarry stool, which results from bleeding in the stomach or upper GI tract. It should be reported to the nurse immediately.

73. **A)** A Health Maintenance Organization (HMO) is a type of health insurance group that contracts, for a relatively low cost, with health care providers who act as primary care physicians and are known as "gatekeepers" because it is necessary to obtain a referral from them to see a specialist. Any health care providers seen by the patient must be a preapproved "in-network" provider.

74. **C)** When a patient is seizing, the medical assistant should remove any surrounding objects that could injure the patient during the seizure. The patient should not be restrained, nor should anything be put in their mouth. The medical assistant should not begin CPR unless there is no pulse or the patient is not breathing. After the seizure, the patient should be moved into the recovery position on their side.

75. **C)** White blood cells, or leukocytes, play an important role in fighting an infection. A patient with a dangerous blood infection such as sepsis will have a markedly elevated white blood cell count (WBC). This is called leukocytosis.

76. **D)** White is indicative of a contact hazard.

77. **C)** The chief complaint is the problem or symptom the patient describes as the reason for the visit.

78. **A)** Eye irrigation can be uncomfortable for a patient. It is much more tolerable if the surface of the patient's eye has been numbed with anesthetic drops.

79. **C)** The red tube contains clot activator. The gray tube contains sodium fluoride.

80. **C)** Results of the allergy test should be recorded after fifteen minutes.

81. **D)** The provider will recommend the child receive the third vaccine at the earliest convenience, as it should be routinely administered any time from six to nineteen months of age.

82. **A)** MMR, VAR, ZVL, and MMRV should be stored in the freezer (−50 to −15°C).

83. **D)** A cerebrovascular accident, or stroke, can cause weakness to one side of the body and face.

84. **C)** The medical assistant can assist the patient in changing their physiologic response by directing them to take deep breaths. This directive will help the patient focus on the present moment and help to alleviate the panic.

85. **C)** A skin avulsion is a tearing of the most superficial skin layer.

86. **C)** When a patient rolls up their sleeve and offers their arm for a blood draw, this is an example of implied consent.

87. **C)** An asset is something that is useful or valuable to a company, such as a building or equipment.

88. **A)** Health care–related surfaces and equipment should be cleaned with sodium hypochlorite (bleach).

89. **E)** The SA node, or sinoatrial node, is the intrinsic pacemaker. It typically sets the heart rate between 60 – 100 beats per minute and is located in the right atrium.

90. **E)** Decreasing sodium intake is an effective way to reduce blood pressure in a patient with hypertension.

91. **E)** In a lithotomy position, the patient will be on their back with their feet in stirrups. This is a common position for a pelvic exam or vaginal delivery.

92. **A)** The V5 lead should be placed in the left midaxillary line.

93. **C)** Stool samples will need to be collected on three different days.

94. **C)** Double-booking is a scheduling method in which patients are scheduled for the same time slot. This method is considered to be ineffective but sometimes unavoidable.

95. **A)** Beta blockers are known to cause a slowing in heart rate.

96. **B)** CPR on infants less than one year old includes a chest compression depth of approximately 1.5 in, or 4 cm.

97. **E)** Cholecystitis is inflammation of the gallbladder.

98. **C)** Two tablets of 325-mg acetaminophen are equal to 650 mg of acetaminophen (650/325 = 2).

99. **A)** The medical assistant should sit or squat when talking with a patient in a wheelchair to be at their eye level.

100. **A)** A minor with a nonemergent medical condition cannot give informed consent. Consent must be given by the patient's guardian.

101. **D)** Suction containers with any fluid collected should be disposed of in a red biohazard container. In general, waste products soaked or dripping with blood, or equipment that can drip bodily fluids if compressed, should be placed in a biohazard container.

102. **B)** PT and INR are laboratory tests that evaluate how long it takes for a person's blood to clot. Patients on warfarin will have elevated PT/INR.

103. **A)** Use the side of the fingertip for skin puncture, not the center. The center of the fingertip has more nerve endings, and skin punctures to this area are more painful for the patient.

104. **B)** Co-payments are designated amounts of money that some medical insurance plans require patients to pay at the time of service.

105. **A)** The full container should be replaced with a new one.

106. **E)** The nurse should not evacuate or move patients until directed to do so by security or police; they can determine the safest area if evacuation is necessary.

107. **B)** The nurse should instruct the patient to eat a low-fat, high-fiber diet, avoiding acidic foods. Tomatoes are highly acidic, and consumption of tomatoes or tomato-based sauces can worsen the symptoms of GERD.

108. **C)** Percussion involves tapping on the outside of a structure, such as the lung or abdomen, to determine its density (solid, fluid-filled, air-filled).

109. **D)** Tachycardia is an abnormally fast heart rate, and electrocardiograms show the electrical activity of the heart.

110. **B)** Side effects of prednisone include hypokalemia (low potassium). Anxiety, confusion, and lethargy are signs of hypokalemia and should be reported.

111. **B)** A directional term for "closest to the point of attachment" is proximal.

112. **A)** Patients should wash their hands before collecting a clean-catch urine sample.

113. **A)** Obtaining a stool sample from the patient is within the scope of practice of a medical assistant.

114. **B)** Remove all PPE before exiting the patient's room EXCEPT a respirator mask. This should be taken off after leaving the room and closing the door.

115. **A)** An accurate equipment maintenance log is often a legally required document for insurance purposes and may be subpoenaed if a patient was injured due to an equipment failure.

116. **C)** The skeletal muscles and the bone are attached by the tendons.

117. **A)** An itemized form listing CPT and ICD-10-CM codes in which the physician will indicate the services rendered to be submitted to the payer is called a superbill (also encounter form or charge slip).

118. **C)** Platelets, also known as thrombocytes, play an important role in blood clotting.

119. **B)** The patient in pelvic traction is on bed rest wearing a traction belt around the pelvis. This patient is the most immobile of the patients listed.

120. D) The kidneys filter the blood to remove waste products such as urea and creatinine, but if they are not working properly, these materials are not removed. This causes an elevation or buildup of BUN and creatinine in the blood.

121. C) C. diff is highly contagious, and soiled linens require special handling. The medical assistant should place all linens in a red biohazard bag and put them in the designated area for biohazard bags in the soiled utility area.

122. A) A side effect of levothyroxine is weight loss.

123. B) Initial order of assessment: circulation (feel for a pulse); check the airway; look and listen for breathing.

124. E) Lacto-vegetarians eat milk, cheese, and dairy but no meat, fish, poultry, or eggs.

125. C) When dealing with an angry patient the medical assistant should remain calm and use a typical tone and volume of voice.

126. E) A membrane exposure or splash should be flushed with water or normal saline. It is not a medical emergency. The sample may be tested for communicable diseases. An incident report should be completed.

127. C) Patients who are NPO should not consume any foods or liquids by mouth. The medical assistant should alert the nurse that the patient has been eating.

128. C) Drug samples left by a pharmaceutical representative should be placed in a locked cabinet or drawer.

129. A) An accounts receivable report that lists unpaid customer debt in specific date ranges and can help a billing department with collection time frames is called an age analysis or aging of accounts.

130. D) The ear is lateral to the eye because it is farther from the midline of the face or body than the eye.

131. C) Viruses are responsible for the common cold, influenza, and HIV (human immunodeficiency virus).

132. B) Vitamin K is essential in the blood-clotting process.

133. E) Clonazepam (Klonopin) is a benzodiazepine.

134. A) In an arterial bleed, bleeding is often pulsatile and spurting.

135. E) Elbow splints are used to prevent infants and children from scratching and touching tubes or incisions.

136. A) Medical assistants can only administer controlled substances under direct supervision of a physician.

137. E) The wave scheduling method provides built-in flexibility to accommodate unforeseen situations, such as patients who end up needing more time with the physician than was allocated, late-arriving patients, or no-shows. This method involves scheduling three or four patients at the top of each hour.

138. D) Proper confirmation of a patient's identity is an important part of patient care. The medical assistant should not proceed until the nurse has fixed the discrepancy.

139. B) Monies owed to a business's creditors are called accounts payable.

140. C) Monocytes use phagocytosis to "swallow" and break down pathogens.

141. C) Standard precautions are recommended whenever the nurse comes in contact with blood or body fluids that could transmit blood-borne pathogens.

142. C) An uncomfortable feeling of pressure, squeezing, fullness, or pain in the center of the chest is the predominant symptom of an MI in women.

143. D) Gout patients should be on a low-purine diet. When the body digests purine, it creates uric acid as a waste. If uric acid blood levels go up, patients can develop a condition called gout. Gout occurs when painful uric acid crystals build up in the joint (often the great toe).

144. D) An adjustment refers to any changes in the patient's financial account unrelated to charges or payments. The most common type of adjustment is a credit adjustment or insurance write-off, often as a professional courtesy or insurance discount.

145. E) Rivaroxaban (Xarelto) is a blood thinner that helps prevent clots and DVT.

146. B) Painful burns with blistering are seen with partial-thickness burns. There is no blistering with superficial burns. Full-thickness burns often have charred skin present.

147. B) A sprain involves ligament damage. A strain involves muscle and tendon damage.

148. A) Examples of proper telephone etiquette include being polite and professional.

149. C) Open-ended questions invite the patient to share feelings, thoughts or ideas; they are different from direct questions, which require only yes or no answers.

150. C) The patient schedule is a legal document, and medical assistants should carefully document any patient cancellations or no-shows in the schedule and in the patient's medical record to protect the physician from potential charges of patient abandonment and negligence.

151. **E)** The dorsal cavity contains the cranial and spinal cavities, both lined by meninges. The other organs are found in the ventral cavity.

152. **A)** Direct contact is the transmission of infectious agents through physical contact between two people, such as kissing.

153. **C)** The chief complaint is an example of subjective data, or data reported by the patient.

154. **E)** Milk is not considered a clear liquid.

155. **B)** In the antecubital fossa, the median cubital vein is a common site for a lab draw.

156. **E)** Fever is not a common side effect of cholesterol-lowering medications.

157. **E)** Only the front of the gown from the waist up and arms is considered sterile.

158. **A)** A head tilt/chin lift is the most common way to assess an airway. If a neck injury is suspected, a jaw thrust maneuver is instead recommended.

159. **E)** When questioning a patient through their interpreter, whether they cannot hear or do not speak English, one should always direct questions to the patient.

160. **E)** An order to appear in court is called a subpoena.

161. **B)** Urgent care facilities use the open office hours scheduling method, in which patients are seen in the order of their arrival.

162. **C)** CPT (current procedural terminology) codes are a numeric or alphanumeric medical code set, consisting of five characters, that is used to report medical, surgical, and diagnostic procedures and services to entities such as physicians, insurance companies, and accreditation organizations.

163. **A)** In patients with kyphosis, the upper back curves more than normal and can look rounded, humped, or hunched.

164. **A)** Social and occupational history details patients' habits, including tobacco use, alcohol use, drug use, occupation, and who lives with the patient (parents, spouse, etc.).

165. **C)** The needle should enter the skin at a 30-degree angle during venipuncture.

166. **A)** Antibiotics stop the growth of or kill bacteria.

167. **E)** The hamstring muscles are in the posterior thigh.

168. **D)** The ratio should be thirty chest compressions followed by two breaths for each cycle of single-provider CPR, with a goal rate of one hundred compressions/minute.

169. **B)** When attempting to resolve conflicts with coworkers or patients in the medical office the medical assistant should not escalate the situation.

170. **A)** Salmeterol prevents asthma attacks and bronchospasms.

171. **C)** Upcoding is a form of fraudulent billing using a CPT code for a more expensive service than what was performed.

172. **B)** The carotid pulse is palpable lateral to the trachea; both carotid pulses should not be measured at the same time.

173. **C)** The skin must air-dry for thirty seconds after cleansing.

174. **E)** Stopping a benzodiazepine (such as lorazepam) can cause an end-of-use adverse reaction or withdrawal symptoms because the body has become dependent on the medication.

175. **C)** Hypertensive patients should be on a LOW-sodium diet. Salt can increase blood pressure and should be avoided in the diet of a hypertensive patient when possible.

176. **E)** A patient may drink water before a fasting test. No additional steps are required.

177. **C)** Fluid-resistant gowns should be removed BEFORE leaving the patient's room to prevent spread of infection into the hallway.

178. **D)** Although the HCPCS level I code set is identical to the AMA's (American Medical Association) Current Procedural Terminology (CPT) code set, technically use of the Healthcare Common Procedure Coding System (HCPCS) is required when billing Medicaid or Medicare.

179. **E)** Alveoli are tiny air sacs at the ends of bronchioles. Their membrane is only one cell thick and is where oxygen is brought into the blood, as carbon dioxide is diffused out.

180. **E)** Linen that is lightly soiled can go in the dirty linen receptacle. However, linen that is heavily soiled by blood should be placed in a biohazard bag.

181. **D)** The normal respiratory rate is twelve to twenty breaths per minute. Tachypnea is abnormally rapid breathing, so more than twenty breaths per minute is considered tachypnea.

182. **C)** A two-hour postprandial urine is collected two hours after a meal to test for glycosuria.

183. **B)** Sublingual means "under the tongue." Nitroglycerin is often given this way. Ondansetron, a medication for nausea and vomiting, is also often administered sublingually.

184. B) This patient has signs of diabetes. A fingerstick glucose will screen for an elevated blood sugar.

185. B) Eosinophils are a type of white blood cell designed to attack multicellular parasites.

186. B) Orthostatic hypotension is a rapid drop in blood pressure when a patient changes position, from supine to sitting or sitting to standing. It is often caused by dehydration.

187. A) The medical assistant should make sure a patient does not use antibacterial mouthwash before a sputum specimen.

188. C) Intradermal injections are injected at 15 degrees with a 25- to 27-gauge needle.

189. D) An open fracture occurs when the fractured bone pokes through the skin.

190. E) HIV attacks helper T cells. If T cell levels get below 200, the patient has progressed to AIDS.

191. C) Albuterol is a bronchodilator that is used for treatment of asthma attacks.

192. B) The abdomen is not a dependable location to measure pulse oximetry.

193. B) Nasopharyngeal swabs are often used to test for RSV and influenza.

194. A) A filtered needle will prevent any broken glass from mixing with the medication as it is drawn into the syringe.

195. C) The parathyroid is responsible for controlling the calcium and phosphate levels in the blood. Each person has four parathyroid glands, located on the posterior surface of the thyroid gland.

196. C) A Pap smear collects cells from the cervix to test for human papillomavirus (HPV) and cervical cancer.

197. A) This describes a wet mount preparation. It is used to examine bacteria that normally move or live in a liquid environment.

198. B) 5 cc = 5 mL.

199. A) Pap smears should be labeled with the patient's name, date of birth, medical record number, and last menstrual cycle date.

200. C) Silence allows the patient time to think and reflect and lead the conversation in the desired direction.

Made in the USA
Coppell, TX
10 May 2024

32264258R00166